HOSPITAL
PUBLIC RELATIONS

Photo by William M. Rittase, courtesy Abington (Penn.) Hospital

Good public relations are built upon a program of high grade service to all the sick of the community, whether rich or poor.

HOSPITAL
PUBLIC
RELATIONS

ALDEN B. MILLS

CHICAGO 1939
PHYSICIANS' RECORD COMPANY

Set up in eleven point Century Expanded type
on thirteen point slug and printed in the United
States of America by the press of the Physicians'
Record Company, Chicago, Illinois, September 1939.

To

H.E.M. *and* J.D.N.

PREFACE

ONE OF THE great troubles of the day is the cultural time lag that exists in many important fields of action. There is a time lag between the acquisition of knowledge and the application of that knowledge by leaders in that field. In the use of effective public relations by non-profit institutions, this cultural time lag is particularly marked.

Social service, educational and similar leaders are so intent upon carrying out their own activities that they often remain oblivious to, ignorant of or completely passive in their relations with the public upon which they are so dependent. But possibly they are no more neglectful than are leaders in other fields of activity. In fact, finance and industry are but now awakening to the need of bridging the gap between knowledge of public relations and its application in actual practice. Great industries and trade associations have recognized that private interest and public responsibility go closely hand in hand. The profession of counsel on public relations has developed to take care of the need.

In this book on hospital public relations, Alden B. Mills bridges the gap between existing knowledge of public relations and the need for that knowledge not only by hospitals but by other types of social service institutions as well. He has not contented himself with giving method alone. He has related method in both public relations and fund-raising to the sociologic and other foundations upon which method rests. His book should serve as a most useful compendium on the theory and practice of integrating social service institutions with their backgrounds in these so rapidly changing times.

One of the great advantages is that the subject matter is here treated so broadly that it will apply to the larger field. Many of those engaged in social service feel that they are Columbuses and Magellans in the field of public relations. They assume they must discover and explore these fields for themselves. Reading Mr. Mills' book will save them from time-taking, troublesome journeys of discovery and exploration. The time and effort they would have spent on these explorations can be devoted to the actual effective handling of public relations.

No library of a social service institution should be without this book. If the institution has no library, this book might well become the nucleus of one.

EDWARD L. BERNAYS

ACKNOWLEDGMENTS

IT IS probably impossible for any author to give full credit to all of the people who have aided him in one way and another. I know this is true in my case. To each person who recognizes some of his own contribution that has not been adequately acknowledged here or in the text, I extend my apologies and my thanks. I have tried to be meticulous in giving credit but it is hard to keep my own thoughts strictly separated from the thoughts I have acquired from others.

My first acquaintance with the basic principles of public relations as expounded in this book was made through Perry Addleman. I gratefully record his stimulating influence. Many people have kindly read the entire text of this book and given me their comments. Dr. E. M. Bluestone was particularly generous and he will find reflections of his brilliant thought in every chapter. Dr. Basil C. MacLean and Dr. Robin C. Buerki can likewise feel that this child is in part theirs. Others who have graciously contributed include Dr. G. Harvey Agnew, president, American Hospital Association; Robert M. Cunningham, Jr., Plan for Hospital Care, Chicago; Michael M. Davis, chairman, council on public education, American Hospital Association; Arnold F. Emch, assistant executive secretary, American Hospital Association; Paul E. Faust, trustee, Evanston Hospital, Evanston, Illinois; Mrs. George T. Gerlinger, vice president, Pacific College, Newberg, Oregon; Benjamin J. Green, Plan for Hospital Care, Chicago; Gerhard Hartman, executive secretary, American College of Hospital Administrators; Dr. Malcolm T. MacEachern, associate director, American College of Surgeons; Ada Belle McCleery, administrator, Evanston Hospital, Evanston, Illinois; Oliver G. Pratt, administrator, Salem Hospital, Salem, Massachusetts; C. Rufus Rorem, executive director, Commission on Hospital Service, American Hospital Association; Sister Mary Patricia, administrator, St. Mary's Hospital, Duluth, Minnesota; Sister Mary Adele Meiser, intern in hospital administration; Raymond P. Sloan, associate editor, *The Modern Hospital* and trustee, Methodist Episcopal Hospital, Brooklyn, New York; Dr. Raymond T. Smith, Holt-Krock Clinic, Fort Smith, Arkansas; James W. Stephan, intern in hospital administration; L. H. Stoneman of Will, Folsom and Smith, New York City; Harold J. Tune, Cleveland Community Fund; E. A. Van Steenwyk, Associated Hospital Service of Philadelphia; Judith Waller, National Broadcasting Company; Harold M. Weeks of John Price Jones Corporation, New York City; and Gerald Wellesley, London, England.

I am especially grateful to Dr. Arthur C. Bachmeyer for the introduction and to Edward L. Bernays for the preface.

Particular thanks are due to Dr. Otho F. Ball for his unfailing aid and encouragement and to Mildred Whitcomb and Gail Moulton, the former for valuable editorial assistance and the latter for careful proof reading.

For permission to quote I am indebted to the American Hospital Association, American Medical Association, Homer J. Buckley, Canadian Medical Association, Cleveland Hospital Council, Crowell Publishing Company, Curtis Publishing Company, *Editor and Publisher*, Grady Hospital of Atlanta, Georgia, Henry Holt and Company, Alfred Knopf, Horace Liveright, The MacMillan Company, Methodist Episcopal Church, The Modern Hospital Publishing Company, New York Hospital, Physicians' Record Company, Rand McNally and Company, *Toronto Star*, University of Chicago Press. Acknowledgments for the photographs are given under each picture. I appreciate the courtesy of those who lent them.

Constant aid for a period of nearly two years has been given me by my wife. She has been my most constructive and critical helper.

While I gratefully acknowledge aid from many people, it should be clearly understood that any errors of fact or conclusion found in this book are entirely my own.

ALDEN B. MILLS

August, 1939

INTRODUCTION

VOLUNTARY hospitals, whether sponsored by religious organizations, public spirited groups of laymen, fraternal or other associations, even though in most instances founded in response to a local demand for hospital service, have in many respects held themselves aloof from the general public. Frequently they were established without due consideration for the specific needs of the community or district they sought to serve. Their development has been so rapid that the attention of those in authority has been primarily concentrated upon the problems of organization and internal affairs.

Hospital administrators, busied with manifold, routine intramural problems, often have not had or have not taken the time to look beyond the walls of their institutions or to endeavor to interpret to the public the functions of their hospitals.

The advances in medical science and consequent changes in the practice of medicine, the many changes in the mode of living, the enlightenment of the people in matters pertaining to public health and to the treatment of disease and injury and many other factors, all of which are constantly increasing the need and the demand for hospital service, tend to stress the importance of the institution's relations to the public which it serves.

Whether the hospital be voluntary or governmental, it is in large measure dependent upon public support, and the need for favorable public opinion is therefore obvious.

Increasing costs, arising largely out of the complexity of its organization which in turn has been occasioned by technological and scientific advances, and declining

xii   *Introduction*

revenues from philanthropic gifts and from invested
funds have served to emphasize the need for interpreting
the institution to the people and of stimulating their
interest in the hospital.

In this volume, Mr. Mills has set forth briefly but in
comprehensive manner the general considerations to
which attention should be given in the development of a
sound and proper public relations program and has
indicated practical means of application.

A properly conducted and sound program of public
relations should result in continued and generous support of the institution. Many hospitals have received
large gifts from spontaneous donors. A good program
of publicity may influence such individuals and stimulate
them to give. It is not, however, the only factor which
may motivate such gifts. They are often actuated by
totally unrelated incidents and by occurrences which in
themselves seem trivial. The personal contacts of trustees and of staff members will continue to be vital factors
in obtaining benefactions for the hospital. The institution, however, which takes advantage of every opportunity to tell its story of service to the public, which
develops a comprehensive program of community relations, not in a spirit of competition with its sister
institutions but rather in a spirit of cooperation and
coordination with them, and which endeavors to develop
an adequate service to meet the needs of the community,
can hope to gain large dividends from such undertaking.

Hospital trustees and administrators should recognize
the activities included in a program of public relations
as an integral part of the management of the institution.
The endeavor to interpret the institution properly to the
public must permeate the entire organization. Such an

endeavor, while requiring active and able direction, cannot be set up as a distinct and separate venture or department but must be integrated with the activities of every division of the institution. The entire personnel — from floor maid, orderly, engineer, mechanic, clerk, telephone operator, hostess, admitting officer, technician and therapist to dietitian, social worker, nurse, physician and administrator — has an important rôle to perform in the development of public relations. Each of these should perform his or her duties pleasantly and efficiently, thinking not only of the immediate task but of the influence which the manner in which that task is performed will have upon patient, visitor and stranger. The conduct of an effective program of public relations cannot be delegated to an officer burdened with other responsibilities and time consuming duties. The best obtainable individual should be secured to assist the board of management in the formulation of the program and in its continued direction.

It is of prime importance that the members of the board of management evidence a deep and alert interest in the relationships of the hospital and its public. Frequent opportunities are presented to those who hold trusteeship in hospitals to promote good will toward the institution and to explain its functions, services and needs to those less well informed. To be able to do so requires a clear understanding of the organization, its purposes, functions, complexities and operation. To obtain such an understanding requires time and effort; it cannot be secured merely through attendance at board meetings and the reading of reports. Frequent visits to the institution, acquaintance and discussions with the administrator and heads of departments are essential to that intimate knowledge of the hospital that anyone must have who seeks to represent it.

The time is long past when a hospital can confine its activities within the four walls of its structure, can neglect or ignore related agencies in the social and health fields, can remain aloof from the general public and still hope successfully to conduct an enterprise which will have public support. Though a hospital may have an excellent medical staff, employ a highly efficient personnel and possess fine facilities and modern equipment, thereby making it possible to provide a high quality of service, it cannot leave the formation of public opinion concerning that service to chance impressions and occasional reports.

To the trustees and administrators who are interested and eager to develop sound public relations, this volume will be a timely and helpful one.

ARTHUR C. BACHMEYER, M.D.

CONTENTS

xv

ILLUSTRATIONS

Part I

GENERAL CONSIDERATIONS

Chapter 1

THE NEED FOR A
PUBLIC RELATIONS PROGRAM

THE RÔLE OF public relations is more important today than it has ever been before. This fact is increasingly recognized by business groups, educational institutions and welfare agencies. Hospitals and other health organizations are also beginning to understand the vital necessity of conscious and comprehensive public relations programs. Even governmental agencies—national, state and local—are giving far more attention than they have done before to informing, educating and understanding the public mind.

There may have been a time when hospitals made no special effort to gain the confidence and respect of the public. Hospitals in those days had little to offer in the way of scientific care and patients went only as a last resort to the dread "death house." In the intervening years, science has made such rapid strides in transforming the death house into a house of health that public understanding has often not kept pace. Although even backward institutions now realize that their existence depends on public approval, many hospitals fail to comprehend that such approval requires more than mere pleasing of the patient, important as this is.

Having satisfied themselves that they are offering a high type of service, some hospitals still leave to chance the formation of the public's impression of their services. They do not stop to realize that a large percentage of

1

people have little or no direct contact with a hospital for long periods of time. Even those who have some contact may have no way of obtaining a clear picture of its community rôle.

In this day of complex living, with the worries of un-settled economic conditions, greatly enlarged avocational interests, the blare and ballyhoo of modern life, only those activities and projects which are most sensational or those which strike a note of genuine appeal and interest will attract any widespread attention. Since sensation-alism is not in accord with the dignity and scientific character of hospitals, they must find other means to achieve widespread attention if they are to have the support that is essential to the high levels of service to which they should and do aspire. A satisfied patient is a legitimate and invaluable public relations asset but his contacts, both with the hospital and with the public, are relatively too random to enable him to act as the sole intermediary between the hospital and the great body of the people.

The realization of this situation has spurred hospitals and other social institutions to follow the example of many enterprising business concerns. No small amount of time and money is spent by such firms in customer research and self-analysis to make certain that they measure up to what the public expects of them and that the public understands and approves their objectives.

So the very old trait of talking about oneself is developing and expanding into a two way conversation which, in its formalized aspect, has been named the "public relations program." Such a program bears the same relationship to ballyhoo and press-agentry that chemistry does to alchemy and that astronomy does to

astrology. It is the respectable offspring of a disreputable
parent.

Definition of a Public Relations Program

There are many definitions of a public relations
program but the following statement indicates the sense
in which the term is used in this book:

> A public relations program is a conscious, sincere,
> directed endeavor to create and strengthen contacts
> which contribute to the development of mutual
> understanding, good will and respect between an
> institution (or business) and its public.

It will be noted that this definition clearly implies that
the program has reciprocal objectives; no longer content
merely to talk about itself, the institution now listens
for the voice of the public. The understanding, good will
and respect must be mutual, not unilateral. An institution will not win respect of the public if it has no respect
for the public and its needs and opinions; it will not gain
understanding where it gives none; nor will it win the
good will of others if it has no good will toward them.
As a result the obligations that are implicit in public
relations are mutual. In other words, such a program is
designed not only to win financial and moral support for
the hospital but also to make sure that the hospital meets
the public's need for hospital service, health education
and training of personnel.

This double purpose is our central theme, which will
be developed from various points of view. Unless this
reciprocity is understood by the reader, however, the
principal purpose of the book will not have been properly
fulfilled.

What is a hospital's "public," the public with whom it has "relations"? The hospital's public is the entire group of people with whom it has or is likely to have any association, whether these people come into contact with the hospital as free or pay patients, as members of the medical staff, as students, as employes, as benefactors or merely as neighbors. The people whom a hospital does or is likely to serve as patients constitute its "service area." Usually, although not always, they live in some reasonably well defined geographic district. Sometimes they may be of a particular racial, religious, fraternal or age group or of a given economic or disease classification.

Since hospitals and other social institutions usually need financial aid, administrators and trustees are sometimes prone to regard only benefactors and potential benefactors as of any significance in a public relations program. Actually such a program should embrace, in one way or another, all of the people listed above as members of the hospital's public. Hospitals need the understanding support of lowly as well as prominent persons if they are to accomplish their legitimate legislative objectives, are to meet their labor relations problems and are to obtain proper patronage. At the same time, people of less education and less means are often the ones most in need of the hospital's service and least articulate in expressing their needs.

The fact that the public relations program is conscious and directed distinguishes it from a mere haphazard trusting to luck. Since it is directed, it must be directed by someone who gives a substantial amount of thought to creating and strengthening the kind of contacts mentioned. This person, by whatever title he may be known, is in fact the director of public relations.

The fact that the program is sincere and that it is mutual in character clearly differentiates it from mere press-agentry. Press-agentry is designed to "sell a bill of goods" and it usually results in abuses, such as distortion of the facts or "slanting" of the news. Sound public relations require accuracy and honesty of the same caliber as characterize the work of a scientist, although in a different field and using different tools.

Granted that, as yet, there is no clearly defined code of ethics for a public relations program for social institutions, a person of honesty, candor and ability can, nevertheless, establish and observe his own standards just as did the physician of dignity and integrity before adoption of a code of ethics by the American Medical Association. One observer has described a public relations program as "good manners and good morals."

Need for a Public Relations Program

We have already attacked the stand of certain administrators that if the institution renders good care to the sick it will automatically win friends and obtain respect and support. Good service to the sick is, indeed, the first essential — the most important single element — in any good public relations program. Without this element such a program will have disappointing results. When a public relations program is expected to "sell" a poor product, it must resort to chicanery, half-truths and deception. It degenerates to mere press-agentry.

But good service, even when coupled with sound business practices and fair treatment of employes and medical staff, is not enough. The days are past, if they ever existed, when an institution could rely entirely upon casual conversation and chance personal contacts to learn all that it should know about the needs of its public and to inform the public adequately about its needs. This is, in part, due to the increasing urbanization and mobility of our population and the consequent loss of direct personal touch and, in part, to the tremendous increase in the competition for public attention.

One needn't labor the point about urbanization. It is obvious that in a city of 500,000 people each person is less likely to know about the work and services of every other than he would in a city of 5000 population. But even in the small city the situation is changing. Today many of the people in the city of 5000 are highly mobile and they think as little of traveling 50 or 100 miles as their parents or grandparents would have thought of going five or ten miles. In other words, they are not hemmed in by geographic boundaries to the same extent as earlier generations. Hence they often do not take as intense an interest in the activities of their own community since it does not occupy such an exclusive and dominating position in their lives.

But even those who do not travel find a changing situation. There is today a tremendous competition for interest. That part of the world which is brought within the ken of any one individual is constantly expanding at a steadily increasing tempo. Political, cultural, social and economic changes come at a dizzying speed and the tremendous expansion of communication brings them to each of us more dramatically every year. If television becomes a practical reality the next generation may see the process speeded up even more.

Most people who can help the hospital have heavy demands upon their time. Their occupations, their hobbies, their civic and philanthropic interests leave few hours free even for their families. Whether they are wealthy persons or manual laborers, the opportunities for utilizing their time are legion.

While a public relations program must try to make itself felt among all these competing interests in the lives of the wealthy and those of little means, it is often particularly difficult to penetrate the former. In addition to the demands of business, family, pleasure, hobbies and self-advancement, each such person finds himself constantly bombarded with appeals from philanthropic and civic enterprises eager to enlist his aid and interest. There are churches and schools. There is a score or more of health organizations. There are character building agencies, child and family welfare agencies, legal aid organizations, civic reform groups, neighborhood clubs, voters' leagues and political organizations of many types. The list is well nigh endless. Some are extremely worthy; others are of questionable merit; all are organized and active. Unfortunately, there is also the charity racket which keeps the generous citizen ever on his guard.

The busy individual must constantly pick and choose. He cannot support all good movements. In fact, often he cannot even take the time to determine which are the best of the many appeals. Usually he must make up his mind quickly to give his aid to some and not to others. To attempt a thorough personal investigation of all appeals would consume too much of his time. How much more likely he is, then, to support an institution which he feels has taken careful stock of itself and is seeking cooperation for developments which are clearly in line with definite community needs.

If, in this situation, the hospital is to enjoy contacts with the public which "contribute to the development of

mutual understanding, good will and respect," it must
not expect the public to come the whole way, probably not
even half of the way. The hospital itself must take the
initiative. It must carry the burden of research and self-
analysis and then must establish avenues of communication through which helpful contact will be created and
maintained. It must carefully check every existing
avenue of communication to assure that contacts there
made really do lead to mutual understanding, good will
and respect.

Good public relations are essential to a hospital and
a definite program is essential to the creation of a positive
or active instead of a negative or passive attitude. Lack
of generous public respect and support will be serious to
governmental hospitals and may be fatal to voluntary
institutions.

To governmental agencies the present is already a
difficult time. The units of government — national, state
and local — have been called upon to carry so many new
responsibilities during the last decade that there is
intense competition for appropriations. Funds for those
on relief, for the aged, the blind, dependent children and
other wards of the state, as well as for the enormous
expansion of regulatory functions of many kinds, all add
to the increasing expenses of government.

In addition to the new functions, there is a constant
pressure for higher standards of administration of existing governmental activities — schools, parks, health
services, highways — all of which require more and
better trained employes and larger expenditures for
equipment. While it is true that governmental units in
recent years have tapped new sources of income, such as
sales taxes, the net final effect of these various expan-

sions of activity is a heavy pressure upon all governmental agencies to reduce their costs.

But, even in the face of this pressure, federal, state, county and city hospitals, like so many other governmental agencies, have been forced to carry a heavier load. Not only are they expected to care for more people, but, upon governmental hospitals, as upon all others, there is the constant necessity of increasing the scope and quality of their services to keep abreast of scientific advances in the practice of medicine.

In view of this situation, the governmental hospitals of all types need to earn and retain the understanding and respect of large sections of the public. Congress, the state legislatures, city councils, county commissions and courts will in the long run reflect the attitude of the majority of the citizens. General citizen support and understanding are the basic bulwark for these hospitals. Such support and understanding are essential to protect the income of the hospitals and to assist them in avoiding the hazards of political control.

And what of the voluntary hospitals? In general, their situation is even more precarious. They, too, have been expected to care for a larger number of free patients or patients who could pay less than cost. The competition for additional income has been even more severe for them than for governmental institutions since they have to rely on individual generosity rather than on the contributions required by the tax collector. At the same time, increasing costs of operation have been particularly marked in the voluntary hospitals, especially in those of high caliber. These institutions have always been regarded as the pacemakers in hospital administration. To sink into a secondary position would be a severe shock to them and a grievous loss to the nation as a whole. The country needs the leadership that they can provide. With a few notable exceptions governmental hospitals cannot provide such leadership. Their form of organization is not so flexible and they usually cannot have as imaginative and creative a type of administration.

To the voluntary hospital, adequate understanding, good will and respect are today vital. Without them the future of the voluntary hospital is dark; with them it can go forward to new levels of community service. If there are important values in the philosophy of voluntarism in hospitals — and nearly all students of hospital service agree that there are — these can only be preserved if the voluntary hospitals will strengthen their public position. This will influence the success of voluntary hospital care insurance plans, the position of hospitals under any form of compulsory health insurance that may be started in this country, the ability of voluntary hospitals to obtain a satisfactory agreement with governmental agencies for the care of the indigent, their ability to deal satisfactorily and fairly with their employes, their position under social legislation and, of course, their power to obtain funds for needed rehabilitation, extension of service, increased educational facilities and replacement of obsolete equipment. As voluntary hospitals strengthen their public position, they also increase their ability to attract private patients, to obtain extra-budgetary endowment funds by legacy or otherwise and to enlist the aid of medical staff members whose service to free patients constitutes an important philanthropic contribution.

Though there is strong feeling among leaders in hospital work that voluntary hospitals are invaluable in the

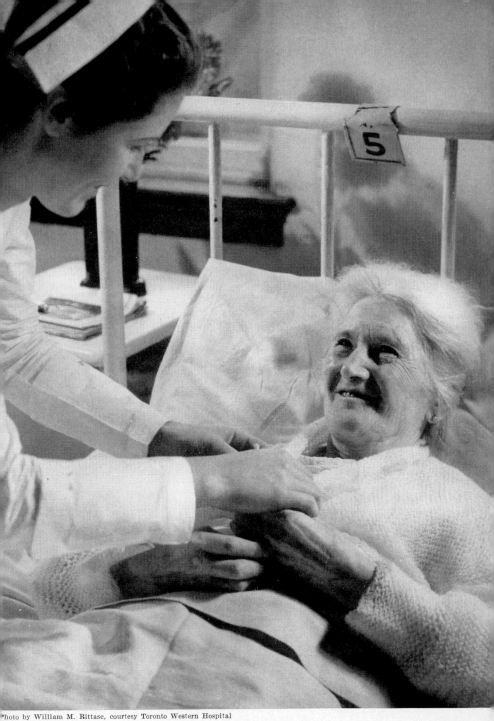

Photo by William M. Rittase, courtesy Toronto Western Hospital

If a hospital provides kindly, thoughtful and intelligent care,
it should take definite steps to inform the public of this fact.

field, in some other quarters there is a growing acceptance of the philosophy that government should now assume full responsibility for all social needs. Many of the people who have built new fortunes in the last 10 or 15 years have not yet formed the habit of contributing funds for social purposes. And many of the supporters from whom voluntary hospitals were wont to obtain money are no longer able to provide funds in such large amounts.

Since this is true, what alternative sources of income can the hospitals tap? Hospital care insurance is held out as one source of additional funds and undoubtedly it will be increasingly important, especially as low-income groups are aided in achieving pay patient status.[1] The enlistment of a large group of people who can donate small sums is a second important proposal. The raising of rates is advocated to keep pace with advancing costs. Governmental subsidies, direct and indirect, are proposed. Higher standards of administration resulting in the further elimination of waste may be of some assistance. To be effective, all of these proposals obviously require public understanding and support.

For both voluntary and governmental hospitals, mere preservation of present standards of income is not sufficient. There is a burden laid upon all hospitals to meet constantly rising standards and to provide constantly widening services. No hospital can long retain its position if it is content merely to maintain itself at the level it achieved yesterday. What institution today, for example, would be satisfied with the x-ray equipment that was considered modern and sufficient in 1929, with nurses who had successfully completed the course of 1929 and had done nothing to keep abreast of the changes of the last decade, or with physicians who are still treating pneumonia as it was treated even a short 10 years ago? The advances in medicine, dietetics, nursing, pharmacy, education, engineering, architecture and all other fields related to hospital service are so rapid that the unprogressive institution will soon be left far behind.[2] Of course, every hospital does not have to install every new gadget that appears. But no hospital can afford consistently to drop behind the procession. If it does, it shortly begins to lose its attractiveness to both its medical staff and its patients.

The tempo of scientific advance is constantly accelerating. Each year brings a larger number of new weapons and technics into the physician's armamentarium. Each year brings more new ideas in hospital administration, hospital planning and construction and hospital service. The demands for new comforts, such as acoustical treatment, air conditioning, improved beds and more attractive rooms, are often heard but are of minor significance compared to the demands for new clinical advances. Blood transfusions, anesthesia, serum treatments and physical, occupational, vitamin, oxygen and intravenous therapies are only a few of the clinical fields that are growing in importance every year.

These new comforts and expanded services cost money and must be paid for in one way or another by someone. They make the cost per patient day higher and increase the spread in cost between mere hotel service and true hospital care. Some of them, of course, make treatment more effective so that the increase of costs is somewhat offset by decrease of length of patient stay in the hospital. Sometimes they save lives, whose money value defies computation.

This necessarily increasing cost of hospital service must be viewed against a background of constantly rising living standards. Twenty years ago people spent little or no money for airplane travel, radios, permanent waves, frozen foods, electric refrigerators or "talkies." Today these and other similar things call for their expanding share of the national income. The competition for the consumer's dollar is keener than ever. Whether they like it or not, hospitals must meet this enlivened competition.

Public Service Through Public Relations

Another important reason for a sound program remains to be discussed. As we have said, a true public relations program is designed to aid the public as much as the hospitals.

First, it informs the public about hospitals. What do hospitals do? How can one use them effectively and discriminatingly? When is home care as good as hospital care? When is it wise to use the hospital instead of the home as the place to care for illness? How can one judge the quality of hospital service?[3]

Second, it aids in disseminating sound information regarding health preservation. It takes a lead in advocating "health inventories" and making it possible for them to be provided to the people on terms that are suitable to their needs and financial abilities. It promotes consciousness of public health objectives and possibilities. It arouses the public to the need for early detection and care of the diseases, including cancer, heart disease, mental disease, tuberculosis and the venereal diseases, which today are the outstanding challenges to a healthy nation. It teaches, by precept and demonstration, the value of good maternal and infant care.

Third, it acts as a sensitive antenna to bring to the hospital knowledge of the public's needs for hospital service, whether these are recognized or not by the general public. When these needs are uncovered through the public relations program, the hospital administrator and trustees can then act upon them intelligently and purposefully.

Fourth, by increasing effective use of the hospital plant, it aids in reducing the unit costs of operation. Many services cost less per unit in large numbers than they do in small numbers. A substantial part of hospital expense is involved in readiness-to-serve costs. If a hospital can find ethical ways of utilizing more fully the money that has been invested in plant and equipment and the money currently spent in general overhead, it owes the public an obligation to do so. The worst waste in hospital operation is the unoccupied bed, the unused x-ray department, the idle nurse or the empty surgery when there are patients in the community who need to utilize them. (Of course, it is necessary to have some unoccupied beds for the protection of the community. The only alternative is a waiting list which, if large, is sure to mean severe hardship on some people.)

Summary

A sound public relations program is a scientific endeavor to create and strengthen constructive contacts between the public and the hospital. It involves mutual benefits and obligations and is built upon a well rounded program of service designed to meet the public's requirements for hospital care.

Such a program is essential to the hospital for the following reasons:

1. Hospitals can no longer rely entirely upon casual word of mouth to tell the dramatic and interesting story of their work or to keep themselves fully informed of public needs. The competition for attention is so great today that hospitals must come at least halfway if they wish the public to understand their problems and appreciate their services and if they are to understand and appreciate the public's various points of view.

2. New threats to the very existence of voluntary hospitals and to the proper growth of governmental institutions are arising. These come from the decrease in the number of large donations, the growth of social and economic legislation affecting hospitals, the advances in medical science and administrative standards constantly requiring more hospital equipment and services, and the growing competition for each dollar, whether it comes from an individual or from a governmental unit.

3. There are various potential sources of additional revenue for voluntary hospitals. These include hospital care insurance, enlistment of a new class of donors, raising of rates, governmental payments for care of the indigent and higher standards of administration. All of these, to be most effective, require widespread public understanding and support.

4. Hospitals owe the public a duty to give sound information about themselves and their intelligent and discriminating use, to aid in the advancement of health education, to promote public health and to reduce the unit cost of hospital services through making the most effective possible use of the physical plant and the available personnel.

Without any attempt at melodrama one can safely state that hospitals in the United States today face the most serious crisis in their history. The intelligent use of public relations programs may spell the difference between continued growth and stagnation.

REFERENCES

1. Oseroff, Abraham: New Areas of Voluntary Service, *The Modern Hospital*, Jan., 1939, p. 69.
2. Mills, Alden B.: Milestones in Hospital History — 1913-1938, *The Modern Hospital*, Sept., 1938, pp. 144-164, and Mills: Major Hospital Trends, *op. cit.*, pp. 166-174, and Patricia, Sister M.: Trends in Professional Education, *Hospitals*, June, 1939, p. 45.
3. Eichenlaub, M. H.: Public Relations of the Hospital, *Hospitals*, Sept., 1938, p. 19, and Spencer, William H.: The Hospital in Modern Society, *Hospitals*, June, 1938, p. 11.

Chapter 2

INFLUENCING
PUBLIC OPINION

WE MAY WELL leave to the psychologists, both those
dealing with individual psychology and those more concerned with social psychology, all theoretical discussion of
precisely what goes on in a human mind in the formation
of that intangible something called "public opinion."
They have been fighting now for some years over such
questions as whether public opinion is merely the sum of
individual opinion or whether it also contains some kind
of an "x" quality which gives it a different character.
Psychiatry and psychology are now developing rapidly
and we may anticipate that soon they will achieve wider
agreement in their interpretations.

The type of public opinion with which we are here
concerned fortunately is somewhat more concrete than
general public opinion on broad social, economic and
political questions. We are concerned with influencing
opinion of all or a majority of the public toward one
specific social institution, the hospital. Whatever theories
may be advanced to explain how public opinion is formed
and whatever logical or emotional procedures may be
hypothecated to bolster these theories, they will doubtless
remain largely theoretical until much more insight into
the process is gained.

But we do not have to wait for the scientific explanation of the functioning of the group mind. Certain
measures produce results. This has been demonstrated

17

time and time again. A scientific explanation might reveal other things that would also work but, while the psychologists are formulating it, let us use the technics we now have.

Stereotypes or Models

Walter Lippmann in his brilliant book, *Public Opinion*, has indicated his strong belief, supported by substantial argument, that most of us tend to think about those things on which we are not expert in terms of "stereotypes" or "simple models." These stereotypes, he believes, are a necessary shorthand in thinking. Without them we should be innundated by the tremendous flood of perceptions that would pour in upon us from all sides.

"The real environment is altogether too big, too complex and too fleeting for direct acquaintance. We are not equipped to deal with so much subtlety, so much variety, so many permutations and combinations. And although we have to act in that environment, we have to reconstruct it on a simpler model before we can manage with it."[1]

Propaganda is the effort to alter the stereotypes to which men respond. The man who can choose and then popularize a stereotype can determine the action of thousands. Note the avidity with which political parties coin and promote catch-words and slogans and the efforts they make to build up certain politically desirable characteristics of a candidate at the neglect of all the other virtues and weaknesses which he, like any other human being, possesses. They try to make him fit their stereotypes.

Enormous power is wielded by those who stand between the general public and the person or institution that they reconstruct on a simpler model. This power carries with it a corresponding responsibility. Propaganda may be and has been used to make the worse seem the better part, to mislead people by giving them a model that distorts or grossly magnifies the real person or thing. Such uses of propaganda have given it a bad name, so bad that one almost hesitates to use the term although it has a splendid history dating back to the famous College of Propaganda of the Catholic Church.

False or essentially distorted propaganda is in reality a crime against the minds of those who are misled thereby. Furthermore, it is highly explosive, likely to backfire and do more damage to its perpetrator than to anyone else. When one attempts to influence the minds of others, he should apply to himself as rigorous standards of honesty and veracity as he expects from a scientist. Anything else is mass prostitution of the mind. We shall discuss this at greater length in Chapter 3.

The problem of hospital public relations may be divided into two parts. First, comes the study necessary to develop a simple model that will be true to the facts in all important particulars, that will be simple enough that it may be grasped by those we are endeavoring to interest and that will be attractive enough that it will stir them to the kind of action desired. To be attractive it must be built to meet the real needs of the people and, insofar as possible, created with their help and participation so that they rightly feel a healthy pride of creation and possession.

Having developed our model we then face the second problem, namely, so effectively and forcefully to bring this concept to the attention of the various classes of people comprising our public that they will adopt it as their own and, insofar as it is a plan for the future, will assume responsibility for helping us to make the concept a reality.

Building a Plan

Before we can intelligently decide what particular concept or model of the hospital we wish to set as an objective, we must decide what level of quality and what scope of hospital service we wish to provide. The word "hospital," which is itself a stereotype of sorts, actually covers a vast range of institutions. Many are the finest expressions of the union of philanthropy and science; some are mere medical boarding houses or less.

Obviously, if our model is to be sound it must be based on a sound program of public service. Without a program of service that represents our best efforts to meet the real needs of the community for hospital care, we are forced either to create a false stereotype, which carries the grave risk of discovery, or to confess the truth, which strikes no responsive cord in the minds of our listeners. The question of what constitutes a good program of hospital care is discussed at length in Chapter 4.

Having formulated such a program, it then becomes necessary to restate it in terms that can be grasped by our constituents. For people with intelligence and interest sufficient to wade through substantial material, our aims and purposes can be stated in considerable detail and supported with the most important sections of our evidence. In a few instances, for example, a hospital or a college has prepared an entire volume on its needs and program just for one prospective donor. He was given nearly as many data and discussions of the data as were the trustees who adopted the project in the first place. Such interest, however, is rare.

For the average intelligent person mildly interested in an institution, a considerable sifting and selection are necessary. He wants to know the essential facts and to learn the broad conclusions based upon those facts. But usually he has neither time nor interest to recapitulate the detailed study that preceded the decision of the board of trustees. When we come to the mass audience reached through newspapers, radio or widespread direct mail campaigns, still further simplification is necessary.

Such simplification and orderly presentation to constituents can be made only by a person who is intimately informed about the subject and who has a clear picture of the people to be reached and why it is desired to reach them. Sometimes the mistake is made of assuming that the newspapers, for example, can best make their own stereotypes. They will do so, as they did in connection with the hospital care insurance plan in New York City, when they labeled it the "three-cents-a-day plan." While this is a convenient label for the plan in its original form, it became somewhat complicated when dependents were included requiring a "five-cents-a-day plan" and a "seven-cents-a-day plan."

From the hospital's point of view, the newspapers' choice of emphasis and of catch-phrases is as likely to be unwise as it is to be wise. Certainly they do not have the background of hospital experience against which to test the validity of a particular stereotype. The best way to avoid this risk is to provide them with well considered and acceptable catch-phrases and stereotypes.

Harnessing the Emotions

The concept, model or stereotype that we develop must not be a mere passive thing if it is to obtain results. It must arouse some emotional response. It must appeal to one or more of the individual's interests, must be of such a character that it can penetrate his present armor of stereotypes, must fit in reasonably well with his previous experience and beliefs.

Each man pursues his own interests. But how he shall pursue these interests is determined not by any fixed laws comparable to those of physics or chemistry but by the habits that have been built up in the particular culture patterns in which he happens to live and to have lived. Which of his interests can be harnessed for the benefit of social institutions, particularly hospitals?

First, perhaps, is man's interest in his own protection and the protection of those who are dear to him. It is no difficult task to demonstrate that good hospital facilities are an essential protective force in the community. They are necessary not only to care for emergency illnesses and accidents but also to provide a center of health education, to train nurses and other personnel and to raise and maintain the general level of the practice of medicine carried on outside of their walls. By and large, good doctors are attracted to a community by good hospitals; they are driven away by poor hospitals or by the absence of hospitals. Well trained physicians can practice better medicine with a good hospital than they can without one. The best way of assisting a good doctor in many instances is to give him the facilities and scientific stimulus of a well administered, progressive and adequately financed hospital. (In certain impoverished or sparcely settled rural communities, of course, even this by itself will not be sufficient to attract and retain good doctors.)

A second interest is civic or group pride. Many a man will respond to an appeal to provide as good an institution as is found in any other community of the size in the state. This string to our fiddle ought to be played with great care. It is often abused, as when one civic, racial or religious group tries to outdo another and succeeds merely in saddling the community with needlessly duplicated facilities. There is scarcely a city anywhere in the United States that has escaped entirely from the unhappy results of misguided local or group pride.

But if a sound plan is adopted this interest need not be abused. There are plenty of opportunities for service open to every group. No community in the United States has all of the hospital facilities and special services of all kinds that it needs. Why shouldn't there be just as much civic or group pride in enlarging a good general hospital, so that it can offer adequate service to chronic disease patients or to convalescents or to mental or tuberculous patients as there is in building a new hospital for maternity cases or crippled children? While the identity, and thus the emotional appeal, of the new unit can remain distinct, common use of expensive equipment and sharing of overhead cost can aid it to function more efficiently. Also cannot civic and group pride be adequately expressed in providing an existing hospital with a badly needed out-patient department, surgery or contagious disease unit or by financing a social service department, endowing education and research or raising funds to provide better care to indigent or "white collar" patients? If combined with intelligent discrimination, "keeping up with the Joneses" can become a virtue.

Many individuals, even in this day of expansion of governmental social activities, have a personal and individual sense of duty regarding the support of social institutions. They feel responsible for doing their share

24 Hospital Public Relations

to make sure that the needy sick are not neglected, that mothers have an opportunity to bring babies into the world under favorable circumstances, that those with chronic diseases have whatever relief medical science can now provide. To such people the hospital's appeal is especially strong. They are found in all economic classes; hence, opportunity should be provided for them to support the hospital in proportion to their means. Herein lies one of the special values of Hospital Sunday and similar occasions.

The economic appeal of the hospital also is strong. Many people can readily be shown that it is "good business" to support the hospital. Most hospitals earn a large percentage of their operating expenses. The contributed dollar often enables the hospital to earn more dollars; thus the investment multiplies. In this respect the hospital is readily distinguishable from many other types of social agency where all or most of the income must come from gifts. These facts appeal to the desire to be considered shrewd and possessed of good business judgment. One hospital has ably capitalized upon this feeling by publishing a series of articles in its monthly house organ under the title "The Gift Lives On." Each tells how a certain gift to the hospital has continued to pay dividends in better service to the sick over a period of many years.

Many institutions have successfully appealed to the vanity of those who like to see their generosity expressed in memorials of brick or concrete. It would be idle to deny that this appeal has aided many socially desirable activities. But like civic, racial or religious pride, it must be wisely guided if more harm than good is not to result. In one small middle-western town, for example,

there are three general hospitals today where one or two
would adequately serve the needs of the community.
Each hospital is struggling along with antiquated equipment, many empty beds, no funds for the care of the
indigent except such as it can obtain from the surplus on
paying patients or can squeeze from inadequate payment
to employes. Undoubtedly there are many unmet medical
needs in this community. But, even if there are no such
needs, the money that has been invested in half-empty
buildings could be far better used if it were divided
between not more than two well equipped hospitals.

Most of us have at least a small streak of vanity. One
hospital has found an acceptable way of catering to this
trait with dignity and intelligence. The name of every
person who gives the hospital a special fund or a building
is recorded in a large gold lettered hand-illuminated book
which is kept in a locked glass case in the front lobby. It
is opened in rotation to each page on which there is an
entry and, of course, on occasion is taken from the case
so that especially interested persons may see all the
entries. A sample entry reads:

Charles Parkhill Whitehouse

Mr. Whitehouse had been a liberal subscriber to this
hospital for many years and his will provided for the
bequest of twenty-five thousand dollars. Mr. White-
house was born at Danville, Illinois, on May Fifth,
Eighteen Hundred Fifty-Six. He was married to
Martha Farwell Simpson on November Twelfth,
Eighteen Hundred Seventy-Nine at Norwood Park,
Illinois. He died on February Twenty-First, Nineteen
Hundred Thirty-Two at Pasadena, California.

In several hospitals the names of those persons who
give a stipulated sum, *e.g.* $5000 or more, are recorded
on bronze name plates and added to a large bronze plaque

in the lobby. This is found to be preferable to putting the names on rooms, wards, laboratories or special sections of the hospital which, in course of time, become outmoded and must be torn down or converted to other uses. One hospital was much embarrassed when the daughter of a formerly wealthy patron took up residence in the room he had endowed many years before. Frequently donors or their heirs think that they are privileged to name the persons who may occupy "endowed" rooms.

Imitation is another human trait that may be turned to useful channels. Most of us like to be in style, to conform to the social pattern of those with whom we associate, to imitate the action of those whom we consider to be just a little above us in the social, economic or intellectual scale. Bernays rests his basic theory of propaganda upon the strength of this trait.

The practice of propaganda since the war has assumed very different forms from those prevalent twenty years ago. This new technic may fairly be called the new propaganda. It takes account not merely of the individual, nor even of the mass mind alone, but also and especially of the anatomy of society, with its interlocking group formations and loyalties. It sees the individual not only as a cell in the social organism but as a cell organized into the social unit. Touch a nerve at a sensitive spot and you get an automatic response from certain specific members of the organism.[2]

Bernays' technic is to utilize group leaders as the "sensitive spots." Once the right kind of leaders are committed publicly to support a given idea or movement, he is convinced that its success may easily be assured by the simple technics of publicity. In financial campaigns it is a well known rule that the public leader of the

The "Memory Book" at Evanston Hospital is a dignified and appropriate appeal to the pride of donors and prospective donors.

campaign must be the most widely respected and followed man in the group.

While there is a great deal of truth in Bernays' contention, it must also be recognized that sometimes the issue will create a leader. An example comes to mind in the case of the proposed merger some years ago of two universities. Undoubtedly there were and still are many reasons why such a merger is desirable. But there was a strong feeling on the part of certain professors in one of the universities that the terms of the merger did not sufficiently guarantee the continuance of some of its worth-while activities. For a considerable period all publicity concerning the merger emanated from the presidents of the two institutions or from others who were favorable to the proposal. The opposing elements, however, were counseled by an able public relations man who began supplying the papers with articles containing a note of doubt, although no person of outstanding reputation could be found who would publicly oppose the plan.

Finally, a comparatively unknown member of the faculty of one school issued a carefully prepared attack on the plan. His name alone carried little weight but the character of his statement and the timing of it were so forceful that he and his statement became the spearpoint of the opposition. Others then rallied to his cause. The newspapers soon took a tone definitely adverse to the merger and within a few weeks the trustees of the two institutions issued a statement saying that the plan was indefinitely postponed because of public opposition.

This instance has been recited at some length because it illustrates the limitations of the leadership principle. Here all the "big names" were on one side yet the other side, by the force of its arguments, was able to utilize a comparatively unknown person with telling effect. The university officials, apparently, relied too much upon the power of "big names" and not enough upon presenting a case that was well conceived and sound from every point of view.*

Satisfying the Intellect

While it is important to harness the emotions, it is vital to satisfy the intellect. In a short intensive fund raising campaign utilizing the high pressure methods so common in the twenties, results were often achieved with appeals and claims that could not stand the light of critical analysis. But the era of such campaigns seems to be drawing to a definite close. Today people do not respond so readily to the "tear-jerkers" and the "sob-sisters." People are more discriminating in bestowing their money and their support. Hospitals are learning also that there are emotional recoils to purely sentimental appeals. These recoils may do injury to the hospital that money cannot erase.

The type of public relations program envisaged here is not designed solely for the purpose of obtaining gifts for the hospital. Increased patronage, a better quality medical staff and a higher caliber candidate for the nursing school, improved relations with employes and a

*An interesting sidelight of this case was the method of timing releases to newspapers. When an important statement was to be made by the opposition, the city editors of the morning papers were notified in advance that it was coming but were told that the material was not yet ready. It was then given to them about 9:30 p.m., too late to make the early evening editions of the local morning papers. The proponents, having seen the early editions, thought themselves secure from attack for another day only to find in the morning that a telling blow was in the widely distributed final editions of the papers. They had no chance to answer it in the same edition but had to wait for the afternoon papers.

better standing with legislative groups are other goals. On the question of patronage, it is well to bear in mind that an increase of $4000 in the annual net income of the hospital is equal to an increase of approximately $100,000 in its net endowment. And, it may be added, increased earnings are today probably nearly as dependable a source of support as increased endowment. This is particularly true if the increase comes about through the development of a sound plan for helping people to finance their hospital expenses, *e.g.* through a hospital care insurance plan.

There are, of course, varying kinds of intellects. Some are easily satisfied; others require the most rigorous examination of facts and conclusions. Still others would approach such a question as the support of hospitals in general or of Jones Memorial Hospital in particular from a definitely hostile point of view. The facts and the arguments should be sound enough to meet every examination that can be made of them by friend or foe.

How can this be assured? The first essential, of course, is to have fact-gathering in the hands of persons who have reverence for facts. As Lippmann says, "In truly effective thinking the prime necessity is to liquidate judgments, regain an innocent eye, disentangle feelings, be curious and open-hearted."[3] Facts that bear on the situation should be pursued regardless of where they lead. It is not enough to collect merely those facts that corroborate the thinking to date. If other facts might disprove or qualify the conclusions, these, too, should be ascertained and the tentative conclusions adjusted accordingly. When all relevant facts have been gathered, and only then, is it time to let conclusions begin to take definite shape.

But facts by themselves do not determine conclusions. Facts must be studied, arranged, compared, evaluated. Various tentative conclusions must be tested against the facts in different ways. Sometimes one set of facts will apparently support inconsistent conclusions. For example, from the now well established fact that sickness and poverty are associated, one person derives the conclusion that poverty causes sickness while another states that sickness causes poverty. Actually, of course, there probably is considerable truth in both statements and the conclusion needs to be stated in quite different terms that embrace both ideas.

But one person's carefully formulated conclusions from critically collected facts may still not carry conviction to another person. One of the best ways to find out and at the same time to check the accuracy of one's own thinking is to submit the facts and the conclusions in tentative form for the other person's criticism and comment. In the interchange of opinion between them, their joint conclusions will be hammered out by a process of give and take on both sides. Each can learn from the other. And both will regard the final product as a child of their joint consideration. What better way can there be to enlist sympathy and support for a project than to make a potential critic its co-author?

Allowing Time for Thought

This joint consideration is, of course, a time-consuming process. But that is one of its elements of strength. In an analysis of 130 fund raising campaigns, John Price Jones found that the successful campaigns averaged 35.8 weeks of discussion as compared with 22.4 weeks for the "below average" campaigns; the former spent 9.1 weeks in preliminary investigation and planning while the latter spent only 7.6 weeks in this activity; the period of active preparation for the campaign was almost the same for both, 13.6 weeks and 13 weeks, respectively. But now the time factors are reversed. The period of cultivation through publicity was 10.9 weeks in the successful and 11.1 weeks in the unsuccessful; special gifts solicitation occupied 11.5 weeks in the former but took 20.4 weeks in the latter; general solicitation took only 4.9 weeks in the former and 17.1 weeks in the latter while the "clean-up" consumed 4.3 weeks in the successful and 5.1 weeks in the unsuccessful campaigns.[4]

From these figures it is obvious that the successful campaign took far longer for discussion, preliminary investigation and planning, and preparation (58.4 weeks as against 43.0 weeks). When it came time to start the campaign, so much better groundwork had been laid that the actual period of cultivation, solicitation and clean-up consumed only 31.8 weeks in the successful campaign as compared with 53.7 weeks in the below average; in other words, only slightly over one-half as long (assuming for the moment that there was no overlapping of the different phases of the campaigns).

Obviously people do not like to be rushed into giving to a campaign without an adequate period of preliminary investigation and preparation. Such a preliminary period gives them time to raise objections, modify conclusions, become accustomed to new concepts. If this is true of fund raising campaigns, it is doubtless just as true of campaigns that have for their objective the development of sufficient confidence in an institution so that one wishes to entrust to it one's own life or the lives of his loved ones.

Summary

In concluding this chapter we may sum up the argument in a few words.

1. Public opinion will ordinarily operate through and within the limitations imposed by the mental stereotypes of the people. The hospital should, therefore, attempt to create and popularize stereotypes that will aid the public in obtaining a correct impression of the hospital's complex and intricate program and service.

2. These models, or stereotypes, must tie in with some of the basic human emotions, such as the desire for protection of self and family; civic, racial or other group loyalty; a sense of duty; vanity, or the desire to go with the crowd.

3. But a program that is based merely on an emotional appeal is on precarious footing indeed. A vigorous and well reasoned attack, even from an unknown person, may upset it. Therefore, it should have a solid and honest intellectual basis. This comes only as a result of careful fact-gathering and analysis of needs for hospital service, proposals for meeting these needs, submission of these proposals for public discussion and ultimate recasting of the proposals to take account of all valid criticisms and suggestions.

4. If the public is asked to participate in the formulation of the conclusions, it will naturally be more ready to accept them and to work diligently for their fulfillment.

5. This is a time-consuming process but it is time well spent.

REFERENCES

1. Lippmann, Walter: Public Opinion, Harcourt, Brace and Company, New York City, 1922, p. 13. By permission of The Macmillan Co., publishers.
2. Bernays, Edward L.: Propaganda, Horace Liveright, New York City, 1928, p. 28.
3. Lippmann, Walter: *Op. cit.*, p. 31.
4. Jones, John Price: The Technique to Win in Fund Raising, Inter-River Press, New York City, 1934, p. 71.

Chapter 3

PRINCIPLES
OF PUBLIC RELATIONS

THE PREVIOUS chapter discussed some of the basic factors that play a part in determining public opinion on any particular question. It was recognized that public opinion usually operates within the accepted folkways and mores, *i.e.* the mental stereotypes, of the people, that it is influenced by both emotional and rational forces and that a sense of participation and possessiveness is most effective in creating and solidifying favorable public opinion.

As was stated in the opening chapter, public relations constitute the complex web of interconnections between an institution and the many persons who compose its public. A public relations program is a conscious effort so to arrange these interconnections that they produce a favorable influence upon public opinion. Public relations are the means; favorable public opinion and the results that flow from it are the objectives.

The present chapter will carry further the discussion of methods of influencing public opinion in order to reach certain general conclusions that may be stated as principles of public relations. Various theories will be contrasted and analyzed in the process.

The Emotion and Prejudice Theory

From certain sociologists we might get a series of statements something like this:

1. Public opinion is influenced primarily by emotional drives. These can be set into motion by that type of propaganda which skillfully plays upon prejudices, associations and symbols, *i.e.* stereotypes. It attempts to ally itself with all applicable folkways and mores.

2. Such propaganda circumvents objections and glosses over inconsistencies or lack of logic instead of meeting objections and resolving inconsistencies. It is sly rather than honest, smart instead of scientific, plausible when it should be rigorous.

3. "Public opinion . . . is formed by verbalized attitudes, beliefs and convictions, which are essentially emotional, and their associated images and ideas. It is formulated in a crisis when people differ in their definitions of new situations. The amount of rational and scientific discussion in public opinion is small, although in special groups, of course, opinion is occasionally based on fact and logic. But even the public opinion based on fact is usually, in the end, incorporated into the larger schema provided by emotional attitudes."[1]

E. C. Lindeman has formalized the steps in the creation of public opinion on social questions as follows: (1) consciousness of need, (2) spreading of consciousness of need, (3) projection of consciousness of need upon the leadership of the community, (4) rise of emotional impulse to meet the need quickly, (5) presentation of other solutions, (6) conflict of solutions, (7) investigation (if conflicting solutions are not suppressed), (8) open discussion of the issue, (9) integration of solutions and (10) compromise on the basis of tentative progress.[2] Obviously such a formal series of steps is seldom followed exactly; yet some or most of these steps are probably involved in any formation of opinion. Much of the conflict that is implied in this outline can be avoided by intelligent forethought and planning.

The Leadership Principle

Bernays relies largely upon leaders and clichés. "Trotter and Le Bon," he states, "concluded that the group mind does not *think* in the strict sense of the word. In place of thoughts it has impulses, habits and emotions. In making up its mind its first impulse is usually to follow the example of a trusted leader. This is one of the most firmly established principles of mass psychology.... But when the example of the leader is not at hand and the herd must think for itself, it does so by means of clichés, pat words and images which stand for a whole group of ideas or experiences. ... By playing upon an old cliché or manipulating a new one, the propagandist can sometimes swing a whole mass of group emotions."[3]

But the public relations counsel is not merely a propagandist, Bernays states:

The stage at which many suppose he starts his activities may actually be the stage at which he ends them. After the public and the client are thoroughly analyzed and policies have been formulated, his work may be finished. In other cases the work of the public relations counsel must be continuous to be effective. ...

While the concrete recommendations of the public relations counsel may vary infinitely according to individual circumstances, his general plan of work may be reduced to two types, which I might term continuous interpretation and dramatization by highspotting. The two may be alternative or may be pursued concurrently. Continuous interpretation is achieved by trying to control every approach to the public mind in such a manner that the public receives the desired impression, often without being conscious of it. Highspotting, on the other hand, vividly seizes the attention of the public and fixes it upon some detail or aspect which is typical of the entire enterprise. When a real estate corporation which is erecting a tall office building makes it 10 feet taller than the highest skyscraper in existence, that is dramatization. Which method is indicated can be determined only after a full study of objectives and specific possibilities.[4]

This technic is not a question of ballyhoo, says Bernays, or of creating a picturesque fiction for the public. "It is merely a question of finding the appropriate modes of expressing the personality that is to be dramatized."

The Beginning of a Scientific Theory

John Price Jones, in his interesting book *The Technique to Win in Fund Raising*, states that there are ten constituent elements in the organization and operation of a fund raising campaign.[5] (A fund raising campaign is, of course, merely a specialized aspect of a public relations program and, if properly conceived and directed, it will not violate any of the principles. A full discussion of fund raising and its relation to the whole public relations program will be found in Chapter 12.) These elements or principles may be summarized as follows:

1. The "case" should be (a) bigger than the institution, (b) sociologically and psychologically sound, (c) practical, (d) timely and (e) connected with some object popular in the public mind. The institution should (f) be wide in scope and (g) have proper personnel available for carrying out the program.

2. The leaders of the campaign should represent all the larger groups which are to be approached for funds or help and must themselves be a strong group, willing to accept the responsibility for the campaign and able to set the proper example to workers and to other volunteers.

3. The "prospects" must be listed with the utmost care and thoroughness so that the campaign directors may have an adequate knowledge of their interests.

4. The volunteer workers must be responsible, energetic, intelligent, informed, courageous and of standing in their community.

5. The campaign budget must be adequate.

6. There must be an articulated organization and clear definition of all the campaign's elements and of the relation of personnel, one to another.

7. Essential preliminaries of a campaign are the studies, discussions, analyses, decisions and plans which must precede actual organization. During these preliminary discussions a clear concept of the purpose of the contemplated effort must be attained; responsibilities for each phase of action must be fixed; policies must be determined and decision made as to whether there are obstacles which must be removed before actual fund raising is attempted.

8. "Operation is the act of putting the campaign organization into motion and steering it to its desired destination."

9. Coordination of all phases of a campaign ensures that "the entire mechanism works together smoothly and with maximum efficiency."

10. Momentum is a spiritual and partly intangible quality which is present in every campaign to a certain degree. It is the sum of enthusiasm, zeal and determination throughout the entire campaign organization.

These elements or principles, as may be seen, are a composite of basic ideas that may be applied to general public relations problems and specific details that apply only to the technic of a fund raising campaign. Numbers

1 and 7 apply particularly to the whole of public relations, whether a campaign for funds is in progress or not.

The Growth of Reason

Let us consider one more set of principles that goes even further in putting reliance upon reason and logic than the Jones' statement. From material prepared by Perry Addleman which appeared in *The Modern Hospital* for August, September and October 1934,[6] the following principles of public relations as expressed or implied in these articles may be summarized:

1. Institutions that expect to receive public beneficence should be entirely aboveboard in all their relations to donors and the public. They should make full, accurate and intelligible accounting for funds and the funds should be used for the purposes for which they were given.

2. The first step in developing a public relations program for a hospital is to make a thorough and rigorously scientific study of what hospital service the people of the community need. People who are or should be interested in the hospital should be invited to participate genuinely in this study in accordance with their abilities.

3. The second step is planning to meet the needs so outlined. The plans should be publicized; therefore, not only must they have built-in values but they must have systematic arrangement which will permit of clear statement of those values. When values are well balanced and clear-cut there is a demand to hear about them.

4. Public relations and promotional methods are organic with internal development. Correct methods of obtaining public interest, support and funds can result only from scientific and rationally planned development.

5. Rational and utilitarian objectives in an institution's development should be given due prominence and not obscured by emotional appeals.

6. The type of publicity used should be dignified and honest, entirely in keeping with the plans.

7. The mediums of publicity selected should be appropriate to the kind of idea to be expressed. Newspaper publicity, for example, should consume not over 15 or 20 per cent of the effort, time and money expended. All types of mediums should be considered: magazines, radio, moving pictures, direct mail (including personal letters, individually prepared statements, booklets, pamphlets and house magazines), "feature" publicity and, perhaps, even paid advertising.

8. The program should not be based on any self-made assumptions of soundness. Such assumptions are subjective and may be grotesque. Even if correct, they are bad tactics. Statements of an institution's soundness and progressiveness, its social utility and recognition of new needs, the comprehensiveness of its service — these statements should be drawn from outside, independent and objective sources. Otherwise they mean nothing, at least for publicity and promotion purposes.

9. Rational and critical resistances, such as are normally engendered in any promotional work, should be dissolved through intelligent meeting of the criticism. They should not be outflanked through high pressure, intensively organized campaigns with strong emotional appeal and some inherent coercion.

10. The realization should be kept constantly in the foreground that the American public built and equipped hospitals and still pays their operating costs. "The public relations man who can best earn his fee is the one who

first looks after the interests of the public, who is the public's representative on the corporate board rather than the corporate board's representative to the public, even though the board pays the bills — with the public's money."

These statements indicate why a low pressure public relations program is preferable to a high pressure program. Whereas the latter endeavors to rush people, often unwillingly, into giving assistance, a low pressure program places emphasis on winning confidence and respect in the belief that a more lasting and vital support will follow. It is usually continuous rather than spasmodic; it presents scientific evidence in support of its general statements and avoids spectacular and exaggerated claims. Persuasion replaces coercion.

Starting this chapter with a theory of public relations that explained all molding of public opinion on the basis of emotions, stereotypes and prejudices, we have now followed the more advanced thinkers in the field to a position where principal reliance is placed on the rule of reason.* While Jones and Addleman would doubtless be the first to admit that emotion plays a large part in human action, they have come to regard it as too fickle to serve as the sole or principal basis for permanent support of social institutions. Jones still has a place in his

*The terms "rational" and "emotional" are used in this paragraph and elsewhere in the book in a popular rather than a scientific sense. Obviously all appeals to reason and logic are forms of persuasion and are shot through and through with emotion. This point will be fully discussed in a forthcoming book by Arnold F. Emch, Ph.D., entitled *"The Structure of Discourse (The Technic of Persuasion)."* For present purposes, rational will be used to describe statements or appeals in which a substantial amount of evidence and of logical reasoning are presented; emotional will refer to statements or appeals which rest almost entirely upon broad emotional responses, such as pity, fear and pride.

campaign setup for "momentum," *i.e.* enthusiasm, zeal and determination. These are, of course, emotional drives but he has harnessed them to rational ends and he purposes to use rational means of expressing them.

Addleman definitely submerges the emotional to the logical appeals. No crippled children parade across his platforms. If you give money or support to his crippled children's hospital, you do so because you believe that the care of such youngsters is an important social problem which his institution is meeting in a sound and intelligent way. He definitely will not draw tears to your eyes with the pathetic story of "little Joe." There is too much likelihood that later you will be annoyed at having fallen prey to such a tale and will vent your anger on the offending institution.

The Task of Interpretation

Neither Jones nor Addleman specifically says anything in his set of principles about the necessity of presenting the ideas developed by scientific study in a way adapted to the level and caliber of the minds they are intended to reach. Such adaptation was doubtless taken for granted, however, as both men are experts in this work.*

It is, however, no easy task to translate complicated ideas that have many ramifications into simple catchphrases or stereotypes that will have a sound emotional appeal and will at the same time be true to the scientific

---

*After this chapter was written, Jones and his associate, David M. Church, published a small book entitled *At the Bar of Public Opinion.* This book sets forth Jones' ideas about public relations more fully than is done in *The Technique to Win in Fund Raising.* Although it is aimed primarily at industrialists, there is much in it of value to hospitals and other social institutions. In this book the need for interpretation is given expression. Particular stress is put upon public opinion as the force in public relations.

investigation which produced them. Suppose, for example, study has indicated the need for a pay diagnostic clinic. It has been discovered that the family physicians of the community need help in diagnosing difficult cases. There are available sufficient specialists to provide the diagnoses but, when they work as individuals without definite pooling of abilities, the results are either incomplete or are too costly for the majority of the population. The matter has been studied from all angles. The specialists are willing and ready to pool their knowledge for certain hours during the week. Thoughtful and conscientious family practitioners are willing to refer patients under conditions that will safeguard their interests in their clients. It has been decided what class of persons will be accepted for diagnosis and what scale of charges will be made. The schedule of payments to the participating physicians has been set. The hospital has agreed to provide adjunct personnel and facilities and to carry the administrative responsibility.

Such a situation is obviously loaded with dynamite for the unsophisticated public relations man. Naturally the service needs to be described to physicians in the service area and to members of the public who might have need of it. Funds may be needed to provide some additional equipment and to assure the project's success during an initial trial period. While the publicity must indicate the need for such a service, it must not cast aspersions upon the general level of diagnosis in the community or in any way deprecate the ability of the physicians. It should clearly not threaten their economic position or embarrass them in their relations with patients. The impression should not be given that by this one move all the medical economic problems of the community will be solved.

It takes careful study to find a method of expressing
the idea of a pay diagnostic clinic in terms that are simple
yet have the right emotional appeal and avoid the dangers
inherent in any simple expression of a complex and perhaps controversial issue. There are two ways of finding
the right answer to this problem. One is by intuition;
the other, by careful analysis of all the factors concerned
and systematic selection and criticism of the various
possibilities involved. The former is sometimes a brilliant success and is at other times a dismal failure. The
second method is always reasonably successful and frequently just as brilliant.

Difficulty in translating complex ideas into simple
language is not unique in the hospital field. For many
years the newspapers and scientists of the country strug-
gled with this task with little success, the scientists
believing that the newspapers garbled and misinterpreted
their results while the newspapers complained that the
scientists wished to carry along so much unnecessary
intellectual baggage that the principal idea was buried
beneath a burden of qualifications, exceptions and conditions. In recent years substantial progress has been made
through the development of newspaper men who are well
grounded in science. Many newspapers rely on Science
Service for this interpretive work; a few have highly
qualified scientists on their own reportorial staffs.

Something of the same sort should happen for hospitals. There should be developed as rapidly as possible
a group of men who are thoroughly familiar with medical
and hospital service and the general aspects of hospital
administration. They should be familiar with the technics of social investigation. Finally, they should be well
grounded in the technical aspects of publicity.

At present there are almost no such people available. The nearest approach to them are a few of the best men in the fund raising firms and a few men that are being developed in hospital care insurance organizations. One or two hospitals have added to their staffs men who have the basic public relations training and are giving them intensive training in hospital service so that eventually these men will be highly skilled. In a few rare and happy instances, an administrator possesses all of the qualities required to direct a public relations program competently. Occasionally an advertising man rises far above the usual routine and qualifies as a public relations counsel.

Under these circumstances the most promising course, for most hospitals wishing to follow the scientific procedure, is to employ a competent hospital consultant for the investigative work and to engage an able public relations man to work with him in interpreting the study to the public at all stages and in carrying forward its recommendations after the study itself has been completed. In a few communities, notably the New York metropolitan area, surveys have already been made by competent experts and the problem is largely one of bringing the program of the individual institution into line with the general program for the community. Fortunately there are several consultants who are qualified to make worth-while hospital surveys.

When community-wide investigative work must be done, it will often be difficult for one hospital alone to find enough money to make it as comprehensive as it should be. Hence, whenever possible, all the hospitals of the community should pool their resources or obtain special funds to finance a thorough and reliable survey. This is most readily accomplished through a strong hospital council or similar organization.

When all of these methods of study and exposition seem to be out of reach, the hospital must of necessity rely upon its administrator or some member of its board of trustees to make the study and to interpret the hospital to the community and the community to the hospital. This requires considerable objectivity, more than most of us possess. While it is unlikely that either the administrator or any member of the board will be expert in all aspects of public relations, valuable work can be done by them and a groundwork laid for the employment of an expert later.

The Place of Ethics

Unfortunately no existing code of ethics gives any clear guidance to hospital authorities regarding the conduct of their public relations programs. But, because of their intimate relation to physicians, hospitals will be influenced by the ethics of medicine. The principles of medical ethics of the American Medical Association contain the following statements which are more or less germane to the present subject.

Chapter I, Section 1. — A profession has for its prime object the service it can render to humanity; reward or financial gain should be a subordinate consideration. . . . Section 2. — The ethical principles actuating and governing a group or clinic are exactly the same as those applicable to the individual. . . .

Chapter II, Section 1. — Patience and delicacy should characterize all the acts of a physician. The confidences concerning individual or domestic life entrusted by a patient to a physician and the defects of disposition or flaws of character observed in patients during medical attendance should be held as a trust and should never be revealed except when imperatively required by the laws of the state. . . .

Chapter III, Section 4. — Solicitation of patients by physicians as individuals, or collectively in groups by whatsoever name these be called, or by institutions or organizations, whether by circulars or advertisements, or by personal communications, is unprofessional. This does not prohibit ethical institutions from a legitimate advertisement of location, physical surroundings and special class — if any — of patients accommodated. It is equally unprofessional to procure patients by indirection through solicitors or agents of any kind, or by indirect advertisement or by furnishing or inspiring newspaper or magazine comments concerning cases in which the physician has been or is concerned. All other like self-laudations defy the traditions and lower the tone of any profession and so are intolerable. The most worthy and effective advertisement possible, even for a young physician, and especially with his brother physicians, is the establishment of a well-merited reputation for professional ability and fidelity. . . .

Chapter IV, Section 1. — Physicians, as good citizens and because their professional training specially qualifies them to render this service, should give advice concerning the public health of the community. . . . They should be ready to counsel the public on subjects relating to sanitary police, public hygiene and legal medicine. . . . Section 2. — Physicians, especially those engaged in public health work, should enlighten the public regarding quarantine regulations; on the location, arrangement and dietaries of hospitals, asylums, schools, prisons and similar institutions; and concerning measures for the prevention of epidemic and contagious diseases. . . .

These principles obviously were drawn up to apply primarily to individuals and not to social agencies like hospitals. Nevertheless, hospital public relations activities should observe the principles regarding public service, delicacy, confidential nature of information about patients, self-laudation and public leadership in health education.

The question of solicitation of patients is, of course, the most difficult one and here the code of ethics is of little help. Obviously many of the public relations efforts of hospitals will be directed toward an increase of patronage. This is a legitimate and proper effort provided the methods used comport with the dignity and scientific character of the hospital.

A little more light is thrown on this question by the following code of ethics for hospital publicity prepared by its committee for public education and adopted by the American Hospital Association.

I — Publicity by clinics, hospitals, sanatoria and other semipublic institutions as to quality of work done implies unusual and exceptional ability and efficiency on the part of their professional staffs and, therefore, is advertising of the medical men concerned. This type of advertising distinctly savors of quackery and is unethical.

II — Publicity by any such institution stating or implying that by reason of its exceptionally fine equipment and material resources it is able to, or does, give the public better medical service than similar institutions are able or willing to render is advertising for purposes of self-aggrandizement. Statements of this type are frequently exaggerated and misleading and are detrimental to the best interests of the public, of the institutions concerned and of true medical progress.

III — From time to time, hospitals, sanatoria and other similar medical institutions must raise funds from an interested public for capital expenditure and maintenance. Furnishing the public with facts concerning such an institution, its work, its aims and its ideals is legitimate and desirable. The public is interested in these facts and, therefore, is entitled to know them. Publicity dealing with these facts is ethical, provided, of course, that it refrains from any comparisons or superlative terms either direct or implied.

IV — Publicity carried on by any one institution should be such as will be beneficial to all like institutions in the community. It should tend to develop public confidence in hospitals, sanatoria and other medical institutions. It should be free from superlative or comparative statements and any implication of rate-cutting or unfair competition.

This code, too, leaves much to be desired in definiteness. For example, may a hospital that never refuses to admit a patient and that has had only four maternal deaths in 2000 consecutive deliveries state that fact in its annual report and in newspaper articles based upon the figures in the annual report? Certainly this is a "fact" concerning the institution's work. The public is interested in this fact. On the other hand, it is publicity concerning the quality of work done and it very properly implies unusual and exceptional ability. In spite of this implication, if no comparisons derogatory to other institutions are made and if the limitations of mortality rates as indices of hospital quality are clearly indicated, such publicity appears to be entirely ethical.

Take another example. A hospital staff has tried a new method of anesthesia on 750 patients and the carefully tabulated results have been published in a medical journal. Is not the hospital justified in bringing that fact to the knowledge of its constituents? Or it has engaged an outstanding pathologist to head its clinical laboratories. Or it is the first hospital in the community to put all employes on an eight hour day and a 48 hour week.

All of these things do indicate a hospital's excellence. But if the facts are allowed to speak for themselves and no derogatory comparisons are made with other institutions, such facts can properly be given to the public.

In his book, *Hospital Organization and Management,* Dr. Malcolm T. MacEachern has attempted to give more definite meaning to the American Hospital Association code.[7] He has added the following five statements.

1. Solicitation of patients by the hospital or by any person connected with it is unethical.

2. The hospital may not admit patients at a rate below the cost of actual care except in dispensing acknowledged charity.

3. Physicians, nurses and others actively employed in hospital work are to be given treatment at the actual cost of the service rendered.

4. The individual hospital is expected to uphold the honor and dignity of the hospital field.

5. Ethical members of the different professions and specialties embraced in the hospital organization will uphold the dignity and honor of their own special lines of endeavor and of the hospital as a whole by becoming members of their respective societies and by devoting time, energy and means to the elevation and advancement of their own particular field.

These principles and the discussion that accompanies them in Doctor MacEachern's book are helpful but they still leave much to interpretation. For example, is a booklet about the hospital, mailed to former patients, "solicitation of patients"? What is "actual cost"? Does it include interest on donated capital and depreciation on investment? Does it include the value of donated services?

Unfortunately the American Hospital Association has set up no judicial council or other body to interpret the code of ethics as it applies to particular instances. Until this is done there will be only *ex cathedra* statements on the subject and the present vagueness will continue.

The entire discussion of ethics really simmers down to a matter of good taste. Physicians and hospitals have an ethical duty to inform the public concerning matters of public health, since they have peculiar opportunities to know about these subjects. They must avoid unscientific statements, unjustified and undignified claims and self-laudation. They should act with dignity. Since there is no body to decide what is ethical in each instance, the responsibility falls upon the individual hospital to enforce these ethical concepts upon itself and, insofar as it is able, upon the independent news gathering and distributing agencies.

Summary

Let us try now to weave together the various theories and see if we can obtain a consistent and workable set of principles of public relations for a hospital or other social institution.

1. The first requisite of a good public relations program is that the institution provide good hospital service. This includes as comprehensive service as could reasonably be expected from each hospital according to its size; emphasis on quality of care in all details; awareness of social responsibilities, and provision of methods of payment that make service available to those who need it.

2. The hospital should adapt its service to changes in public needs, placing emphasis upon qualitative as well as quantitative aspects. To determine these changes it should periodically or continuously make rigorously objective and scientific analyses of needs.

3. Its service program should be in accord with progressive and important public movements, should be "bigger than the institution," as Jones phrases it.

4. The institution should be entirely open and above-board in all dealings with donors and the general public. There is no excuse for secrecy regarding important facts.

5. Its work should appeal to the emotions or personal interests of most people.

6. Its emotional appeal should not be allowed to overshadow or submerge its rational appeal.

7. Its work should appeal to the intelligent, informed minority on logical and rational grounds.

8. Its trustees and other leaders should be strong influential persons representing all the larger groups in the service area. They themselves should be thoroughly convinced of the institution's social utility.

9. It should be competently and intelligently administered. Every dollar spent should produce a full dollar's worth of service.

10. Rational resistance should be dissipated by welcoming honest criticism, regardless of how unintelligent it may be, rather than by suppressing or overpowering it.

11. The public relations program should not be based on any self-made assumptions of soundness. Such assumptions make the institution vulnerable to criticism. Without them it can welcome criticism without embarrassment.

12. Publicity methods should be organic with and grow out of plans for internal development. Proper publicity can assist in ascertaining needs and developing plans for meeting them. Likewise, study of needs and development of plans are themselves the best materials for publicity.

13. Publicity should be in keeping with the ideas and organizations publicized. Hence, for hospitals it should be dignified, entirely honest and rigorously scientific.

14. While dignified, a hospital's publicity should, nevertheless, be prepared in terms suited to the amount of time, interest and intellect which the recipient will probably give to it. This requires selection, interpretation and highspotting of the facts, a process of simplification without distortion.

15. All mediums of publicity should be considered and those utilized which are most appropriate to the particular idea to be expressed.

16. The publicity and promotion must be ethical. To be ethical they should avoid any form of exaggeration, should not reflect adversely upon other institutions, should be strictly scientific and honest in expression and should be in good taste. To date, the rules determining what is ethical are so vague that actual decisions must be left to each institution.

17. High pressure efforts do not allow opportunity for rational criticism and adjustment. They rely primarily upon emotional drives. Hence, in most instances low pressure programs are distinctly preferable. This involves what Bernays calls continuous interpretation. It does not preclude dramatization of the hospital's needs or objectives so long as the dramatization is sincere and genuine.

18. While the soundest program is low pressure in character, the tempo will naturally be stepped up from time to time to accomplish specific objectives in the total program, *e.g.* to raise funds for a needed building or a new department.

19. The program should be permeated throughout with the realization that the public has paid the bill for hospitals in the past and will do so in one form or another in the future. Hence, the institution should be alert to

discern public needs and protect public interests. This requires a community-wide viewpoint of hospital problems that is broad enough to assure cooperation and integration of the services of various hospitals. Cutthroat competition between institutions is decidedly not in the public interest.

20. To carry out this program, a hospital needs to have available, on full or on part time, a person who is skilled in (a) scientific technics of social investigation, particularly as they apply to needs and problems in the hospital field, and (b) technics of interpretation and publicity. If this combination is not available in one person, a competent hospital consultant may work with an able public relations counsel. As Jones and Addleman have pointed out, hospitals should not think that a survey made by a fund raising organization as a part of its new business promotion is the type of study and survey required as a basis for a public relations program.

21. The public relations program should be, in theory and in fact, a real service to the public. It should assist people to take better care of their health and to receive the maximum value from their medical and hospital expenditures. It should also interpret to the hospital the needs of the public.

REFERENCES

1. Young, Kimball: Source Book of Social Psychology, Alfred Knopf, New York City, 1927, p. 580.
2. Lindeman, E. C.: The Community, Association Press, New York City, 1921, Chap. IX. (Quoted in Young, *op. cit.*)
3. Bernays, Edward L.: Propaganda, Horace Liveright, New York City, 1928, pp. 50-51.
4. Bernays, Edward L.: *Op. cit.*, pp. 43, 69.
5. Jones, John Price: The Technique to Win in Fund Raising, Inter-River Press, New York City, 1934.
6. Addleman, Perry: Hospital Support and Development — A Public Relations Problem, *The Modern Hospital*, Aug., 1934, p. 33, Sept., 1934, p. 73, Oct., 1934, p. 71.
7. MacEachern, Malcolm T.: Hospital Organization and Management, Physicians' Record Company, Chicago, 1935, pp. 790-794. See also Editorial: Progress and Publicity, *The Modern Hospital*, Dec., 1932, p. 88, and Code of Ethics, Canadian Medical Association, Toronto, 1939.

Chapter 4

GOOD
HOSPITAL SERVICE

THE VERY cornerstone of a sound and effective public relations program is the provision of good hospital service. Without it a public relations program may merely stir up smoldering antagonisms and bring hospital shortcomings to public attention, thus building up resistance. It is important, therefore, to analyze just what is meant by good hospital service.

In a community where there is only one hospital, the responsibility of that institution is reasonably clear. It must do its best to provide all the types of hospital service which are needed by the residents of its service area, except such types as can properly be provided only at some center serving a larger number of people. Thus a 50 or 100 bed community hospital would be expected to provide medical, surgical, obstetric and pediatric services but would not today be expected to have a serum center, a radium bomb or a fever therapy service.

In metropolitan communities, of course, there is need for greater specialization. If the entire hospital facilities of the community adequately meet all of the important needs of the whole population, it is quite proper that some institutions should care for one group in the population and others, for another, provided this specialization is not carried to the point where it interferes with the quality of service or becomes uneconomic. The Hospital Survey for New York[1] recommended that the smaller special

56

hospitals be merged with general hospitals to improve quality of service and cut down needless duplication of overhead expenses. Metropolitan communities should study their hospital facilities as a whole, as New York City has done, and prepare programs based upon this whole view of the situation.

No one can lay down a definition of good hospital service which will remain true indefinitely. Good hospital service changes as rapidly as do the basic medical, physical and social sciences upon which it rests. Without attempting to define it rigidly, however, we may set up the following criteria for testing a hospital as to quality and scope of its service. An institution offering good hospital service will meet its proper share of the responsibilities enumerated under each of these criteria.

In-Patient and Outpatient Service for All Major Types of Disease

Nearly every community that has any hospital facilities will care for medical, surgical, obstetric, gynecologic and pediatric cases. Special provisions, however, are often advantageous for various subgroups under these broad classifications, provided the specialization has not gone too far.[2] Under medicine, for example, special outpatient and in-patient services may well be set up, in metropolitan communities, for endocrine, gastro-intestinal, metabolic, diabetic, cardiac, pulmonary, allergic and similar cases. Special provision for the care of premature infants has been influential in reducing mortality among them.[3] Many progressive hospitals provide maternal welfare clinics.

Dermatology is another specialty of medicine that merits recognition in the hospital. If the department of dermatology does not include the care of patients with a venereal disease, some other provision should be made for meeting the needs of this large group of people and adequate follow-up should be provided to keep them under treatment.[4]

Often surgery, also, may be advantageously divided into brain surgery, abdominal surgery, orthopedics, emergency and traumatic surgery and similar branches. Adequately manned and equipped tumor clinics should be available throughout the country at strategic locations.[5] The eye, ear, nose and throat department or departments of surgery are of long standing in large hospitals. Whether organized as separate departments or not, skilled service in these fields should be available to all people.

A separate department of urology and proctology has been found to be important in rendering improved service to patients with diseases in these categories. At least one hospital of only 100 beds successfully operates such a department.[6]

Most of the services so far mentioned have been relatively well supplied by hospitals in the past, although sometimes not with the degree of specialism that is now considered desirable. There are types of patients, however, that often are inadequately served or entirely neglected. They include convalescent, chronic, mild psychopathic, tuberculous, epileptic, alcoholic and narcotic patients and persons with communicable and dental diseases.

Facilities for mental and tuberculous patients are restricted almost entirely to government owned hospitals and a few proprietary institutions. Patients in these categories who would prefer to pay a modest amount for

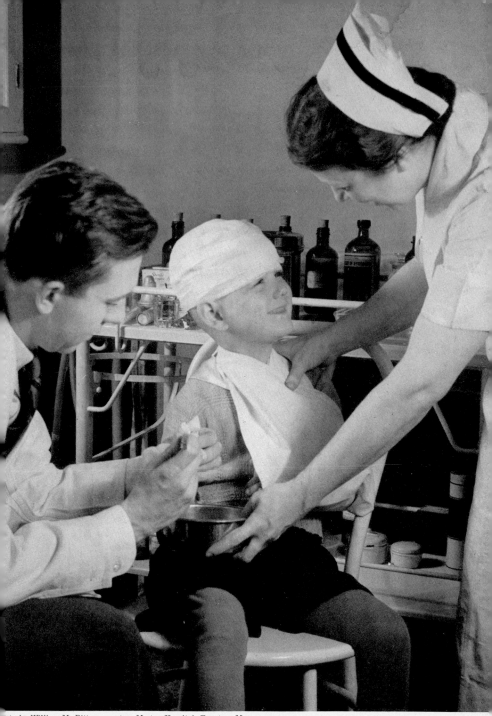

oto by William M. Rittase, courtesy Morton Hospital, Taunton, Mass.

A progressive and intelligent medical staff serving outpatients
as well as bed patients is the brain of the modern hospital.

their care usually find that voluntary hospitals do not accept such cases. They must either pay high rates in proprietary institutions for service which in some instances is of questionable quality or must accept care in government owned institutions. Furthermore, facilities in the latter are frequently overcrowded and the hospitals have long waiting lists.[7]

The need for additional hospital facilities for convalescent and chronic patients has been repeatedly demonstrated.[8] Yet, to date, in most communities the services are distinctly inadequate in amount and often in quality. New York City, although it already has the largest voluntary hospital in the country for chronic disease patients, is now also taking the lead in providing facilities for these patients through government action. As yet almost no other community has seriously tackled this problem.

Epileptics and alcoholics and patients with drug addiction are sometimes refused treatment for these conditions because hospitals are not equipped to cope with the special problems that they present. Somewhere in the community, however, there should be facilities for their care.

The care of communicable diseases in a general hospital presents peculiar difficulties because public understanding has not kept pace with the development of scientific aseptic technics; the fluctuation in demand involves serious economic problems.[9] This is an important service, however, and one that the public should be taught to support on a scale sufficient to the community.

The amount of uncared for dental disease and defects is appalling. In 1935, for example, the committee on community dental service of the New York Tuberculosis and Health Association stated that among adults not over 25 per cent paid for anything approaching adequate

dental care and only 3.5 per cent of the population of
New York were cared for in clinics.[10] This latter figure
is probably lower in most other communities. Thus over
70 per cent of the people obtain inadequate dental care
or none at all. While this problem is probably too large
for hospitals to solve individually or even collectively, it
would be well to make a start on it.

As medicine advances, other specialties or special fields
of service will be suggested. The foregoing list is not
intended to be exhaustive but merely illustrative. Certainly every hospital should make a careful analysis to
determine how fully it provides all these services.

In nearly every instance the services listed above
should be provided to outpatients as well as in-patients.[10a]
The outpatient department should be well organized,
under competent medical and administrative direction
and provided with sufficient space, equipment and personnel to facilitate the service. Its value in the teaching
of nurses and of the resident medical staff should be
fully realized.

Whether to organize a special department for each
specialty or merely to group the services in a few broad
divisions will depend upon the circumstances in each
individual case. Ordinarily a special department is justified only when there are one or more strong able men to
serve in it. Hospital trustees and administrators should
recognize that it is relatively easy to add departments
but quite difficult to abolish them.

Service for All Racial, Economic,
    Social and Age Groups

All persons in the community must have some place
to obtain good hospital care. If there are many hospitals

and they choose to specialize in caring for various groups, this may be acceptable provided no groups are consistently given poor care. Such specialization is dangerous, however, and likely to lead to discrimination.

A community may be classified into various divisions, depending upon one's point of view. There are in most American communities various racial and religious groups. The ones most frequently neglected are those with the least secure economic positions or those against which there is some racial antipathy. Hospitals should be sure that good service is available to Negroes, Orientals, Mexicans or any other racial groups found in the community. Likewise, there should be good service for Protestant, Catholic and Jew.

All economic classes need hospital care, although the well-to-do apparently need somewhat less care than those with little means, since sickness decreases as income increases. Hospitals should analyze their facilities to see that they have appropriate service for the wealthy, the white-collar workers, the industrial and agricultural laborers and those who are partially employed, transient or indigent. Many hospitals in the past have built as though they thought the majority of people were wealthy, an assumption that does violence to the facts.[11] Hospitals need not provide a degree of luxury that is out of keeping with the habits of the community.

Unmarried mothers present a special problem to the hospital. They need and should receive maternity care of just as high quality as is given to other mothers. Furthermore, the hospital should be willing and prepared to help them in their social adjustments. The consensus today is that in most such cases the major responsibility for social adjustment should be carried by a child or family welfare agency, but the hospital should cooperate whole-heartedly and intelligently with this agency.[12]

The need for care of those persons with venereal diseases has already been mentioned.

On an age classification, too, there are special services needed. Premature infants, full-term infants, children, adolescents, adults and the aged all have distinctive requirements. Hospitals should analyze their services from this point of view.

Well Rounded Care to Each Patient

The mere fact that a patient is accepted by a hospital does not, of itself, ensure that he will receive good hospital care. Some patients receive little or no benefit from their hospital stay even when it is in a good institution. When this is true because there are still gaps in our scientific knowledge, there is little the hospital can do except wait for the advance of medical science to mop up on these unoccupied areas. But when it is due to lack of proper tools and services and those tools and services have already been made available by science, it constitutes a distinct challenge to the administrator, the board of trustees, the medical staff and the contributing public.

Well rounded service to even a single patient makes a great many different requirements of a hospital. Such service to all types of patients multiplies these requirements. Without attempting to list every possible skill or tool that is essential or desirable, some idea of the scope of the requirements will be given.

The first requirement for well rounded care is a visiting and resident medical staff composed of able, ethical and conscientious physicians. Without good physicians, the best of equipment and of ancillary services will be of little use. A progressive and intelligent medical staff is the brain of any hospital, activating, directing and co-ordinating the work of all the other departments in the institution. Various aspects of the work of the medical staff are discussed elsewhere in this chapter and in later chapters.

Skilled nursing service is the backbone of good hospital care. No hospital today is worthy of the name unless it has a staff of capable nurses. They must be adequate in number, well trained in their various duties, courteous and considerate in attitude and working on a schedule and under conditions that preserve vigor and effectiveness and stimulate a desire for higher standards of service and knowledge.[13] If a nursing school is maintained, a sufficient number of graduates must be employed to provide good service to patients while permitting the student nurses to take time for their studies. Through the use of aids or attendants, many hospitals today provide better nursing than they otherwise could. If properly regulated and controlled, such attendants can help to stretch a strained hospital budget without lowering standards of nursing service.[14] Good hospitals are beginning to provide floor nursing service in sufficient amount and quality to meet all the real needs of the patient. Private duty nursing is gradually disappearing.

A third vital function is an adequate food service. Hospital food must meet more rigorous demands than food prepared for healthy persons. It should be more attractive to the patient and must be nicely adjusted to his needs, both clinical and psychological. Many stories of hospital thoughtlessness in food selection pass from person to person today, even though hospital food standards have been extensively raised in the past two decades.

But some hospitals still serve coarse scratchy food to patients who have just had their tonsils removed or put a heavy workman's meal before a patient accustomed to delicate servings.

The first contact with patients is often in the admitting department. While some persons might consider that it was stretching a point to call the admitting and discharging department one that served the patient, actually it should do so. It should make as sure as humanly possible that the patient is assigned to the proper type of accommodations and is received in such a courteous, friendly manner that his confidence in the hospital is strengthened or restored. Care should be exercised to convey to the patient the fact that the hospital is interested in him as much as or more than it is interested in his pocketbook.[15] The same care should be exercised in discharging patients since often the final impression is psychologically important.

For patients who have serious economic and social problems, a good medical social service department is an essential, at least in a large city. The prime function of this department is to aid the doctor in treating the patient by providing him with as clear an understanding of the mental and emotional processes at work on the patient as he has of the physical handicaps under which the patient is suffering. The doctor and the social worker must often work out a social therapy just as carefully as the doctor and his medical colleagues work out a physical course of treatment.[16] Another hospital responsibility which the social service department may assume under the direction of the medical staff and administration is the systematic follow-up of discharged patients to determine the end results of in-patient and outpatient care.

Only by such a follow-up service can the hospital accurately judge the effectiveness of its work.

In addition to the personalized attention of the medical social worker, there are other aspects of the patient's general well-being that can be served while he is in the hospital. A hostess may usher him to his room, assist in getting in touch with relatives, write letters or telephone for him and in other ways express the hospital's concern for his mental comfort.[17] Many patients appreciate the ministrations of religion while they are confined in a hospital. Such comfort should be available and arrangements made for obtaining rabbi, priest or minister, promptly, when desired. A well trained hospital chaplain can be an exceedingly useful person in an institution that is so large that it tends to become impersonal.[18] A third personal service, recently labeled "bibliotherapy," requires the presence of a skilled librarian. She assists patients in choosing books that are suitable to their interest and their condition.[19] "To allow patients to read without expert supervision is analagous to allowing a diabetic to eat indiscriminatingly," according to Dr. Gordon R. Kamman.

An adequate ambulance service is essential. In most large communities this is provided by the city and in a few, by undertakers or other miscellaneous persons. It is, however, a specialized work and should not be entrusted to any Tom, Dick or Harry. Arrangements should be made with the proper governmental officials so that competent ambulance service is always available, even to those who cannot pay.[20] If interns ride the ambulances, the cars should be housed in or adjacent to hospitals so that the interns' time between calls can be properly utilized. There is considerable doubt today whether the educational value of this service justifies taking an intern's time for it.

Discussion of ambulance service naturally leads to thought of the emergency department. Good hospital care cannot be given to accident cases without an organized emergency service, ready within a few minutes to deal with any emergency that may arise.

The compounding of prescriptions is a service of important trust.[21] Most large hospitals have this well organized with an experienced registered pharmacist in charge. In some of the smaller institutions, however, compounding is done by amateurs — nurses and others. This is a dangerous and unwise expedient. If arrangements cannot be made to employ a qualified hospital pharmacist either full time or shared with another hospital, a contract should be made with the best qualified pharmacist in the community.

Clinical and pathologic laboratory service is a vital point in hospital care. It is short sighted to look upon this department of the hospital as a revenue producer. The pathologist should be a man of unquestioned ability, meriting and commanding the respect of the members of the medical staff and constantly stimulating them to higher standards. Obviously he must make any criticism of the medical staff tactfully. If he is too blunt, for example, in pointing out shortcomings of the surgeons, he may jeopardize his own position, for it is a rare and courageous board of trustees that will support the pathologist against the united opposition of the surgical staff. The pathologist should lead rather than drive the staff. He should stimulate an abiding interest in pathology on the part of other staff members, particularly surgeons.[22] The autopsy percentage should be substantial and, more important, each necropsy should be fully utilized for its teaching value to the visiting and resident medical staffs.

The larger hospitals should examine their laboratory service to determine whether it is providing all of the types of investigation and advice which the medical staff can effectively use. There may be need for the services of a biochemist or a physicist or some other type of scientist or technician not customarily employed in hospitals.[23]

The scope and value of radiologic service grow year by year. A quarter century ago hospitals had relatively little x-ray equipment and what they had would now seem most primitive. Today all hospitals have some x-ray apparatus and many of them have large departments with facilities for meeting all present x-ray needs. A competently trained radiologist, like an expert pathologist, is a hospital necessity. Equipment for deep therapy, fluoroscopy, dental x-rays, stereoscopy, radium therapy and other types of radiologic service should all be considered by the hospital. Radium and deep therapy, of course, can be provided only by the larger institutions and should not be offered except when the personnel is thoroughly trained.

An adequate anesthesia service is becoming increasingly important as the available anesthetics multiply in number. Putting reliance upon general practitioners or other physicians without training in anesthesia to perform anesthesia service is hazardous. The progressive hospital today insists that its anesthesias be given by persons, whether physicians or nurses, who have had special training in the field. And the well organized hospital provides as competent direction for its anesthesia department as it does for its radiologic or pathologic departments.[24]

Closely allied to the anesthesia department is the gas therapy service. Today the administration of oxygen is firmly established as a hospital procedure for many types of patients. Helium is also being widely tried. The use of resuscitation and artificial respiration is among the most dramatic of hospital services, often commanding wide public attention. The fact that these have sometimes been injudiciously exploited for publicity purposes should not blind the hospital to their true merit. A well trained medical anesthetist can often take over the entire field of gas therapy, much to the benefit of the quality of hospital care.

In the larger hospitals, at least, the physical therapy department has proved to be of untold value. As in so many other fields of hospital activity, the quality of personnel in this department is far more important than the amount and scope of equipment. "Many hospital physical therapy departments with good equipment and poorly trained personnel have failed in their functions," state Drs. J. S. Coulter and W. H. Northway, "but a department with good personnel, with or without elaborate equipment, will grow and expand."[25]

The use of fever therapy for certain conditions now seems to be well established.[26] Such therapy should only be administered by specially trained personnel.

Electrocardiography is now a well established and useful hospital procedure. New equipment is placed on the market from time to time to make the findings more exact or more readily available.[27] Metabolism tests also are used with increasing frequency and here, too, both the tools and the skills are advancing.

Intravenous therapy has grown tremendously during the past decade and no limit seems yet to have been reached. Year by year more and more patients are benefitted by injections of one type or another.[28]

Blood transfusions are given now with much greater frequency than they were a generation ago. Occasionally, of course, a transfusion is given merely to impress the patient or the relatives. But far more often it is ordered because of a sincere and well founded belief that it will be of definite benefit. The mounting cost of blood for transfusion has led recently to the exploration of new sources. Many hospitals use blood "banks," which assure them a ready supply of tested and typed blood for immediate use. Some have experimented with placental blood and, in Russia at least, with cadaver blood. Other hospitals and the American Red Cross have built up groups of voluntary blood donors to aid those who need transfusions but who are too poor to pay the cost of employing donors.[29]

The use of convalescent human serum in the treatment of various contagious diseases has apparently proved of value. Several hospitals in various parts of the country have set up serum centers in order to meet this need. While one serum center is usually all that a particular community needs, there are still many communities without this service.[30]

Practically any hospital of size needs an occupational therapy department. This work is beneficial to the psychological condition of patients; it often aids in restoring function to maimed or crippled limbs and joints, and sometimes it helps effect vocational readjustments that are necessitated by illness and its sequalae.[31] Entertainment and diversion for convalescent and chronically ill patients is often under the direction of the occupational therapy department.

Another essential of good care to patients is a careful system of medical records. These should be full and complete, properly indexed and cross-indexed and filed in a readily accessible manner. Accuracy of the medical record is of even more importance than accuracy of the financial record. Medical data should be studied as carefully and thoughtfully as any balance sheet or statement of income and expense. The confidential character of medical records must, of course, be respected at all times.

Many other types of service might be mentioned but the foregoing list covers the leading ones. Before it can be printed, however, it probably will be out of date. New discoveries and inventions constantly challenge hospitals to keep abreast.

As was mentioned at the beginning of this chapter, small hospitals are not expected and should not try to provide all of the services here listed. But they should come as near as possible to giving complete care to those patients whom they accept for treatment. Frequently, in order to do this, workers must be found who combine two or three skills. For example, a dietitian may also be a housekeeper; the record librarian may also keep the accounts and handle admissions; a pharmacist may also have received training as a laboratory, physical therapy or x-ray technician.

A medical school or state university might assist several small hospitals to develop a plan whereby they could send their specimens and films to the medical school laboratories and receive prompt reports by telephone. To be truly effective, however, this work should be supplemented by regular visits to the hospitals by a radiologist and a pathologist associated with the medical school who would supervise the work of the hospitals' technicians, be available for consultation with the medical staffs and participate in the staff meetings. Skilled dietetic service might also be made available on a comparable system, with a dietitian spending one or two days a week in each of several hospitals and being available for consultation by telephone at any time.

It is even more important to make arrangements whereby difficult medical and surgical cases can be sent in to a central hospital for diagnosis, surgery or complicated therapy for which the small hospital does not have suitable equipment or personnel. The family doctor in the small hospital should be kept in close touch with the case and it should be referred back to him as soon as he can safely resume responsibility.

Highest Attainable Quality

Many of the things previously discussed have an important bearing on the quality of hospital service as well as upon its quantity and scope. Quality is so important that the board of trustees should keep this subject before itself constantly and also make special inquiry from time to time.

It is difficult, of course, for any lay group to judge the quality of medical care. Certain tests can easily be made, however. Has the hospital won the full approval of the American College of Surgeons? If large enough, is it approved for intern training and for the training of residents by the American Medical Association? Are the heads of its various clinical departments certified as specialists by the appropriate specialty boards? Are the heads of administrative departments recognized as competent by their professional confreres, especially where this recognition involves the meeting of definite professional requirements?

These more or less objective tests of quality are useful but not conclusive. They all rest upon the theory of standardization at high levels. Standardization is valuable as a milepost and direction sign. It is not an end in itself. The hospital that has achieved approval by the various standardizing bodies must not rest content; if it does, standardization becomes a sedative and a bar to progress instead of a stimulus.

Each hospital and each individual that have won approval of standardizing bodies must take that as a base from which to push on to higher peaks. This can be achieved through the pursuit of distinguished service — systematic and rational individualism based upon real needs and special talents to meet those needs. In such a situation encouragement should be given to the individual or group with the special talent so that it may be developed to its fullest extent. Where there is no unusual aptitude, distinguished service is still possible through systematically uncovering and defining public needs, selecting those which the hospital can best fill and persistently endeavoring to fill them to the best of the hospital's ability.

The effect of distinguished service upon the hospital has been aptly phrased by Dr. O. F. Ball. "A hospital may be a distinguished institution no matter what its size. If it is great in spirit, original in its outlook, creative in its service and inspiring in its community relationships, it will assume a definite personality. Distinctive personal character on the part of an institution compels interest, commands respect and augments support. It is the most potent force in attracting and holding friends for the hospital and is a true and effective stimulant to progress."[32]

No concept of excellent hospital service can long be valid if it is static. A hospital rendering a high quality of service today will be only mediocre tomorrow if it does not constantly progress. Often the advances in hospital service are so gradual as to be almost imperceptible. At other times they are more rapid and widely heralded. When the latter occurs a board of trustees can readily determine whether its hospital is keeping pace.

An example of a widely heralded advance in hospital standards is ready at hand. For the past decade or longer, special attention has been focused upon the care of mothers and their children by such organizations as the specialty societies concerned, the Maternity Center Association, the Ohio Hospital Obstetric Society and the committee on maternal care of the American Hospital Association's council on administrative practice and community relations.

Then early in 1938, the various proposals of these groups congealed in new regulations adopted in Chicago and New York City governing the care of mothers and infants in hospitals.[33] The outstanding hospitals, of course, had been meeting the new standards or exceeding them voluntarily. The adoption of these regulations forced the hospitals of lower grade to pull themselves up rapidly to the level of the better institutions. Hospitals throughout the nation are watching the Chicago and New York experience with interest and many are falling in line with these standards voluntarily.

In its zeal for higher standards, the hospital should not be misled into thinking that these can be attained merely or primarily through the addition of better facilities and equipment. Tools are important but the mind back of the tools is vital. Standardizing programs have been severely criticized because of reputed overemphasis on equipment.[34]

A new type of audit is finding its way into the hospital field. This is the medical or professional audit, which subjects the work of the medical staff to the same type of objective evaluation that a firm of certified public accountants gives to the business office. A hospital should be far more concerned with the results of its medical audit than with those of its financial audit. One deals only in dollars; the other, in lives.[35]

If voluntary hospitals are to survive, they must be prepared for the changes which are inevitable in the provision and the distribution of medical service. Many able students of the social aspects of medicine believe that group practice organized around a hospital is as important and as inevitable as group payment. The principal benefit expected from group practice is a distinct improvement in the quality of service.

As previously stated, a comprehensive administrative survey that takes into account the financial, professional and social aspects of the hospital's work is invaluable in the development of a proper public relations program. Such a survey will aid the trustees materially in evaluating the quality of service which the hospital is rendering. Only a few people are competent to make such surveys but when properly made they are revealing and stimulating.

One aspect of a high quality of service that is often lacking in otherwise good hospitals is an adequate safety program. Such a program is designed to protect patients,

per photo by William Rittase, courtesy Toronto Western Hospital
ver photo by George U. Wood, Peralta Hospital, Oakland, Calif.

The medical social worker (above) and the Chinese girl serving early morning coffee are two symbols of the humane spirit.

employes and visitors from the many hazards of the hospital. Even in fine institutions, inspection sometimes reveals hazardous conditions in stairs and elevators, equipment not maintained in a safe condition, procedures in the pharmacy which may permit patients to receive the wrong prescriptions, incomplete controls over narcotics and other drugs, surgeons allowed to operate without adequate preoperative study, explosive gases carelessly stored or their safety caps removed prematurely, and anesthesia equipment which is not kept entirely clean and free from explosion hazards. Hospitals have all of the accident hazards found in hotels and scores of others in addition.

Fire and panic hazards also are peculiarly great in hospitals, since so many of the occupants could not walk to safety in case of fire. Of course, the fact that personnel are on duty 24 hours a day is a safeguard. Instruction and drill of all personnel should be regular procedures.

Safety engineers who are especially trained in hospital inspection work are not too plentiful but there are a few of them. The alert hospital should employ such men, either in connection with its insurance program or independently, to check all possible hazards at least annually.[36]

Cooperation in Public Health Work

No medical dollar is spent more advantageously than the one that prevents disease. Leadership in the prevention of disease must, of course, continue to rest in the hands of public health authorities. In the predictable future it appears unlikely that hospitals will devote as much of their effort to disease prevention as they do to treatment. Nevertheless, every hospital should be highly receptive to suggestions for preventive services and should do preventive work when it is indicated.[37]

The alert hospital administration is conscious of manifold opportunities for assisting in public health and preventive medicine. The various preventive clinics offer perhaps the most obvious and most frequent service rendered in this field by hospitals. These include prenatal, well baby, venereal disease, tuberculosis, psychiatric or mental hygiene, and health examination clinics. Some hospitals are carrying on important health education services through special clinics (*e.g.* food clinics), through lecture courses, radio talks, newspaper articles and other means.

The home care of certain types of patients apparently is satisfactory and is less expensive than hospital care. If there is no other agency that is better prepared to give this home care, an alert community hospital might well sponsor it, particularly in a small community. This would require the employment of visiting nurses and visiting housekeepers and, perhaps, even of physicians for the care of the indigent.

Adequate provision for the care of communicable disease was mentioned earlier under the first criterion of good hospital service. This, of course, is a public health service of major importance.

In some communities the hospital can cooperate effectively with the public health department by providing needed laboratory facilities. This is particularly true in smaller communities where it would be unnecessarily wasteful to have two pathologic laboratories, neither being used to more than a part of its capacity.

Intelligent and effective public health work is dependent in part upon prompt and accurate knowledge of disease conditions. Here is another place where a sympathetic hospital can assist the health department. Studies of various disease groups are essential from time to time to guide public health work. When a hospital is called upon to permit its records to be used for this purpose, it should respond generously, taking due safeguards, of course, to preserve the confidential character of the records and to keep them intact for their major purpose, the service of the patient and his physician.

Being a health agency, a hospital should practice the health precepts which it preaches. This requires a comprehensive health program for all personnel from the administrator to the ward maid. Such a program will save much illness among students and employes.

Cooperation With Other Hospital and Social Agencies

If a hospital is truly concerned with giving the public the best possible return for its investment, it will realize that cooperation rather than competition among hospitals is most productive of results. To take a simple illustration, when one hospital in a community has developed a serum center, if that center is adequate to the needs of the public, it would be shortsighted for another hospital to duplicate that service while at the same time the community lacked a tumor clinic or a physical therapy department. Likewise, when a community has adequate facilities for the care of maternity patients, a hospital should have good reasons indeed before it adds further maternity wards.

On a larger scale, also, hospitals should be ready to work together. In many instances it would be highly desirable if special hospitals would consolidate with well managed general hospitals so that a better service could be rendered by both. In other cases amalgamations could well be effected so that hospitals could reach the minimum size necessary for efficient administration. In large cities this has been set at 200 beds by Dr. Haven Emerson in his survey of the New York City metropolitan area.[38]

The need for coordinated community-wide hospital planning becomes more apparent each year. In the past entirely too much money and effort have been wasted in needless duplication of facilities while other more pressing needs have been neglected. This does not mean, of course, that all hospitals should be gathered into a few mammoth medical centers. As in industry so in hospitals, there is a point of optimum size. Beyond that, there is danger of increasing unwieldiness, advancing administrative costs and multiplication of administrative controls to the point where initiative is hampered by red tape and human contacts tend to yield to mechanization. But there are so few institutions that even approach this optimum size that this danger is much less real than the danger of poor administration, incomplete service and inadequate facilities and personnel inherent in a large number of small and uncoordinated hospital units.

In the larger cities there is obvious need for vigorous hospital councils that not only are concerned with rendering certain common services to their constituent members but also are continuously engaged in studying the hospital needs of the community and assisting in meeting those needs.[39] Hospital councils will not achieve their full potentialities unless they keep constantly before themselves this larger social usefulness as well as the specific services they can render through central credit and collection agencies, finance corporations, statistical studies and similar activities. The councils must achieve a position of such public confidence and trust that individual hospitals will be ready to make their own plans fit into a sound community pattern sponsored by the council.

In cities where there are too few hospitals to form an effective hospital council, the hospitals may well join with other health agencies in a health council. Even in cities where there are hospital councils, there should be close relation with other health agencies, either directly or through a health council. Physicians, dentists and nurses must all be considered as important parts in the health picture.

The fact that hospitals should cooperate with one another does not mean that all institutions should be reduced to a dead level of mediocrity. There is plenty of room within any rational community plan for development of distinguished service. True distinguished service, as was stated earlier, is based on community need and would, therefore, be given consideration in a proper community plan.

In addition to its relations to other hospitals and health agencies, the hospital should cooperate as occasion may offer with childcaring and family welfare agencies, with character building agencies, with safety groups and with other organizations for community betterment.

What specific relations hospitals should have to community chests or welfare councils and to councils of social agencies must depend upon the circumstances. In some cities, notably in Cleveland, the community chest and welfare federation provide hospitals with generous support. In other places, hospitals are nominally in the community chest but are given little support. In still other communities, hospitals are no longer members of

the community chest or have never been members. In
New York City, hospitals conduct their own joint fund
raising campaigns through the United Hospital Fund.
After much discussion this was finally chosen as preferable to making a common appeal with the Welfare
Federation; subsequent events seem to indicate that the
public will respond to both appeals put on separately at
least as well as they would to an amalgamated campaign,
and the hospitals will net a larger sum. Whether the
same would be true in another city, however, is not
known.

While hospitals are fully as important to the community as are any of the other agencies that are federated
in the community chest, their position is somewhat different from that of most of these agencies because of the
large funds required to operate them and the relatively
large percentage of their operating expense that comes
from earned income.

Whether hospitals should join their fund appeals to
those of community chests depends upon the conditions
in each instance, which can only be ascertained by a careful and impartial analysis of all the facts. Will a joint
campaign result in a more effective public appeal? Will
it reduce the cost of raising funds? Will the control
exercised over hospitals by the chest be intelligent, progressive and stimulating to higher standards or will it
serve to discourage and hinder needed development?
Will the chest give hospitals a fair share of the receipts
or will it use the undoubtedly strong appeal of hospitals
to raise funds for less popular and less essential agencies? Will chests have a sympathetic and understanding
attitude toward the entire hospital problem or will they
be so concerned with that aspect relating to the care of

the indigent that they hamper the hospitals' other essential service to part-pay and full-pay patients? Will hospitals brand themselves in the public eye as isolationists among social institutions if they stay out of the chest? Can community chests provide them with valuable statistical, publicity and research assistance? Can association with the chest give hospitals a better picture of community needs? Can chests stimulate and furnish funds for education and medical research in the hospital or must they be restricted to routine financing of the care of bed patients and outpatients? Does the community chest allocate its funds to hospitals on a basis of service rendered or in accordance with the influence and pressure of trustee groups? Does the chest insist upon sound and uniform systems of accounting and statistical methods? Without these, proper evaluation of claims is impossible.

Amelioration of Medical Costs

It is too well established to require argument that the American people do not receive the best medical service which the science of medicine now can offer and that this situation is partly due to the hurdle of medical costs. The bearing of this problem on hospital public relations is definite and obvious. Hospitals, representing as they do the most important publicly sponsored and publicly financed institutions in the medical field, have a definite responsibility to help the public solve this troublous problem. Their responsibility pertains particularly to that portion of the whole problem that is concerned with the work of hospitals but, as experts in the field of organizing medical services, hospital administrators and trustees may well be called upon for counsel and advice in a wider field.

That this responsibility has been widely accepted is indicated by the vigorous hospital leadership in many hospital care insurance plans. The rapid growth and development of such plans are undoubtedly one of the most beneficial public relations steps ever taken by American and Canadian hospitals. The potentialities of the new economic arrangements are so important that they will be discussed at length in Chapter 5.

Professional Education

The educational work of hospitals becomes increasingly important as the scope of medical service broadens. To do a good job educationally requires adequate materials and personnel, both of which cost money. It is becoming increasingly plain that the segment of the public that happens to utilize hospitals in any one year should not be forced to carry the major cost of this educational work which is provided for the benefit of the entire public. Insofar as the cost of this education cannot be assessed against the student concerned, either through services or tuition fees, it should be met by funds obtained from the general public for this purpose. It is not good public relations to conceal certain expenses, to say that they are for one thing when actually they are for another. Frankness demands that educational expenses, where significant in size, be labeled as such and not buried in costs of caring for the sick.

When hospitals obtain special funds for their educational work, the public will rightly ask whether this education is conducted on a plane commensurate with the needs of the students. Hospitals which meet the standards set up by the various professional bodies concerned will have a much more attractive case for the public than will those of lower standards. A hospital with an accredited school of nursing, for example, will be able to make a much more forceful appeal than will one that has been refused accreditation.

Here again, too much emphasis must not be laid on formal standards. Some schools of nursing, for example, will undoubtedly be accredited because they meet all of the tests laid down by the National League of Nursing Education yet will fail to turn out nurses with the sympathy, tact, kindliness and personality which are essential to a good nurse. There is no sound reason to believe that these qualities of spirit and personality are in opposition to fine intellects and good scientific training. The nurse of today needs attributes of both types.

Sixty years ago all temperatures were taken by physicians. Today nurses not only take temperatures but they do scores of things that even physicians of an earlier generation did not dream of doing.[40] As a result, the type of education formerly given to nurses is not adequate for the responsibilities now placed upon their shoulders. What is true of the nurse is true also in varying degrees of the several other ancillary workers concerned with the organized care of the sick — dietitians, medical social workers, clinical laboratory technicians, x-ray technicians, medical record librarians and similar workers.

Hospitals have a large share in the education of these various groups. For some, the hospital provides the entire technical training, requiring only that candidates be high school graduates or have a certain number of years of general college work. For others, the hospital acts as the laboratory where the students learn to apply what they have gained elsewhere from lectures and textbooks. In either event the hospitals have educational responsibilities which they must fulfill competently for their own benefit and for the benefit of the public.

The hospital's part in medical education has taken an enormous spurt in the past five years.[41] The training of interns has long been an accepted hospital responsibility, although one which, it must be admitted, has not always been discharged creditably. With the formation of the specialty accrediting boards, the training of residents in their specialties has taken on vastly greater importance. As the new requirements become fully effective, the pressure upon the better hospitals to provide both internships and residencies with richer educational content will become heavy. The intern and resident must be regarded as doctors still in training and opportunities and facilities for training must be provided. The amount of repetitious routine which can be expected from residents and interns must be reduced and their opportunities for carefully guided study and experience greatly increased. Residents should also have time and facilities for research. These changes will necessarily throw a somewhat larger financial burden upon both the hospital and the resident. In order that it may not become too onerous upon either, special funds for graduate medical education may be necessary. Good teaching is the best guarantee a hospital can give that the quality of its service to patients is on a high level.

In addition to the education of residents and interns, the hospitals that are doing the best work are constantly providing more and better educational opportunities for their visiting medical staffs. Pathologic, radiologic and departmental conferences, other regular staff meetings, journal clubs, visiting lecturers and good libraries of medical books and periodicals are some of the important

tools in this work. Careful thought should be given to
the possibility of making some or all of these opportunities available to any physicians in the community who
do not have medical staff appointments.

The training of the nonprofessional staff, including
orderlies, housekeeping employes, ward aids or attendants, elevator operators and similar persons, is undertaken primarily to increase their efficiency and value to
the hospital. As such, it is a proper charge upon income
from patients and would hardly merit the solicitation
of special funds.

Progressive Trustee Leadership

Whether a hospital will offer the broad scope and
quality of services outlined in this chapter will depend in
considerable measure upon the intelligence and progressive attitude of the board of trustees. Membership upon
the board should be given only to persons who are willing
to devote the necessary time and energy to the welfare
of the institution. An active board of 10 members is far
preferable to a board of 30 or more members of whom
only 10 are really interested. Membership is an honor
but it is also a responsibility. Even a small board should
be broadly representative of the various groups which
the hospital will serve, including those people who "live
on the wrong side of the tracks."

Ten duties for board members have been outlined by
Michael M. Davis.[42]

1. To know why the organization exists and annually to
review why it should.

2. To govern a board or a committee through joint thinking, not by majority vote.

3. To give money or help get it, or both.

4. To face budgets with courage, endowments with doubt, deficits without dismay and to recover quickly from a surplus.

5. To deal with the staff as partners.

6. To keep far enough ahead of the community to be progressive and close enough to it to be practical.

7. To interpret health work to the public in words of two syllables.

8. To deal with physicians on the assumption that the highest ideals of the profession dominate its every member and to face difficulties with recognition that both doctors and board members are human.

9. To be proud of a tradition but eager to improve it.

10. Always to combine a New England sense of obligation with an Irish sense of humor.

Competent Administration

Under a proper method of organization, the board of trustees of a hospital decides the basic policies that are to govern the institution and then leaves the execution of these policies in the hands of an administrator whom it has chosen.[43] If the board has been unwise in the selection of an administrator, money, time and perhaps lives may be lost. A hospital is a complex organism with ramifications in the fields of medicine, business, social service and community organization. To coordinate all of these matters effectively and to obtain the greatest possible return on the public's investment in hospital care require a high degree of competence.[44] It is not the kind of task that should be given to some individual who has made a failure of his own business or profession, nor to a physician who wants a quiet berth for retirement.

Good hospital care requires good administration. The various departments of the hospital must coordinate their services for the best interests of the patient. Wasteful expenditures must be avoided and needed expenditures made at the most opportune time and in the most productive manner. Today in a medium sized or large hospital the administrator is head of a group of department executives who are well trained for their tasks. He cannot obtain and retain their confidence and respect unless he, too, is well prepared for his own work.

The hospital should be so directed and should maintain such records and accounting methods as to instill public confidence in its financial reports.[45]

In the endeavor to achieve efficiency in the finances of the hospital and in its teaching activities, the administrator must not overlook the humane aspects of hospital care. Dr. E. M. Bluestone of Montefiore Hospital, New York City, has aptly summarized one important aspect of this matter in a classic article.[46] He cites a dozen instances of the unconscious inhumanity that often creeps into the work of distinguished physicians when their attention is concentrated entirely upon the research or teaching aspects of their work and concludes that "sympatheic control by the administration of the scientific enthusiasm of the staff doctor, whether at the bedside, in the operating room or in the classroom, should be given more attention than it has thus far received."

Fortunately it is less necessary than it was a decade or two ago to appoint an untrained person and let him learn entirely through experience. There is a growing and important body of hospital literature, both books and magazines. There is an increasing number of men and women who have served apprenticeships of from two to ten years under competent administrators. There is one university course of graduate caliber for training hospital administrators as well as one undergraduate course for nurse administrators.[47] Others are in contemplation at various universities.

There are six or more institutes presented annually or biennially for the benefit of persons now engaged in hospital administration to enable them to review quickly the major factors in the field and to come into direct contact with the best minds. There are numerous state, regional and national conventions offering information and guidance on administrative problems. But with all these there is no excess supply of competently trained administrators with the necessary qualities of character and personality. Most of the people coming into the field today do so expecting to work hard to remedy whatever lacks there may be in their own background and professional training.

Today no board of trustees need entrust the operation of its hospital to a person who is entirely unfamiliar with hospital work and unable to cope with its complexities. It may not be easy to find a qualified administrator but neither is it impossible. To merit public support the trustees should insist upon appointing a competent administrator and then give him authority and responsibility for administering the institution within the framework of general policies which they have adopted. Nothing less will produce good hospital care.

Summary — A Check List

Various methods may be used in examining a hospital to determine the quality and scope of its services. An approach differing somewhat from that presented in this chapter is given by Dr. E. M. Bluestone in a thoughtful outline presented as Appendix I.

The material in this chapter may be most usefully and conveniently summarized in a check list of the functions and services of a large hospital that gives good hospital care. (Smaller hospitals, of course, must limit themselves and will omit some of the services listed in 1, 3 and 8.)

1. In-Patient and Outpatient Services for All Major Types of Disease
   a. Medical: Endocrine, gastro-intestinal, metabolic, diabetic, cardiac, pulmonary, allergic, dermatologic, psychopathic, neurologic and psychiatric, tuberculous, epileptic, alcoholic, narcotic, communicable and similar branches
   b. Surgical: Brain, abdominal, orthopedic, emergency, traumatic, tumor, eye, ear, nose and throat, urologic and proctologic, dental and similar subdivisions
   c. Obstetric: Newborn, both normal and premature, maternal welfare
   d. Pediatric
   e. Convalescent
   f. Chronic
2. Service for All Groups
   a. Racial groups
   b. Religious groups
   c. Economic groups
   d. Special social groups
   e. Age groups
3. Well Rounded Care to Each Patient
   a. Medical service by visiting and resident staff
   b. Nursing service
   c. Dietary service
   d. Admitting and discharging service

    e. Medical social service

    f. Care of patients' morale: Hostess service, religious ministration, bibliotherapy

    g. Ambulance service

    h. Organized emergency care

    i. Pharmacy service

    j. Clinical and pathologic laboratory service

    k. Radiology

    l. Anesthesia

    m. Gas therapy: Resuscitation, artificial respiration, oxygen, helium

    n. Physical therapy

    o. Fever therapy

    p. Electrocardiography

    q. Metabolism tests

    r. Intravenous therapy

    s. Blood transfusion service: Blood donors and blood banks

    t. Serum service

    u. Occupational therapy

    v. Medical records

4. Highest Attainable Quality

    a. Approval of standardizing bodies

    b. Competent heads of medical staff departments

    c. Able administrative department heads

    d. Development of distinguished services

    e. Constantly advancing standards

    f. Medical audit

    g. Administrative surveys

    h. Adequate safety program

5. Cooperation in Public Health Work

    a. Preventive clinics

    b. Public health education

The key to advancement in the quality of service given by the
hospital is often found in well run pathological laboratories.

  c. Home care service
  d. Care of communicable disease
  e. Cooperation with health department: Laboratory work, disease reporting
6. Cooperation With Other Hospitals and Social Agencies
  a. Avoidance of needless duplication
  b. Consolidation of hospitals
  c. Coordinated community-wide hospital planning
  d. Support of hospital councils
  e. Support of health councils or councils of social agencies
  f. Cooperation with community chests and welfare federations
7. Amelioration of Medical Costs (See Chapter 5)
8. Professional Education
  a. Equipment and personnel for teaching
  b. Special educational endowments or gifts
  c. Segregation of educational expenses
  d. Education for interns and residents
  e. Education for nurses, dietitians, technicians and similar students
  f. Education for medical staff members
  g. Training programs for nonprofessional staff
9. Progressive Trustee Leadership
  a. Interested and representative membership
  b. Willingness to assume obligations fully and to discharge them effectively
10. Competent Administration
  a. Qualified administrator
  b. Administrative authority centered in administrator
  c. Policy formation centered in board of trustees

REFERENCES

1. Emerson, Haven, *et al.*: The Hospital Survey for New York, United Hospital Fund, New York, 1937, Vol. II, pp. 48-49. An excellent statement regarding hospital service and hospital standards is embodied in Chapter IX of this volume which is entitled "Essentials for Good Care of Hospital Patients."

2. Ranson, John E.: As to the Special Clinic, *The Modern Hospital*, Feb., 1937, p. 126.

3. Hess, J. H.: Chicago City-Wide Plan for Care of Premature Infants, *Journal of the American Medical Association*, Aug. 8, 1936, pp. 400-404, and Stoesser, Albert V., and Engelstad, Ella: The Newborn Infant in the Large Hospital, *Hospital Management*, Sept., 1938, p. 27, and Adair, Fred L.: The Care of the Mother and the Newborn in the Hospital, *Hospital Management*, June, 1938, p. 14.

4. Usilton, Lyda J.: Chicago's Syphilis Clinics, *The Modern Hospital*, June, 1938, p. 73, and Kaplan, Regina H.: Rôle of the Hospital in New Nation-Wide Venereal Disease Control Program, *Hospitals*, March, 1937, p. 58.

5. Newell, Q. U.: Importance of the Organized Cancer Clinic, *Southern Medical Journal*, Feb., 1936, p. 212, and Scammell, H. L.: Cancer Patient and the General Hospital, *Hospitals*, Dec., 1936, p. 21.

6. Perry, Margaret L.: Complete Urologic Setup, *The Modern Hospital*, July, 1938, p. 44.

7. Hospital number, *Journal of the American Medical Association*, March 26, 1938, p. 969, and Hamilton, Samuel W.: Psychiatric Service in the General Hospital, *Hospitals*, Nov., 1936, p. 98, and Oatway, William H. Jr.: The Management of Tuberculosis in General Hospitals, American Hospital Association, Chicago, 1939.

8. Goldwater, S. S.: Crusading for the Chronically Sick, *The Modern Hospital*, May, 1935, p. 65, and Jarrett, Mary C.: Chronically Ill and Aged, *The Modern Hospital*, Aug., 1938, p. 45, and Goldsmith, Samuel A., *et al.*: Three Views on Convalescent Care, *The Modern Hospital*, Sept., 1935, p. 55, and Coleman, L. M.: Development of the Chronic Hospital and Its Place in the Community, *Hospitals*, Sept., 1936, p. 31, and Bluestone, E. M.: Chronic Disease — A Problem in Philanthropy, *Bulletin of the American Hospital Association*, July, 1935, and Bluestone: Unfinished Business — Chronic Patients, *The Modern Hospital*, Sept., 1938, p. 82, and Bluestone: Hopeless Yesterday — Cured Today, *The Trained Nurse and Hospital Review*, April, 1939.

9. Roper, Jeanette M., *et al.*: Technique of Medical Asepsis for the Communicable Disease Ward, *The Hospital Yearbook*, 14th Edition, 1935, p. 128.

10. Committee on Community Dental Service, New York Tuberculosis and Health Association: Health Dentistry for the Community, University of Chicago Press, Chicago, 1935, p. 31.

10a. Wing, Frank E.: Community Planning for Complete Medical Relief Service in Clinics, *Hospitals*, Dec., 1938, p. 35, and MacCurdy, Frederick J.: The Future Significance of Outpatient Care in the Country's Hospital and Medical Program, *Hospitals*, Nov., 1937, p. 46.

11. National Resources Committee: Consumer Incomes in the United States — Their Distribution in 1935-36, Government Printing Office, Washington, D. C., 1938.

12. Russell, Marian E.: Responsibility of the Hospital to the Unmarried Mother and Her Child, *Hospitals*, Aug., 1938, p. 101.

13. Division on Nursing of the Council of the American Hospital Association and a Committee of the National League of Nursing Education: Manual of the Essentials of Good Hospital Nursing Service, National League of Nursing Education, New York, 1936, and Rogers, Dorothy: The Nurse's Contribution to Adequate Patient Care, *Hospital Management*, Sept., 1936, p. 28.

14. Jensen, A. C.: Training Nurse Attendants, *The Modern Hospital*, Nov., 1938, p. 68, and Hamilton, James A., *et al.*: Standardized Training Course for Ward Aids, *The Modern Hospital*, Dec., 1938, p. 65.

15. Stokes, John H., *et al.*: A Committee Looks at the Central Admitting Office, *The Modern Hospital*, Sept., 1935, p. 45, and Roszel, Irene M.: Management of the Front Office and Information Service, *Hospitals*, June, 1939, p. 48, and Wilson, Ruth C.: Business Methods in Dealing With Patients, *The Canadian Hospital*, Feb., 1938, p. 17.

16. Berger, Samuel S.: How Standards in a Social Service Department Affect the Practice of Clinical Medicine, *Hospitals*, Feb., 1937, p. 30, and Cannon, Ida M.: Social Work in Hospitals, Russell Sage Foundation, New York, 1923, and Webb, Mrs. Charles W.: The Importance of Established Standards in a Social Service Department, *Hospitals*, Dec., 1936, p. 95, and Becker, S. William: The Place of the Social Worker in the Medical Team, *Hospitals*, Oct., 1937, p. 102, and Engel, Gilson C., and Jacobs, Ellen: The Follow-Up Service at Lankenau Hospital, *Hospital Management*, March, 1938, p. 18.

17. Simon, F. R.: Going the Second Mile, *The Modern Hospital*, March, 1937, p. 61.

18. Cabot, Richard C., and Dicks, Russell L.: The Art of Ministering to the Sick, The MacMillan Co., New York City, 1936.

19. Kamman, Gordon: The Rôle of Bibliotherapy in the Care of the Patient, *Bulletin of the American College of Surgeons*, June, 1939, p. 183.

20. MacEachern, Malcolm T., *et al.*: Outline of a Plan for a Public Emergency Ambulance Service, *Chicago Hospital Council Bulletin*, Nov., 1938, p. 10, and Stalker, H. S.: Emergency Hospital Unit, *The Canadian Hospital*, Nov., 1936, p. 10.

21. MacEachern, Malcolm T.: The Forgotten Department, *The Modern Hospital*, Feb., 1939, p. 102.

22. Hertzler, Arthur E.: The Horse and Buggy Doctor, Harper & Bros., New York, 1938, Chapter 8, "I Educate Myself," and Manheimer, Stephen: Necropsies — Not How Many, But How Utilized, *Hospitals*, Feb., 1937, p. 54.

23. Wilson, J. Stuart: The Department of Biochemistry at the Toronto Western Hospital, *The Canadian Hospital*, March, 1936, p. 39.

24. Cameron, Catherine: Progress in Anesthesia and Its Effect on Hospital Administration, *Hospitals*, Aug., 1938, p. 31.

25. Coulter, John S., and Northway, W. H.: Fundamentals in Design for Physical Therapy, *The Modern Hospital*, March, 1938, p. 62.

26. Elkins, Earl C.: Essentials for Fever Therapy, *The Modern Hospital*, March, 1938, p. 44.

27. Asher, Graham, and Hoeker, Frank: Instantaneous Electrocardiograms, *The Modern Hospital*, Nov., 1938, p. 78.

28. Dutton, Walter Forest, and Lake, George Burt: Parenteral Therapy, Charles C. Thomas, Springfield, Ill., 1936.

29. Fantus, Bernard: Cook County's Blood Bank, *The Modern Hospital*, Jan., 1938, p. 57, and Goodall, J. R., *et al.*: Placental Blood Transfusions, *The Modern Hospital*, Dec., 1938, p. 44, and DeKleine, William: Red Cross Blood Transfusion Project, *Journal of the American Medical Association*, Dec. 3, 1938, p. 2101, and Yudin, S. S.: Transfusion of Cadaver Blood, *Journal of the American Medical Association*, March 21, 1936, p. 997.

30. Thalheimer, William: Convalescent Serums Have Proved Their Value, *The Modern Hospital*, Nov., 1935, p. 53.

31. Merritt, Mary E.: Occupational Therapy Modernized, *The Modern Hospital*, Dec., 1938, p. 75.

32. Ball, Otho F.: Distinguished Service in the Hospital — A Stimulus to Progress, *The Modern Hospital*, Sept., 1934, p. 49, and a series of three unsigned articles on distinguished service which appeared in *The Modern Hospital* in April, June and July, 1935.

33. Adair, F. L., *et al.*: Chicago's Maternity and Infancy Regulations, *The Hospital Yearbook*, 17th Edition, 1939, p. 725, and Osborn, Stanley H.: Minimum Requirements for Licensing Maternity Hospitals, *Hospitals*, Feb., 1938, p. 98.

34. Hertzler, Arthur E.: *Op. cit.*, p. 272.

35. Ponton, Thomas R.: The Medical Staff in the Hospital, Physicians' Record Co., Chicago, 1939, Chapter 8, "Professional Accounting."

36. Hinenburg, Morris: Hospital Accidents — A Check List, *The Hospital Yearbook*, 14th Edition, 1935, p. 95, and Doane, Joseph C.: Why Didn't I Think of That? *The Modern Hospital*, March, 1936, p. 92.
37. Wilinsky, Charles F., *et al.*: Report of Committee on Public Health Relations, Transactions of the American Hospital Association, 1936, p. 104, and MacLean, Basil C., *et al.*: Report of the Committee on Public Health Relations, Transactions of the American Hospital Association, 1937, p. 186, and Munger, C. W.: The Community Hospital as an Essential Agency in the Field of Public Health, *Hospitals*, July, 1936, p. 9.
38. Emerson, Haven: *Loc. cit.*
39. Schweppe, Charles H.: Working With Your Neighbor, *The Modern Hospital*, Feb., 1939, p. 75, and Pyle, David H. McAlpin: The Hospital Council of Greater New York — Its Development, Purpose and Program, *Chicago Hospital Council Bulletin*, Jan., 1939, p. 15.
40. Newton, Mildred: Streamlined Nursing, *The Modern Hospital*, Oct., 1936, p. 63.
41. An interesting and important statement of the hospital's responsibility in the education of interns and residents will be published in a few months by the Commission on Graduate Medical Education.
42. Davis, Michael M.: Duties for Board Members, *The Modern Hospital*, Sept., 1937, p. 75.
43. Editorial: The Great Divide, *The Modern Hospital*, July, 1937, p. 38.
44. Carter, Fred G., *et al.*: The Hospital Administrator — Duties, Responsibilities, Relationships and Obligations, American College of Hospital Administrators, Chicago, 1934, and Goldwater, S. S.: The Future of Hospital Administration, *Hospitals*, Nov., 1938, p. 15.
45. Class, James V.: Value of Uniform Accounting Methods to Hospitals, *Hospitals*, July, 1937, p. 107.
46. Bluestone, E. M.: Some Fundamental Problems in Hospital Administration, *The Modern Hospital*, Dec., 1924, p. 514.
47. MacEachern, Malcolm T., *et al.*: University Training for Hospital Administration Career, A Report by the Committee on Educational Policies, American College of Hospital Administrators, Chicago, 1937, and Davis, Michael M.: Studies in Hospital Administration at the University of Chicago, *Hospitals*, March, 1936, p. 24, and Davis: Some Experiences in the Education of Administrators, *Hospitals*, Jan., 1938, p. 11.

Chapter 5

AMELIORATING
THE COSTS

THE COST of hospital service is high. It is going up. And there are no signs indicating that the trend will be reversed, either now or later. Even before the depression there were complaints about high hospital costs. During the depression many thousands of people went without needed service because they could not afford to purchase it and either could not obtain free service or would not ask for it. But the cost is not high in relation to the quality of service. There is no better bargain for a sick man than good hosital care. Still, in relation to his income, the cost often will be high. Thus, hospital costs constitute a public relations problem of major importance.

Reasons for Advancing Costs

The reasons for advancing costs are not hard to find. The preceding chapter gave some indication of the wide expansion of hospital service. We do more for patients in hospitals today than ever before. We give them types of treatment that were undreamed of a generation or two ago. Oxygen therapy, blood transfusions, intravenous injections, fever therapy, the whole extensive range of physical therapy, a vastly expanded x-ray service and a clinical laboratory service likewise enlarged, air conditioned operating rooms, isolation technics in the nursery, extended dietotherapy, occupational therapy, these and

96

countless other enlargements of hospital service have naturally contributed to increased cost.

But this is only part of the story. Another substantial element in the advancement of costs has been the necessity of engaging a higher grade of employe and of paying him more adequately for his service. The trend of the times is toward a full cash payment to hospital employes equivalent to what is paid for similar work in industry. No longer is it considered ethical for the administration to force hospital employes to bear a substantial part of the hospital's charitable burden by accepting remuneration that is distinctly below the going rate in the community.

The improved hospital service with its higher per capita costs has been of distinct benefit to patients. Death rates are lower. Recoveries are more rapid and assured. The length of hospital stay and, in many instances, the length of absence from work are reduced. All this saves the patient's pocketbook. But an unexpected hospital bill of $50, $100 or $150 is still a real hurdle to the average middle class individual, particularly if it is accompanied by a physician's or surgeon's bill of an equal or greater amount. Sometimes there may also be a charge for special duty nurses. Even though a man may stay only 10 days instead of the 20 days he might have stayed a generation earlier, he finds the hospital bill and the other costs associated with it hard to meet.

Hospital administrators and trustees are charged, by their position in the community and because of their special knowledge of the factors involved, with a special responsibility to help ameliorate this burden. As a general rule no other group is so well situated to understand the problem and to take action on it. Any sound effort

to lessen the impact of these charges is sure to benefit the
hospital's relations with the public. There are many
methods that have been tried in various communities to
ease the burden of hospital costs. As yet no one remedy
has been found that is applicable in all instances. Most
hospitals, therefore, must utilize several methods if they
are to meet the problem fully for all classes of people.

The principal efforts have been made along the following lines: (1) obtaining charitable or tax funds or both
to permit rendering service free or at less than cost to
those who cannot pay; (2) creating hospital finance
corporations to permit paying bills in installments after
they have been incurred; (3) offering inclusive rate
plans so that the patient may, on admission, estimate
closely the total amount of his bill; (4) providing hospital
care insurance. Each of these will be discussed in some
detail.

Free and Part-Free Service

It is one of the glorious traditions of the best voluntary as well as of tax-supported hospitals that they never
turn a patient from their doors if they can possibly
accept him. Because of this tradition, millions of dollars
have been provided by governmental bodies and charitable individuals to build and endow hospitals. Furthermore, the voluntary hospitals in most communities have
been relieved of tax burdens, often given free water and
otherwise made objects of public largesse.

Even with this aid, however, the burden of free or
nearly free service has today grown so great that voluntary hospitals are financially unable to carry the increasing overflow from governmental hospitals which often
are seriously overcrowded. Because the voluntary hos-

pitals have the accommodations, however, it is wiser public policy to use them for this overflow than to build additional governmental institutions. But to accept this task, the voluntary hospitals must have some help. They cannot today carry the increasing free load entirely on the basis of their gifts, endowment income and net income from private patients.

In many communities, therefore, governmental bodies have agreed to pay voluntary hospitals part of the cost of caring for free patients. If intelligently and honestly done, this is a sound procedure. It economizes public funds. It utilizes existing facilities. It helps to preserve the voluntary hospital system that has had and can continue to have such a stimulating effect on hospital development in this country.

But, if voluntary hospitals are to preserve their position in the affection and esteem of the public and if they are to merit tax exemption and various free services, they, too, must carry part of the load. They cannot expect that governmental bodies will pay the entire bill for the care of the indigent. The voluntary hospitals must not relax their own efforts to obtain charitable funds. They must expect to give in service more than they get from tax monies. As soon as tax support frees their budgets from one load they must be ready to take up some other of the many loads waiting for a bearer. To a hospital that is awake to the demands of its public, there is never any problem in finding needed public services to render. There are always more needs than available funds can cover.

The general principles that should govern the payment of tax funds to voluntary hospitals for the care of the indigent or other governmental wards have recently been stated by a joint committee of the American Hospital Association and the American Public Welfare Association, working under the chairmanship of Michael M. Davis. They are as follows:[1]

1. It is recognized that the provision of general hospital beds by local governments in the larger cities is generally insufficient to meet the needs for free or low-pay hospital care, and that in the great majority of small cities and towns there are no governmental hospitals and these localities must depend on voluntary hospitals in which a large investment for building and equipment has been made.

2. It is recognized that the use of tax funds from local governments to pay voluntary hospitals for the care of the needy is a widespread and, under some local conditions, a reasonable policy.

3. It is the unanimous belief that such payment to hospitals should be on the basis of service actually rendered, and that payment in a lump sum or subsidy basis is undesirable.

4. Public welfare officials will find it advantageous to deal with the hospitals of their community jointly. The experience of local public officials indicates that this can best be accomplished through the organization of hospital councils within each community or political unit of sufficient size. Where, because of the smallness of the community or for other reasons, hospital councils are not practicable, public officials may wisely suggest that the local hospitals constitute a committee to represent them jointly in conferences with public authorities.

5. Public officials should recognize that good hospital service is increasingly complex and costly, that a high standard of care of patients is important and an ultimate economy, and they should appreciate the close relation of hospital service to general medical practice and to public health.

6. The hospitals, on their side, should recognize the advantages of presenting a united front to the community concerning their needs, of avoiding internal dissension and competitive action which would lower standards of service.

The public-spirited citizens on voluntary hospital boards should present their case to governmental officials without a competitive attitude and from the point of view of community needs.

7. Both the public officials and the hospitals of each community should recognize that the rate of payment for service must be adjusted through conference, taking into account operating costs and other considerations which will vary among communities, and that no fixed simple formula controlling rate of payment can be generally applied.

8. Voluntary hospitals, through hospital councils or otherwise, should cooperate with other community forces in an honest effort to control future expansion of bed capacity beyond community requirements. Excessive new building by individual institutions has not infrequently led public officials to indicate that any payment to voluntary hospitals would tend to encourage further unnecessary expansion.

9. In seeking payment from public sources, hospitals must recognize that the accepted policy today is to the effect that public funds should be expended through public authorities; that some inspection or supervision of accounts, procedure for charging and admission of patients must be expected by voluntary hospitals when they are dealing with governmental units or requesting funds from them.

10. The utilization of voluntary hospitals for the care of indigent persons at public expense requires, furthermore, encouragement by public officials and by the hospitals themselves of a uniform accounting system and of standards such as those required for the approved lists of the A.C.S.

Another possible development in the hospital care of the indigent is suggested later in this chapter.

Hospital Finance Corporations

The majority of people, of course, do not come in the free class. They can and wish to pay something for their hospital care. But frequently they find it difficult to pay at the time of admission. Since people buy radios, automobiles, pianos, refrigerators and other rather expensive items through installment payments, the question has been asked why they should not buy hospital care the same way.

In Cleveland a hospital finance corporation was formed to try out this plan. The corporation has had a slow growth. At the end of five and one-half years, *i.e.* in 1938, it financed about 1100 accounts a year involving a total of about $90,000 in hospital charges. This represents a substantial reduction from 1937 when there were 1600 accounts involving about $140,000. The growth of hospital care insurance in Cleveland may explain the decrease. Twelve hospitals were participating in 1938, although only seven belonged in the beginning in 1933.

The hospital membership in Cleveland seems to be satisfied that the plan has substantial merit and will continue to make a modest place for itself in the future.[2]

Inclusive Rate Plans

Originally hospitals had a single service provided at a single rate. The service was merely room and board with floor nursing, such as it was. But, as the ancillary services became more numerous and more costly, hospitals made special charges for them. In some institutions the special charge system has been carried to extremes. A patient may be charged, for example, 10 or 15 cents for a dose of cathartic that he knows can be purchased at the drug store for 1 or 2 cents. Sometimes every dressing given a patient is billed separately.

This system makes it difficult for a patient to estimate the total amount of his hospital bill in advance. Perhaps even more important from the good will viewpoint is the annoyance aroused. It is a strange but human trait to be more annoyed by trivial than by important matters. The special charge system, moreover, brings a steady pressure on the patient to curtail the scope of his hospital care as much as possible. This is not medically important as related to drugs and dressings, which are not ordinarily curtailed, but it becomes very important when it prevents the patient from obtaining needed special diagnostic methods and therapies.

Certain hospitals have pioneered a new system, the inclusive rate plan.[3] This plan is based on the philosophy that hospital service is the product that hospitals offer the public. Each patient should receive whatever treatment or service the hospital can offer to whatever extent he can benefit by it. When a patient enters a hospital he is not going into a medical boarding house but into an institution with a social and scientific purpose, namely, to bring him all the benefits which medical science can offer persons in his condition.

There can now be no doubt that the inclusive rate plan is popular with patients. That is the experience with it wherever it has been given a fair and intelligent trial. The patient knows when he enters the hospital that his bill will be a certain amount for a certain number of days. If he has a rapid and uneventful recovery, needing little special service, he almost never complains at the cost even though it naturally is somewhat higher than it would have been on the fee for service basis. If, on the other hand, his illness takes a serious turn requiring oxygen therapy, repeated operations, much laboratory service and x-ray therapy, he does not need to complicate his illness and delay his recovery by worry over a rapidly mounting hospital bill.

Staff physicians are usually enthusiastic about the plan. Of course, it lies in their hands to make it a success or a failure. If they take unfair advantage of the opportunity to have unlimited service, if they seek to cover up with accessory treatments their own lack of understanding of the case, they can punish the hospital financially.

Most physicians, however, recognize that the inclusive rate plan gives them an opportunity to practice better medicine. They cooperate, therefore, to avoid unnecessary services so that they can retain the plan for the benefit of their patients who really need it. By keeping records from time to time of the amount of work ordered by each physician, it is possible for the chief of staff to ascertain if any staff members are unfairly exploiting the plan. These men can then be dealt with individually through the chief of their service or the executive committee of the medical staff.

What effect does the inclusive rate system have upon the hospital? Its benefits in public relations have already been mentioned. On the financial side the rate schedule can be adjusted to produce any result desired. Rates may be set to produce less, the same or more income from each hundred patient days. There is nothing inherent in the philosophy of the inclusive rate plan that requires the hospital to pile up a deficit. The problem is merely one in arithmetic. There will be an increase in the use of ancillary services, of course. For laboratory and x-ray services, the increase is about 25 to 30 per cent, according to studies made at the University Hospitals, Cleveland. Increases in other services, such as oxygen therapy, blood transfusions and intravenous injections, will probably be influenced more by the state of medical opinion than by purely economic considerations. In computing charges under the new plan, the hospital administration should give due weight to the reduction in unit cost that comes from an increase in utilization of services. Most x-ray departments, for example, can carry a much higher load of service with only a small increase in outlay.

Although it is common for tuberculosis and nervous and mental hospitals to provide full nursing service to all patients on an inclusive fee basis, general hospitals have not often gone this far. This, however, is a logical extension of the inclusive rate principle. If private and semiprivate patients need extensive nursing service, ultimately hospitals will provide it and not require them to employ special duty nurses. The special duty nurse is unduly expensive to patients and brings an element of uncertainty into the carrying out of hospital routine. When hospitals have fully adjusted themselves to the new situation caused by employing graduate nurses for floor duty, this service can be just as attractive and as remunerative to the nurse as private duty. Given proper hours and pay, the nurse can be better off at the end of the year when employed on salary than when dependent upon the intermittent demands for private duty service. To solve this problem requires honest efforts on the part of both hospitals and nurses.

One caution should be voiced in connection with the inclusive rate plan. The volume of work piled on to the special therapy departments should not be so great that it adversely affects the quality of their service. Laboratory and x-ray examinations, for example, may be done in a purely routine fashion with bad effects on their quality. Of course, this can happen and probably does happen in some hospital laboratories even without any change in method of charging. But special cautions should be followed when making this change-over since it will probably increase the work of these departments by 25 per cent or more.

Hospital Care Insurance

So much has been written about the benefit of hospital care insurance on public relations that the hospital field is well acquainted with this general subject.[4] Certain aspects of the matter merit reemphasis, however.

As far back as February 1933, the American Hospital Association declared that hospital care insurance should be conceived as a public service, not as a means of rescuing hospital finances. Even now, however, some hospitals have not fully appreciated this principle. The matter comes to a head in connection with setting rates to be charged the plans for the hospital care of their members.

The American development of hospital care insurance, in marked contrast to that in Britain, has been based upon the assumption that these patients will pay full actual cost for the services that they receive. But what is full actual cost for semiprivate patients? In the present state of hospital bookkeeping, few institutions have cost accounting systems that give them a true picture of the cost of various classes of patients. Hence, insurance plans have had to rely upon present charges as a substitute for costs. The weakness in this situation is that charges often bear only a vague and general relationship to costs. Furthermore, the charges to private and semiprivate patients have, from time immemorial, been loaded with a certain percentage above cost to help bear the expense of caring for free patients. But under a hospital care insurance plan should not most or all of this charge be transferred from the subscribers to the community?

On the other hand, if in the future it is to be increasingly difficult for voluntary hospitals to obtain large gifts to implement or replace their present capital investment, it may become necessary to include in the charge for hospital care insurance a certain amount as a sinking fund for capital expenditures. This is a subject that has been little discussed as yet either by hospital administrators and trustees or by service plan executives.

Another problem concerning payments to hospitals arises from the fact that "hospital service" is not the same in all institutions. Hospitals could be divided into classes according to the scope and quality of their services. At the top would be institutions that are fully abreast of all major scientific advancements. They have sufficient funds and such an aggressive management that they provide every new service as soon as it has been tested and found desirable. They carry on valuable teaching services and their graduate nurses, interns and residents are always in demand. A second group falls somewhat below the leaders. It provides good service as far as it goes but lacks many of the elements of a well rounded institution. It may excel in certain fields but may fall far down the scale in others. At the bottom are the low grade institutions, rarely excelling in anything and often providing little more than a surgical workshop. They frequently serve the surgical case acceptably but have little to offer a medical case; on the social side, their service is most deficient.

Hospital care insurance plans to date have compensated all types of hospitals equally. Since no accepted classification exists, this has been an administrative necessity. But it works rather unfairly. The high grade institution often finds that it must render service below cost while the low grade institution makes a profit at the same rate. Hospital insurance organizations have assumed that when subscribers were free to choose a high or low class institution without any financial penalty for taking the better hospital, they would favor the latter to an extent that would bring pressure on the poorer hospitals to advance their standards. As hospital care insurance plans grow in enrollment, this probably will, in fact, happen. But the choice of a hospital is influenced to so great an extent by the staff affiliations of the family's physician that this pressure does not arise very rapidly.

Eventually it probably will be necessary for hospitals to be graded according to the scope and quality of their service and for insurance plans to pay differently for what is, in fact, a different service. It has recently been suggested that the American College of Surgeons ought to broaden its program so as to differentiate more clearly between the various "approved" hospitals.

The question of who should control hospital service plans has received considerable attention in recent years. The American Hospital Association has taken the stand that the plans should be controlled by the hospitals and this position has been generally accepted. The other point of view is that the plans should be controlled by independent self-perpetuating trustees who represent a position halfway between public control and hospital control. The question of control may affect the public's attitude toward the plans and the member hospitals.

In view of the recent actions of the American Medical Association and the American Hospital Association, it now appears probable that some plans, at least, will be expanded to include medical service benefits. If this happens, the control also will shift, as physicians will rightly insist on an appropriate voice in determining policies. The result will probably be a three-way partnership with the viewpoints of physicians, hospitals and the public all adequately represented. Various devices can be utilized to effect this partnership. If approximately equal representation is given to all three interests, the question of "who should control" can be laid on a shelf and allowed to gather dust.

Whether medical service benefits are included or not, however, best opinion today indicates that physicians, hospitals and the public should all have a voice in the control of hospital service plans. Obviously in the long run hospitals cannot be seriously injured by plans because collectively they always hold the power of refusing to provide service under any particular circumstances. While eventually it may develop that hospitals cannot exist without hospital service plans, it is true now and will always be true that the plans cannot exist without hospitals.

It may be found to be sound public policy for hospital care insurance plans to make contracts with local governmental agencies for the care of the indigent. Such an arrangement would have the following advantages: (1) It would enable the hospitals to deal collectively and on an approximate equality with the governmental agency. (2) Within limits it would extend to the indigent the same right of free choice of hospital which is so valued by those who pay their own way. (3) The government's share of the administrative expense of such an insurance plan could probably be set at a lower figure than the government could achieve through its own agencies. (4) It would avoid setting up a separate system of medical service for the indigent, a system that would in most instances be on a definitely lower level than that provided for the paying patients.

If the service included medical as well as hospital care, the benefits of a unified system would be even greater. Of course, governmental agencies would rightly insist that the service be provided so efficiently that it would not cost them any more than services of the same amount and quality provided directly under their own auspices. If a substantial number of such patients were given hospital care insurance with free choice of hospital, some provision might have to be made to assure to university hospitals the supply of patients needed for teaching. This is not a serious problem, however, although it might require of such institutions a little more emphasis on the humane aspects of their service to teaching patients. Occupancy in those governmental general hospitals which are now overcrowded would probably be reduced somewhat by such a plan. The reduction should not be carried beyond the point of optimum operating efficiency, *i.e.* about 75 to 85 per cent occupancy for a year.[5]

Summary

Financial considerations play an important rôle in hospital public relations. Much of the criticism of hospitals has centered about their charges. Any means that will remove this criticism should, therefore, be carefully explored.

The methods suggested in this chapter, if widely adopted and fully developed, will obviate a large part of this criticism and at the same time should provide hospitals with sufficient funds to enable them to maintain good standards of service. If these methods do not themselves provide sufficient operating funds, they will improve the hospitals' relations with the public so that the hospitals will be in a better position to ask for the necessary additional funds.

The methods proposed are four.

1. The cost of hospital care for indigent patients should increasingly be shared between governmental bodies and voluntary hospitals. Governmental payments to voluntary hospitals should follow certain general principles which, while safeguarding the standards of medical service, will protect adequately the interests of taxpayers, of indigent and medically indigent patients and of voluntary hospitals.

2. Hospital finance corporations may be formed to arrange for installment payments for those people who can pay but who are not able to meet the full cost in a lump sum at the time of hospitalization. The experience in Cleveland seems to indicate that there is a certain need for such a corporation but that the need is limited and decreases as hospital care insurance plans grow. The Cleveland Hospital Finance Corporation handled fewer accounts in 1938 than in 1937.

3. Inclusive rate plans have been extensively tried in various portions of the country and found to improve the quality of service rendered to the patient, to aid him to meet the costs of care and to encourage physicians to put forth their best efforts for the welfare of the patient. They can be arranged so as to bring in the same, a higher or a lower amount of income per patient day. I know of no instance in which the inclusive rate plan has been given a fair and intelligent trial and has been subsequently abandoned. It appears to meet with the universal approval of patients, administrators and physicians.

4. All the benefits of the inclusive rate plan and others, too, are embodied in hospital care insurance. This has undoubtedly been the most important advance in hospital public relations in the past decade. As yet, however, it is not available to many persons. No one knows whether it can operate successfully in rural areas. The experiments in this field are promising but they are too new to be conclusive. The same is true of its expansion to cover the lower income groups. Also, it is not yet demonstrated whether hospital care insurance under voluntary auspices can be expanded to include physicians' services, dentistry, nursing and other related types of care and extended to all groups of the population rapidly enough to make it unnecessary to develop comprehensive plans under governmental auspices. Developments in this field are coming so rapidly that the outlook is hopeful but specific prediction is dangerous.

Taken altogether, the four methods here suggested will alleviate much of the hardship of hospital costs and thus will improve the basic relationship between the hospital and the public.

REFERENCES

1. Hospital Care for the Needy, *Hospitals*, Jan., 1939, p. 23, and Erickson, E. I.: Governmental Subsidy or Relief Funds, *Chicago Hospital Council Bulletin*, May, 1939, p. 17, and Hoehler, Fred K.: Tax Funds and the Voluntary Hospital, *Hospitals*, Oct., 1937, p. 72.
2. Harmon, E. L.: Cleveland's Credit Plan, *The Modern Hospital*, July, 1938, p. 51.
3. Mannix, John R.: Cleveland Likes Inclusive Rates, *The Modern Hospital*, Jan., 1938, p. 48.
4. Rorem, C. Rufus: Hospital Care Insurance, American Hospital Association, Chicago, 1937.
5. Mills, Alden B.: Insurance for Indigents, *The Modern Hospital*, Dec., 1938, p. 47.

Chapter 6

RESPONSIBILITY
FOR PUBLIC RELATIONS

OBVIOUSLY A sound and progressive public relations program is not going to develop without someone to assume the responsibility of carrying it forward. Major responsibility rests with the trustee, the administrator and the expert publicist. Secondary responsibilities rest with many other persons, including staff members, nurses, department heads, women's auxiliary members and all persons who have contacts with the public in the name of the hospital. The primary responsibilities will be discussed in this chapter and the secondary ones, later.

Before discussing responsibilities, however, the importance of the experimental point of view should be emphasized. Obviously many opportunities for improved relations with patients, contributors, employes, physicians, governmental officials and the general public are as yet undeveloped. All those concerned should be able to conceive, entertain and examine critically all possibilities. If such an attitude is maintained, the future will undoubtedly witness the development of many new plans and methods of value to hospitals and to those persons whom they serve.

The Trustee's Responsibility

The type of public relations program visualized in this book obviously affects all aspects of the administration of the hospital. It is vital, therefore, that it have the support of the trustee since, in the final analysis, he determines what type of administration a hospital will have. Without his understanding and support, the finest program in the world would be blocked.

There are several reasons why this is so. In the first place, a true public relations program costs money. Most of this money will be spent in the purchase of brains rather than of printed matter, radio time or other physical things. But this is one place where penny-wise is distinctly pound-foolish. The woods are full of ex-newspaper men and others who think that, just because they have written for publication, they are automatically qualified as expert public relations counsel. Such an assumption is far from the truth. A man (or woman) is needed whose quality of thinking and scope of experience qualify him to discuss all matters of administration intelligently and effectively. Such an individual, even though not employed full time, will command a substantial salary or retainer. It is better to have the right man one day a week than the wrong one on full time.

In addition, there must be funds and facilities for undertaking necessary research. Hospitals are not going to know accurately the needs of their communities unless they spend time and effort studying those needs. There is much published material today from governmental and other sources that will help in this study. But the application to a particular community must be made by someone who knows how to find, interpret and verify such studies.

Then, of course, there will be certain incidental expenses for stenographic services, printing, photography, compilation of mailing lists, supplies and other physical adjuncts of publicity.

Altogether, the expenses may be expected to amount to 1 or 2 per cent of the hospital's gross income, a not inconsiderable figure.

A second reason for intelligent and understanding trustee support of the public relations program lies in the fact that a sound program, because it follows low pressure technics, will probably not show financial results immediately. Trustees, of course, should realize before they authorize such a program that it is not designed solely to obtain gifts and bequests. To be effective, therefore, the effort must be carried on continuously, through good times and bad, when people are giving to hospitals and when they are not. When times are bad, the financial obligations of the trustees come more sharply to the fore. They may forget the other purposes of the public relations program and be tempted either to throw the program overboard entirely or change the tactics to high pressure, hoping to obtain immediate financial returns.

Both courses are short sighted and, even from the purely pecuniary point of view, tend to kill the goose that lays the golden eggs. When monetary returns are low it might be advisable to curtail the program somewhat but it should not be abandoned entirely. In any public relations program there will be cycles of greater and less activity, depending upon the situations that are to be met. Obviously when a special effort is being made to obtain funds for a new building or endowment for the school of nursing or a tumor clinic, the tempo of expositional effort can be stepped up. When this has been achieved, the tempo can again be slowed. But the program, to be effective, should never stop entirely.

There is a third aspect of the program that also requires trustee understanding. A complete public rela-

tions program for a hospital will probably be quite new
to most hospital trustees. The methods employed may
seem to them quite different from the ones they are
accustomed to use in their own activities, particularly if
they are engaged in some field of commerce. Unless they
see the program as a whole and understand its ultimate
as well as its immediate objectives, they may criticize
the methods. They may feel, for example, that low pressure promotion is too slow; they may not appreciate the
value of understatement rather than overstatement; they
may wish to use dramatic or even sensational devices
that would in the end defeat the very objectives they are
pursuing. Hence, it is important that they grasp the full
program.

Finally, it lies in the hands of the trustees in most
instances to determine whether the recommendations that
arise from a public relations program shall be put into
effect. Obviously in such matters as the adoption of
inclusive rate charges, the development of the outpatient
service and the extension of hospital service in any one
of scores of other channels, the trustees must finally say
"yes" or "no." If new funds are required, the trustees
must assume the responsibility of finding them. Even if
no new funds are required, the trustees should ratify any
major change of policy.

The Administrator's Responsibility

The administrator should be just as well informed of
the philosophy, intent and methods of the public relations
program as the trustee — and for the same reasons. He,
too, is concerned with the money and time required by
the program; he needs to understand the objectives so
that he can appreciate the methods, and he also must

give his support to the recommendations if they are to be fully put into effect.

More than this, of course, the able administrator has a day to day knowledge of the hospital's operation that is not possessed by anyone else. He should be of the greatest possible assistance to the public relations counsel in suggesting sources of information, methods of studying various problems and possible solutions of them. His practical knowledge of administrative possibilities and impossibilities should be invaluable to the public relations counsel in determining what is feasible in the way of administrative changes.

When it comes to putting recommendations into effect, of course, the support of the administrator is almost a *sine qua non* to success. If he counsels and advises during the preparation of the program and then, once adopted, throws his active support behind it, that helps assure success. The opposite is almost a guaranty of failure.

It follows, therefore, that trustees should not force a public relations program or a particular public relations worker upon their administrator. It would be better to have no program at all than to have one that is continually opposed by the administrator. Great care should be taken, of course, in the selection of a public relations worker to obtain one who not only is competent to do the job but is primarily interested in public relations in itself and does not regard it as a stepping stone. Extremely embarrassing situations have arisen occasionally where a board of trustees has employed an "expert" whose principal desire seemed to be to obtain the administrator's job for himself.

In many situations the administrator will have the responsibility of informing the trustees concerning the advisability of a public relations program. He will understand and appreciate the potential values of such a program before his board members do. Here he should be careful not to force the issue too soon. Until at least one or two trustees are thoroughly convinced of its value, a program will almost certainly be premature. It would have to be carried out on such a pitifully small scale as to be ineffective.

The Responsibility of the Public Relations Counsel

The public relations counsel must be the driving force in the program. He plans the studies of community needs for hospital care; he helps the administrator and trustees to interpret these needs in terms of hospital facilities and services required, thus formulating a development program. By approved expositional methods he presents this program to the public and directs the appeals to the hospital's constituents for the support necessary to effectuate the program.

To do the entire job himself, the public relations counsel needs two general types of ability. They may be outlined as follows:

1. Research and Investigative Abilities
   a. Understanding of the basic principles and methods of social research as applied to the hospital and health fields
   b. Familiarity with the basic source materials in these fields, such as hospital and health surveys, morbidity and mortality studies, income studies, census materials
   c. Familiarity with all important aspects of hospital administration, particularly with the developments in hospital service that have come

about in the last ten or twenty years. (This includes, of course, such related fields as nursing education, intern training and medical social service.)

d. Ability to study the history and service of a particular institution or group of institutions and to correlate public needs with the institution's potential developments

e. Ability to prepare a clear, intelligible and convincing summary of the study; to outline a program of advancement which can be followed by the administrator and trustees, and to separate the important from the minor points in such a report

f. Ability and courage to see points of weakness in the hospital's organization, administration or functioning; to recommend methods of correcting them, and to insist that they be corrected before the appeals to the public are begun

2. Promotional and Expositional Abilities

a. Ability to plan an effective expositional program, embracing all appropriate expositional methods. (This requires a good sense of timing and relationship. The program can have certain natural peaks and valleys.)

b. Ability to prepare copy for all types of mediums or to supervise its preparation by others. (This includes newspaper stories, magazine articles, radio scripts, movies, displays and exhibits, pamphlets and brochures, letters, annual reports, house magazines, speeches to be presented before a variety of audiences and similar types of material.)

    c. Ability to prepare a budget for the public relations program and to utilize it to the best advantage

    d. Knowledge of how to check the effectiveness of various steps in the program and when to stop those that are no longer effective

    e. Ability to enlist the support and utilize effectively the aid of various volunteer workers who are ready to help in the hospital's public relations program. (These include trustees, women's auxiliary members, members of the medical and administrative staffs and others who are sympathetic to the hospital's service program.)

    f. Understanding of what constitutes a sound appeal for funds, of when such an appeal should be made and of what the proper response to an appeal ought to be from a given community at a given time

Such a person may not be available, of course. Earlier in this book it was suggested that in this case it would be desirable for the work to be divided into two parts. An experienced hospital consultant could be employed to make the social and administrative investigations and a trained public relations counsel could undertake the exposition of the results. It would be preferable to have these two individuals work simultaneously and in close cooperation with each other. The hospital consultant would probably soon finish his task while the work of putting the recommendations into effect through public exposition would continue indefinitely. Until such time as persons are developed who can do both types of work effectively, the division of function is doubtless the most efficient procedure for most hospitals. Today some of the leading administrators are themselves well able to do the necessary research and investigation and a few are skilled in the technics of promotion and exposition.

Position of Consultant and Public Relations Counsel

The consultant obviously bears a different relation to the administrative organization than would other persons on the pay roll. His position is analagous to that of an outside firm of certified public accountants invited by the board of trustees to make an independent audit of the hospital's books. He makes an independent audit of the hospital's service and administrative practices. He is most useful if he is appointed directly by the board of trustees and is accountable directly to them. This is permissible and does not violate sound hospital organization principles because the consultant's purpose is clearly defined and his term is relatively brief.

With the public relations counsel who becomes, either on a full-time or a part-time basis, a permanent member of the hospital staff, the situation is somewhat different. He should not be a floating rib in the hospital organization because he will carry a certain amount of administrative responsibility like any other department head. Yet his situation differs from that of the dietitian, housekeeper or most other department heads because his work is so intimately tied up with the activities of the trustees.

Various devices may be used to meet this situation. For instance, the public relations counsel might work under the direction of the public relations committee of the board of trustees with the administrator an ex-officio member of this committee as of all other committees of the board. Even with this arrangement, however, the public relations counsel should discuss all major matters with the administrator before they are presented to the committee.

Where the administrator himself has a clear understanding of the public relations program and is in hearty agreement with it, the public relations counsel might find it preferable to make all recommendations to the board through the administrator. The public relations work might be directed by a separate committee comparable to the committees that some hospitals have set up for their schools of nursing. These committees include outside authorities as well as trustees and the administrator. Whatever solution is chosen will depend in some measure at least upon the particular circumstances and personalities involved.

A situation might arise in which a board of trustees would be willing and anxious to have a sound public relations program while the administrator would oppose it, either through misunderstanding or because of fear that it would disturb the peaceful quiet of his ways. If this situation becomes acute enough, the board must either abandon the program or substitute a new administrator. No program can be successful if sabotaged by the administrator.

Summary

Major responsibility for carrying forward a sound and progressive public relations program rests with the trustee, the administrator and the expert publicist. Secondary responsibilities, to be discussed later, rest upon many other persons.

1. Trustee understanding and support of the public relations program are essential for several reasons: (a) A true public relations program costs money. (b) A

If the hospital renders a high quality of service to patients, why not dramatize this by some extra personal attention, such as an alert page smartly attired in white and burgundy uniform?

sound low pressure program may not show immediate financial results, yet it should be carried on continuously since there are objectives other than financial ones. (c) The methods used will probably be somewhat new to most trustees. (d) The trustees usually decide whether the recommendations that arise from a public relations program shall be put into effect.

2. The administrator, since he acts as agent and executive for the trustees, therefore needs to understand and appreciate the program for the same reasons. Furthermore, he has a detailed practical knowledge of the hospital which is invaluable to the public relations expert.

3. The public relations counsel has direct responsibility for planning and executing the program. This requires two types of ability: (a) research and investigative ability and (b) promotional and expositional ability. Each of these is an important specialty and rarely as yet will both be found in the same individual.

The public relations counsel, if a permanent member of the hospital staff on a full-time or part-time basis, should be under the general direction of the administrator like any other department head. Yet his work is so closely related to the activities of the trustees that his channels of communication with them should be somewhat closer and more direct than those of the dietitian or housekeeper.

PART II

SOME MATTERS OF APPLICATION

Chapter 7

PERSONAL CONTACTS IN THE PUBLIC RELATIONS PROGRAM

IF THE hospital is invited to send a person to represent it at a public function, over the radio, in court or in some similar situation, hospital officials usually coach such an individual carefully. This is quite proper. Yet how much more important it is to coach those who represent the hospital informally hundreds of times a year, often without realizing that the public may judge the hospital by their conduct.

The board of trustees, administrator and department heads obviously represent the hospital whenever they talk about it to members of the community. But the number of their contacts is small indeed compared to the contacts of three other groups: the hospital's professional and non-professional employes, the hospital's physicians and the hospital's auxiliaries and guilds. Yet often this important ambassadorial function is completely disregarded. Persons are put in a position to make or mar the hospital's reputation without being given any kind of sound preparation for representing the hospital.

Hospital Employes

Every hospital employe who meets patients or the general public has in his hands some control over the hospital's prestige. This is true not only of the nurse, telephone operator and cashier, but also of the elevator operator, dietitian, housekeeper and her employes, pur-

127

chasing agent and the electrician called to fix a radio. Even the laundry and kitchen employes, when they discuss the hospital with their friends and neighbors, affect its reputation.

These public contacts can be divided into two groups: the informal discussions about the hospital that any employe will have with his friends and acquaintances and the more formal public contacts where the employe acts in his official capacity, whatever that may be.

Because every employe, even one who never sees a patient or any other member of the general public during his working hours, does, nevertheless, discuss the hospital and its spirit during his hours off duty, he should have at least a certain minimum of accurate and significant information about the institution. He should know, for example, something about the volume of free service which the hospital renders; he should know in general where the funds for operating the hospital are obtained; he should have some opportunity of hearing those little human interest stories of hospital service that, if they truly express the hospital's personality, can travel far and do much good. These facts, skillfully presented, will give to each employe a basis for pride in his institution. They will tend to displace in his conversation petty or even malicious gossip concerning the "boss" in which employes often indulge.

But hospital employes cannot learn these facts themselves. The account books are not open to their inspection, nor would they understand them if they were. So the information must be given them in a way that they can grasp, remember and use. There are many ways to get this basic minimum of information into the minds of all employes. It can be transmitted through the department heads; occasional employe meetings may be held for this and other purposes, or bulletin boards or exhibits may be used. One of the best methods is through the publication of an effective and well edited house magazine. Details concerning the publication of house magazines will be given in Chapter 8.

From those employes who have contacts with patients and with the general public, more is expected. They must display patience, consideration, imagination, delicacy, in short, good manners and good etiquette activated by true sympathy and understanding. Countless little cruelties to patients and their relatives happen in hospitals every day because of absence of these qualities.[1]

To obtain good attitudes on the part of employes, the basic personnel practices of the hospital must be essentially sound. This involves the entire field of personnel administration from the original employment interview through to the final exit interview. It includes such things as job analysis, job grading, preparation of an equitable salary scale and ladder of promotion, development of adequate vacation and sick-leave policies and training programs for employes of all grades. Furthermore, a good personnel program includes preparation of department heads for their responsibilities in personnel administration and an adequate method of handling complaints and grievances of employes. It should also nourish employe ambition and self-esteem by giving opportunities for advancement, by developing group consciousness, and by removing the fears of insecurity, domination, old age and similar threats to their peace of mind. A disgruntled employe will not be a thoughtful, courteous representative of the hospital. Neither will one who is beset by personal fears. The best way to en-

courage employes to display patience, consideration and
delicacy toward the hospital's guests is to evince these
qualities in dealing with employes.[2]

In some situations, hospital employes may believe that
the only certain method to assure themselves of reasonable security, to make sure that their complaints are
given a fair hearing and to obtain the best available
wages, working conditions, vacations and other terms
of employment is through membership in an organized
union. Sometimes they are justified in this belief; often
they are not. In any event, the employe has a right to
join a union if he so desires. The formation of a hospital
union presents the administrator and the board of trustees with one of their most delicate and difficult problems
in public relations. Their first duty, of course, is to
patients. No acts must be permitted which will actually
jeopardize the lives or safety of patients. Yet this
dramatic factor should not be utilized by the hospital
to deny proper recognition of the rights of employes. In
a few instances, wise administrators have enlisted the
aid of union officials to improve the quality of work done
by employes.

Training programs for employes should lay particular
stress upon the psychologic conditions of patients. This
applies not only to nurses but to all employes who see
patients. A few examples may illuminate the point.
Recently a man entered a large eastern hospital for an
operation and his poise was given a body blow when the
admitting clerk said, "Well, you certainly are cheerful
for a man who is going to have a double operation
tomorrow."

A friend of mine probably had her recovery from an
operation delayed by a maid in the housekeeping depart-

ment who came to clean the room shortly after the patient regained consciousness. Recognizing her from a former stay in the hospital, the maid insisted upon gossiping about all the hospital events that had transpired since her previous visit. When the nurse in charge finally discovered her and shooed her from the room, she objected declaring that the nurse did not have authority to do so. Every day thereafter, no matter how sick the patient was, this maid spent an hour or so going through the motions of cleaning the room while she kept up an incessant chatter. The fact that she was rarely answered seemed to give her no hint whatsoever.

Of course such examples are not typical. Yet they could be multiplied a thousand-fold. That they could happen in good hospitals indicates that there is much yet to be done in training personnel.

Goldwater has said that "the best hospitals today assume a duty toward their patients which is more inclusive and more humane than a strict interpretation of the term 'medical service' requires, for the patient's mental states — anxiety, fear, ennui, worry, depression, shame, loneliness, irritation — are objects of the hospital's solicitude apart from the physical conditions and the pain and discomfort to which they give rise."[3]

Certain types of persons are of particular importance in this connection. These include, of course, nurses and front office employes (especially admitting officers), clinic personnel and telephone operators.

Good nursing is the backbone of good hospital service. Many a hospital that is far behind the procession in its scientific standards of care remains popular with both its patients and its physicians because the nurses are thoughtful, kindly, patient and adequate in number.

A fine type of nursing care is usually one of the
attributes of hospitals run by the Catholic sisterhoods.
The present day trend to secularism in hospitals appears
in many instances to have had a deleterious effect on the
human qualities of nursing. Nursing schools should be
alert to recognize and to cultivate the growing social
consciousness of their students so as to preserve in nursing its fine spirit of service, devotion and self-effacement.

The foregoing criticism of some nurses should not be
taken as a derogation of the type of scientific training
they are now receiving or as a plea to return to the older
period when nursing students were expected to do the
heavy housekeeping and maid service. Nurses today need
training that prepares them for giving intravenous injections, caring for patients in oxygen tents and fever
therapy cabinets and doing hundreds of other things that
relieve physicians. But with their scientific training
should also be included enough of the spirit of kindness,
humanity and service so that they will always think of
their patients as individuals. One hospital, in trying to
vitalize this idea, suggests to student nurses that they
treat every patient as though he were a parent or someone equally dear.

While nurses, of course, are nearly always rushed, a
gracious attitude toward patients need not take extra
time. Actually it will often save the nurse's time since
patients cooperate better when a nurse is pleasant and
apparently doing all she can to be helpful. A brusque or
sarcastic nurse may arouse the patient's own indepen-
dence and lead him to insist on service whether it is essential or not. The qualities of patience, consideration,
imagination and delicacy are frequently more necessary
in serving ward patients and those in inexpensive accom-

modations than they are in serving patients in expensive private rooms. A kind word to an ignorant or friendless person may do more to speed recovery than the most potent medicine.

The necessity for tact, patience and friendliness at the front desk has been emphasized so often that it is almost trite to mention it again. The only excuse for doing so is that even today many hospitals have people in this department whose milk of human kindness has turned to vinegar. It is easy for the persons at the front desk and in the admitting department to do serious damage to a hospital's reputation. Alert business firms give meticulous training to their receptionists; they realize the importance of gracious yet efficient handling of every person who enters their doors. Hospitals should be even more particular on this score, since many of their visitors are emotionally upset. Whatever his emotional state may be, every person who comes into the hospital should receive prompt and friendly attention. Casual visitors, salesmen and relatives of patients, as well as the patients themselves, all represent potential friends of the institution. Every employe they meet should look upon them as such and should try to merit and win this friendship. Such an attitude will, perhaps, avoid the danger of allowing repetition to make these contacts brusque or curt.

One common hospital policy may well be scrutinized, namely, the requirement that patients pay in advance. This is contrary to the practice of most businesses and is a frequent source of annoyance, if not actual hardship, to patients. Of course, hospitals must collect for their services and obviously every dollar not collected from persons who should pay means one dollar less that is available to render free service to those who really need it. But department and grocery stores, fuel merchants and many others find it possible to allow people to have charge accounts and do not suffer too great a loss. Hotels do not usually require payment in advance. To grant credit, hospitals need to know their clientele. This is possible if adequate credit records of patients are kept and if use is made of the community's agencies for this purpose, *e.g.* the retail credit men's association. Staff doctors should be trained to avoid setting hospital rates and promising discounts independently of the admitting office. This may cause embarrassment at time of admission. Some hospitals avoid this difficulty by providing their medical staff with floor plans showing exact room accommodations and rates.

Whatever the general policies of the front office may be, the execution of these policies should be entrusted only to people who can make friends of all those whom they meet. It is particularly important that those who deal with the poor shall be considerate. This applies to all those who work in the outpatient department and wards of voluntary hospitals and in city and county general hospitals. Indigent clients vary from well educated but unfortunate persons to those of no education; the latter need kindness all the more to allay their fears. If the hospital is going to accept the medically needy, it should minister to them as tenderly as to any others.

In visiting hospitals in various parts of the country I have frequently noted a certain brusqueness and even surliness in front desk employes, particularly in city and county institutions. Their daily contact with poverty and chicanery and misery seems to have hardened them. If they are brusque to a casual visitor, how much more likely are they to be unsympathetic to persons who are sick of body and mind and who, therefore, may well make unreasonable demands.

Many people know a hospital only over the telephone. Efficient, pleasing telephone service is a valuable asset to any institution. Some hospitals attempt to get along with too few operators or insufficient telephone equipment. Neither situation permits adequate, unhurried service. But, whatever the financial limitations may be, any hospital can improve its telephone service by giving thought to it. The telephone company has coaching schools for telephone operators which will assist them to become expert in their services and will help them to develop a courteous manner over the wire. This coaching is available without cost, yet apparently few hospitals have used it.[4]

The standard reply of the telephone operator to an inquiry regarding a patient's condition, "He's doing as well as can be expected," is so meaningless as to be the butt of comedians on the stage and screen. A system has been worked out in several hospitals whereby all calls concerning the condition of patients are referred to a central information desk where a specially trained operator has records of every patient and can quickly give an intelligent statement to the inquirer. This system gives a distinctly more satisfying service.[5] Other hospitals refer calls to the nursing clerk on each floor. This also is reported to be a satisfactory system.

When a hospital has done all that it can to assure good relations between its employes and the public, why not offer some personal attention that will serve to symbolize and dramatize the institution's basic attitude toward patients and the general public? There are several ways in which this can be done. Evanston Hospital, Evanston,

Illinois, has a courteous and helpful doorman at the automobile entrance to the hospital. He assists patients in and out of cars, has ready a stretcher and a wheel chair in case of need, helps with luggage, calls the floor nurse to announce that the patient is arriving, directs strangers and otherwise expresses the desire of the hospital to make patients and visitors feel that they are welcome. A similar plan is used at Touro Infirmary, New Orleans, where page boys in white and burgundy tailored suits with pill box caps give as smart a service as is found in any hotel.

Peralta Hospital, Oakland, California, dramatizes its personal interest in patients by having a Chinese girl dressed in a beautiful mandarin coat who serves coffee or other beverage to all patients early in the morning. The girl, who has been chosen because of her attractive appearance and her gracious personality, wheels her serving cart from room to room and floor to floor throughout the hospital. Many a patient starts the day more happily because of her brief and friendly visit. The gift of a morning paper with the compliments of the hospital or a local business concern is also cheering.

At Emory University Hospital, near Atlanta, Georgia, and at several other institutions, hospital hostesses are employed.[6] A hostess serves as a special liaison officer between hospital and patient. The duties of a hostess are manifold: to do whatever she can to make patients feel secure, comfortable and welcome. Insofar as possible the hostess at Emory University Hospital receives all patients on admission, escorts them to their rooms, introduces them to their nurses and, in general, makes them feel acquainted with the hospital. She visits all patients as often as she can thereafter. She makes such little purchases as stamps, stationery, magazines, cigarets. She sometimes reads to patients or writes letters for those who are too ill or illiterate to write for themselves. Occasionally she does errands downtown for patients who have no friends or relatives to do them. At time of death she assists the relatives to make arrangements and by encouragement aids them to accept the new situation.*

Many hospitals now routinely supply patients with a card on which to record their impressions of the service and to make suggestions for its improvement. This aids somewhat in gaining their good will and, more impor-

*Certain other types of personal services to patients and the public might well be considered by the administration. The most important and socially significant is the provision of physicians' offices in the hospital. This is a convenience to the doctors and their patients, conserving the time of physicians and often that of patients as well, and it provides an opportunity to use more fully the existing service departments of the hospital, namely, clinical laboratory, x-ray department, physical therapy department, pharmacy and any other ancillary medical services available. A variety of economic arrangements may be made between physician and hospital to care for the extra costs.

If a hospital is located away from the business district, as it should be if possible, there are other conveniences that are appreciated by patients and by visitors. These include a cafeteria or guest dining room, a gift and toy shop and a flower shop. The Johns Hopkins Hospital has a branch bank in the building for the convenience of visitors and employes. The Baptist Memorial Hospital at Memphis, Tennessee, has installed a branch of a downtown department store. One of the New York hospitals has an excellent barber and beauty shop. Orange Memorial Hospital, Orange, New Jersey, has a guest suite that accommodates persons who enter the hospital merely to rest as well as those who want to stay near sick relatives. Various other hospitals have similar services.

Some administrators oppose the provision of such facilities on the ground that they lower the dignity of the hospital, they build ill-will on the part of local merchants and they endanger the hospital's tax exemption. Hospitals that have installed them, however, have not been impressed by these arguments. Many of them have been careful to have all such departments face on inside corridors and not on the street. Thus practically all of the patronage of the department comes from persons who are in the hospital and not from those outside who would normally patronize neighborhood merchants.

tant, it permits them to unload their complaints privately while they are in the hospital rather than publicly later over a bridge table. Furthermore, it gives the hospital administrator an effective answer to the doctor who has a chronic complaint that his patients do not get good service.

Any dramatization of thoughtfulness and considera- tion for patients and the public will defeat its objectives if it is forced and insincere. It is unsound to use it as a smokescreen to cover up deficiencies in the basic services of the hospital. But when the basic services are good, when thoughtfulness and consideration actually char- acterize the attitude of the hospital administration and its employes, it is quite proper to dramatize this attitude by having one or more employes who render an unusual service.

Medical Staff

A hospital without physicians soon closes its doors. A physician without a hospital is seriously handicapped in the conduct of his work. This mutual dependence of physicians and hospitals carries with it a mutuality of interest. Today the physician needs the hospital as never before if he is to practice scientific medicine to the full extent of his powers. The hospital has a right, therefore, to expect him to give it vigorous support and aid. But the hospital has always needed the physician and always will. It must, therefore, be ready to give him the kind of aid and assistance that only a good hospital can provide.

If there is any one factor that is more important than others in a hospital's public relations program it is the caliber of the medical staff. A good medical staff can keep a poor hospital going for years while a mediocre medical

When properly organized in guilds or auxiliaries and adequately trained, women can be a great source of strength to a hospital.

staff can defeat the best efforts of a competent board of trustees and of an able administrator to build up a hospital's reputation and character. Of course, such a board and administrator will not long be satisfied with a poor medical staff. Nor would they, in fact, have to be satisfied indefinitely; good doctors will usually accept an opportunity to join a hospital's staff when they are convinced it is rendering good service.

Just what is it that attracts good physicians to a hospital? There are many factors. Some will be of greater weight with one doctor and others, with another. Among those that deserve special mention are the following:

1. Patients are given excellent kindly service including good nursing, competent dietetics, adequate laboratory and x-ray service, efficient personnel in the surgical and obstetrical departments, etc., through the whole range of hospital services.

2. Suitable equipment is available to permit the physician to treat or diagnose his patients properly.

3. The doctor is given opportunity to keep in practice through work on ward and clinic patients. This is particularly important to surgeons whose digital dexterity deteriorates without practice.

4. Opportunities and facilities, including equipment, books, periodicals and good medical records, are provided for research and study.

5. There is the stimulus of a vigorous teaching program. Through the teaching of nurses, dietitians, medical students, interns and residents, the visiting medical staff keeps itself mentally alert. Of course, many hospitals cannot have an affiliation with a medical school but all those that can should do so. Those without medical school affiliation can still be true teaching insti-

tutions if they will take seriously their responsibilities to their student nurses, interns and residents.

6. The hospital's reputation confers prestige on the physician. Staff appointments at a good hospital are a legitimate and highly desirable form of advertising for the physician.

7. Opportunities may be provided for the doctor to develop his special talents or to follow his selective interests in certain categories of disease.

8. Fellowships, subsidies for special study, full-time and part-time salaries may attract certain physicians.

9. In large cities, convenient location will aid in enlisting good physicians. Their time is so full that many of them hesitate to give much of it to a hospital which is located a long distance from their offices or homes.

A hospital can assure itself a good staff, first of all, by meriting such a staff. In addition, staff appointments should be made carefully and solely on the basis of competence. Fortunately the smaller hospitals no longer need be baffled by the problem of ascertaining competence among specialists. Already the specialty boards have certified about one-half of the specialists of the country. By 1942, assuming they continue at the present rate, practically all of the competent specialists will have been certified. By that time it will probably be the exception for any man to head a department of the medical staff of a good hospital without being certified as competent in his specialty.

Other physicians, and particularly surgeons, ought to be limited to those procedures which they are competent to perform. The conscientious hospital gives an implied guarantee to its patients that they will receive good care when within its doors. How can this guarantee be fulfilled? The Tacoma General Hospital has a system of grading its surgeons that seems to answer this question satisfactorily.[7] Surgeons are divided into three groups. The minor surgeons may perform only those operations given on a certain limited list. As they gain experience and demonstrate their competence and moral stamina, they are advanced to junior major surgeons and can perform a much larger group of operations, some of them only after consultation, however. The top group or senior major surgeons are allowed to carry out any surgical procedure. The plan has succeeded at Tacoma General Hospital. It ought not to be considered as a substitute for a surgical residency, however.

A third method of controlling physicians is to give them annual appointments to the staff. This gives members of the medical staff warning that they must meet the hospital's standards of excellence if they hope to continue to use its facilities. An alternative is to appoint for longer terms but to make all staff appointments subject to termination at any time at the pleasure of the board of trustees.

Encouragement of consultations is a vital part of any program for maintaining high medical standards in a hospital. In the obstetric department some hospitals now provide free consultation by the senior men of their staff in any obstetric case and require a consultation in the more dangerous types of obstetric procedure. This puts something of a burden on the senior men of the staff but in recent years obstetric leaders have been so anxious to reduce maternal mortality that they have gladly assumed the load.

In addition to giving the best medical service of which they are capable, can the hospital expect anything else

from its medical staff? Yes. If it is working sincerely
with the doctors, it can expect them to recipricate in
several ways: (1) by understanding and supporting the
aims and objectives of the administration; (2) by co-
operating in the hospital's efforts to improve its services
without, however, attempting to usurp the powers and
duties of the administration; (3) by upholding the
hospital in the eyes of the public, by suggesting it to
wealthy patients as a proper object of beneficience and
by giving actual assistance as workers when the hospital
engages in a financial campaign; (4) by manifesting
only kindness and consideration for patients at all times;
(5) by contributing as much as they are able to the
advancement of medical science and art; (6) by helping
in the educational program for the interns, residents
and junior attending men; (7) by serving faithfully
and to the best of their ability on the medical board
whenever chosen, and (8) by observing the highest
medical ethics in all their practice, both within and
without the hospital.

Members of the medical staff, therefore, play an
important part in the public relations program. If they
are to play this part most effectively, they should be
well informed of the reasons why a hospital undertakes
such a program. Usually every physician on the staff
is eager to have the hospital buy further equipment for
his department or provide additional technical assistance
or improve the care of his patients in some other way.
Unless he is well informed of the need for a public relations program, he will be tempted to resent the money
that may be spent for salaries and incidental expenses.
This may seriously affect the success of the entire effort.
Perhaps it is impossible to win the active support of

every member of the staff. If so, sufficient effort should be made so that the doctors realize that there are good reasons for undertaking the program and are not actively critical of it. If every physician can become an enthusiastic supporter of the hospital, that fact builds real power into the public relations program.

Auxiliaries, Guilds and Similar Groups

A woman's auxiliary or guild can be an important source of strength to the hospital.[8] The primary object of such an organization is to develop a group of persons in the community who are informed about the hospital, friendly to it and ready to act as good-will ambassadors for it. An important part of this function is for these women to act as the eyes and ears of the institution, keeping the administration informed through proper channels of the public's state of mind concerning the hospital. Another purpose, probably secondary in value but nevertheless often of substantial aid to the hospital, is the provision of funds and services.

The public relations function of the auxiliary will be carried on more or less automatically. A group of women cannot work enthusiastically for a project without discussing it with their friends. This discussion can be most effective if the group is given definite facts on which to feed. The problem here is much the same as that of giving employes basic facts about the hospital, except that each hospital employe at least knows a little about one department while the auxiliary members frequently have to start from scratch. The same methods that are used to tell employes about the hospital may be used for auxiliary members, namely, talks by the administrator and by department heads, house magazines, bulletin boards, exhibits, periodic letters and carefully planned tours of the entire hospital, perhaps taken on the install-ment plan.

It is probably best not to ask the auxiliary members to speak in praise of the hospital. If they are supplied with proper information, if they are enthusiastic about the organization, asking them to tell others will be unnecessary and might perhaps offend them.

To arouse and maintain interest, the women must have a feeling that they are actually doing something worth while for the hospital. There are almost limitless opportunities to use their services or financial support effectively. Some years ago I prepared a check list of possible functions of a woman's auxiliary. This origi-nally appeared in *The Hospital Yearbook* and is re-printed as Appendix II. Without going into all details it might be mentioned that the possible activities can be classified into the following groups:

1. Raising Funds
   a. To purchase special equipment
   b. To care for special needs of patients
   c. To encourage graduate and student nurses
2. Obtaining Goods in Kind Through Showers and Solicitation
3. Serving the Hospital in Various Capacities
   a. Clerical service
   b. Assistance to nurses in providing personal services for patients
   c. Assistance to social service department
   d. Sewing
   e. Making surgical dressings
   f. Arranging social activities
   g. Promoting publicity and public education

h. Landscaping and gardening
i. Interior decorating
j. Occupational therapy

If a hospital is a member of a community chest, its auxiliary must be careful not to attempt to raise funds by unapproved methods. Policies adopted in Cleveland to cover this subject are given in Appendix III.

Outstanding among hospitals for the way it has made use of its auxiliaries is the Windham Community Hospital, Willimantic, Connecticut. Not only does it have unusually fine women's auxiliaries but it has enrolled groups of high school girls as "Juniors" with excellent results.[9] These girls come to the hospital on certain schedules and have proved extremely helpful as pages, information clerks and hostesses. They read to children or older people, write letters for patients who cannot write for themselves, arrange flowers, operate elevators during visiting hours, serve as hostesses in the reception room, assist the nurses in serving beverages, amuse children with games, prepare supplies and perform many other extra services. Their work is carefully organized and supervised. Over 160 girls are enrolled as Juniors. This has proved an excellent means of stimulating social consciousness, creating understanding and building an attitude of trust among the girls of the community and their families.

A method of arousing interest among the leading men of a hospital's service area has been utilized by Albany Hospital, Albany, New York, and Blodgett Memorial Hospital, Grand Rapids, Michigan. The various men's organizations in the community are invited in rotation to have dinner and to spend the evening at the hospital. Following an excellent dinner (which is served at a nominal price), the aims and work of the hospital are explained by the administrator and his associates. This talk is followed by a carefully planned trip through the hospital in small groups. Each group is guided by a member of the administrative staff who has been specially coached. This procedure has been found to create real interest on the part of the men.

Administrator and Other Officers

Much valuable public relations work can be done by the administrator, and often by department heads and trustees, through making addresses before various groups in the community. Some administrators are such excellent speakers that they are called upon frequently for all kinds of functions. If the address is not devoted primarily to hospital service, they can always find some legitimate way of bringing in that theme.

The administrator should also consider the value that he can be to his hospital as well as to the community through active work in civic enterprises. His help and guidance can be especially valuable on a council of social agencies or in a health or hospital council because of his special knowledge of health conditions. Many hospital administrators are active members of service clubs, of neighborhood associations, of the health committees of chambers of commerce, of park boards, or of local chapters of the American Red Cross or similar groups. Women administrators often play an important part in the League of Women Voters, the American Association of University Women and in other women's organizations. Because of the educational responsibilities in the hospital, an administrator may be of unusual value on a school board or the education committee of a civic organization. Some administrators have taken a prominent part in the Boy Scouts, Girl Scouts, Y.M.C.A. and similar character-building organizations.

Community services of this type give the administrator an opportunity to make influential friends who will almost automatically be friends of the hospital. Department heads, too, should be encouraged to carry a reasonable load of community service. They are often men or women of culture, education and ability whose assistance on civic enterprises would be most welcome.

In connection with matters of this kind, however, it is well for the administrator to remember that joining a club cannot take the place of doing a good job of hospital administration. If he must choose between the two, his duty to the hospital obviously should be the first call.

The administrator and his department heads, like the other hospital personnel who serve patients directly, should always remember that they are dealing with human beings. This point of view has often been voiced, perhaps most effectively by the late Dr. W. H. Mansholt, director of a university hospital in The Netherlands.[10] Equipment and forms of organization do not of themselves assure good care. Just as Mark Hopkins on one end of a log is the basis for good education, so is a competent, intelligent, humane physician the basis for good medical service. No amount of equipment or high degree of education and skill on the part of nurses or other hospital employes can make up for the lack of these qualities in the physician. Administrators, department heads and trustees should never lose sight of the crucial importance of the physician in the scheme of hospital service.

Summary

Too much emphasis must not be placed, of course, upon the personal contacts discussed in this chapter. Although important in building public support and good will, they are secondary methods. It will always be true that the basis for good public relations is the maintenance of a good institution and the provision of service which is nicely adjusted to public needs of all kinds, clinical and economic.

Subject to that qualification, however, one of the basic next steps is to tell the public what the hospital is doing. Personal contact, if wisely guided and stimulated, is one of the most direct and effective methods. The hospital employes, the physicians on the staff, the women's auxiliaries and junior auxiliaries and the administrator, trustees and department heads can all play important parts in this person-to-person transmittal of the hospital's story of service.

333333

33333

REFERENCES

1. Parlett, Samuel: Patient's Lament, *The Modern Hospital*, Feb., 1938, p. 49, and April, 1938, p. 79, and Price, Alice L.: Hospital Visitors, *Hospital Management*, Nov., 1938, p. 24.
2. Hamilton, James A.: An Approach to the Hospital Personnel Problem, *Transactions of the American Hospital Association*, 1938, p. 649, and Emch, Arnold F.: Hospital Personnel Policy, *Hospitals*, May, 1938, p. 43, and Tead, Ordway: Employe Welfare in the Broader Sense, *Hospitals*, June, 1937, p. 21, and Doane, Joseph C.: Personnel Relations, *Hospitals*, Sept., 1937, p. 15.
3. Goldwater, S. S.: The Correction by Administrative Methods of Undesirable Mental States in Hospital Patients, *Nosokomeion*, 1930, No. 1-4, p. 70.
4. Sloan, Raymond P.: Good Will by Wire, *The Modern Hospital*, Feb., 1937, p. 49.
5. Giddings, Emanuel: Information Cheerfully Given, *The Modern Hospital*, Feb., 1939, p. 43.
6. Simons, Florence R.: Going the Second Mile, *The Modern Hospital*, May, 1937, p. 61.
7. Cummings, C. J.: Controlling Surgical Technique, *The Modern Hospital*, April, 1935, p. 45, and Rankin, W. S.: The Control of Surgery — Who Shall Do Major Surgery?, *Hospitals*, April, 1937, p. 14, and Agnew, G. Harvey: The Medical Profession and the Hospital, reprint of address to joint meeting of British Columbia, Western and Northwestern hospital associations, Aug., 1930.
8. Hyde, Florence S.: Welfare of Patient Is Goal of Women's Auxiliary Activities, *Hospitals*, Oct., 1938, p. 101, and Houston, Mrs. Wm.: The Value of a Women's Auxiliary in Relation to the Hospital, *Saskatchewan Hospital Association Transactions*, 1935, and Fishbein, Mrs. Morris: The Rôle of the Woman's Auxiliary in the Modern Hospital, *Hospitals*, June, 1936, p. 14.
9. Sloan, Raymond P.: Those Windham Juniors, *The Modern Hospital*, Nov., 1938, p. 44.
10. Mansholt, W. H.: What Can European and American Hospitals Learn from Each Other? *Nosokomeion*, 1930, No. 1-4, p. 185.

Chapter 8

EXPOSITIONAL METHODS — GENERAL PRINCIPLES, ANNUAL REPORTS, HOUSE MAGAZINES

EXPOSITION, as the term is used in this book, is the function of defining, explaining, analyzing and interpreting those aspects of the hospital and its work that are of concern to the public. It may be contrasted with purely emotional appeals which define, analyze and interpret little or nothing. Of course, emotion cannot and should not be excluded from hospital exposition. But it should be subordinate to the rational appeals.

Need for Exposition

The task of exposition in the hospital public relations program is to acquaint the public with the hospital's work, its difficulties and limitations, its objectives and ideals. Exposition is essential in modern life. As was pointed out in Chapter 1, if a hospital relies purely upon chance to do the job of exposition for it, there are so many other competing demands on attention that the hospital's story may never be heard. Not that the hospital does not have a good story and one that the public would find interesting, but without a narrator it may be overlooked.

Exposition, therefore, tells the hospital's story — honestly, fairly and effectively.

150

A hospital which is engaged in a program designed to meet the hospital needs of its community should employ sound expositional methods to inform the public about that program at every step in its development. This is desirable for three reasons: (1) to test the soundness of the ideas that make up the program, (2) to create acceptance of the ideas once they have been proved sound and (3) to win the moral and financial support which is necessary to carry any significant program into effect.

Exposition in Practice

Just what do these generalities mean in actual practice? Let us imagine the case of the Jones Memorial Hospital, the only hospital serving two counties with a total population of 65,000 people. The hospital, which has 150 beds and is directed by an able, well trained administrator, has been crowded for some years and a building program is under consideration but has not yet been started. The administrator and the board agree that the hospital should be thoroughly studied and a sound development and public relations program instituted before any further money is put into buildings.

They, therefore, retain on a part-time basis an able public relations counsel with hospital experience. His first recommendation is the employment of a competent hospital consultant to make a thorough survey of the hospital and its community responsibilities. This fact is duly reported to the public through the newspapers and the reasons why a survey should be made are also publicized. After suitable inquiry, the administrator and the board agree on the employment of a nationally recognized expert who is familiar with all aspects of hospital administration and also with the basic mortality, morbidity, economic and demographic data relating to the need for hospital service. His appointment and qualifications are announced to the public.

The hospital consultant supervises the collection of significant data about the hospital and the characteristics of its service area and analyzes these facts in relation to one another. He then prepares a report which indicates the hospital services that are now adequate and efficient and points out those that need improvement or expansion. He may recommend the addition of entirely new services. The full report in all detail is discussed first by the public relations committee of the board of trustees and then by the entire board; the board members may also coopt a few other community leaders to counsel with them. On the basis of their discussion, a plan is developed for the progressive improvement and expansion of the hospital to meet the needs revealed by the survey.

The major highlights of this report the consultant may then present at a public meeting attended not only by those connected with the hospital but also by leading citizens representing important groups in the service area: potential contributors, wage-earners, salaried people, farmers, women's groups and similar classes in the community.

The principal facts of the survey and the major outlines of the improvement and expansion plan are then submitted in pamphlet or mimeographed form to a large group of people for their comments and suggestions before the plan is brought before the board of trustees for final adoption. The comments and suggestions are studied carefully and the development program is restudied in the light of the comments; changes are made where these are indicated. When the plan appears to be the best that can be worked out by the consultant, the public relations counsel, the administrator and the public relations committee of the board of trustees, it is submitted to the entire board for adoption.

The plan as finally adopted is resubmitted to an even larger group of the public, all those, in fact, whose support of the hospital is important. These include not only potential contributors wherever they may be found but also persons who influence the patronage of the hospital, such as women's club and parent-teacher association leaders, officers of business, civic and labor groups, and professional organizations, particularly medical, dental and nursing groups. Various methods are used to give them the information and to solicit their opinions and advice. These include, for example, letters, tests of opinion, pamphlets, addresses at meetings and newspaper articles.

An alternative method of creating in the public mind a sense of participation and partnership is through the use of carefully prepared tests of public opinion. These may be designed to bring out public desires and needs in the field of hospital service as well as any criticisms of the hospital as it is now operated. When properly studied, these can be helpful in guiding the development of the program and, when effectively publicized, they can also indicate to the public that the hospital is definitely eager to obtain public counsel on its development program. A discussion of the technic of the public opinion poll will be presented in Chapter 12.

The hospital should then start work on the first item of its development program. This might be, for example, the installation of an inclusive rate system of charges. Several variations are possible and the institution could well consult a substantial segment of the public concerning its preferences. For instance, would the public prefer to have a flat rate per day regardless of the length of stay or would it rather have a higher rate for the first few days when expenses are greatest, dropping down on the third or fourth day almost to the basic rate for room, board and floor nursing service?

The second item in the development program might involve the construction of new quarters for the outpatient department, thus temporarily relieving the pressure for space. Here, too, there may be various alternatives that involve questions of broad policy in which the public's viewpoint is important.

In this process of taking the public more fully into partnership, the issue should not be confused by asking questions that concern purely administrative details. Within this limitation, the procedure of consulting the public step by step during the development of the hospital promotes a feeling of participation and partnership in its management. Representatives of the public realize that the hospital is earnestly trying to mold its service to meet public needs. They appreciate that it wants to use public money in the way that will be most effective in safeguarding health. Such appreciation evidences a sound relation between hospital and public.

Range of Expositional Mediums

There are many vehicles of exposition. They include such things as annual reports, bulletins or house magazines, letters, pamphlets and booklets, bound books, newspaper and magazine articles, exhibits, moving pictures,

WRENCE HOSPITAL
BRONXVILLE, NEW YORK

1936

NEW YORK
POST-GRADUATE
MEDICAL SCHOOL
AND HOSPITAL 1937

FIFTY-FIFTH YEAR

1937

SEVENTY-FOURTH ANNUAL REPORT
RHODE ISLAND HOSPITAL

80TH ANNUAL REPORT
FOR THE YEAR 1938
BUFFALO GENERAL
HOSPITAL

That life
may
go on

A MANSION OF MERCY

er left, Presbyterian Hospital, Chicago,
lower right, Jewish Hospital, Philadelphia

When annual reports are physically attractive and intelligently
edited, they give effective aid in a public relations program.

slide films, dramas and pageants, meetings, lectures and addresses and radio broadcasts.

Because there is such a range in expositional mediums, a wealth of technics may be employed by the skilled public relations counsel. This very wealth of opportunity makes it important that a wise selection be made. Much time and money can be wasted through selecting the wrong medium. For that reason considerable space will be devoted to discussions of the various mediums, where and when they should be used and how they may be used effectively.

Annual Reports — Basic Considerations

Every hospital should issue an annual report. Many of them do. The main purpose of such a report is to give a public accounting of the hospital's stewardship of the public's funds and support. Actually many reports fall far short of performing this function. Most of them fail because they are not prepared in a manner that will attract and hold interest.

The preparation of an annual report obviously deserves careful attention by hospital officials. The first question to be settled is: What group of people should the hospital try to interest by means of the annual report? The kind of report to be prepared will differ somewhat according to its audience.

It should be sent only to those for whom it has been planned and to whom it will be interesting. There is no point in sending an annual report to anyone who will probably look at the cover, thumb hurriedly through the pages and then consign it to the wastebasket. But, if prepared so as to be interesting, an annual report may well be sent to all trustees, auxiliary members, department heads and employes, members of the medical staff, alumnae of the nursing school, former interns and residents, former patients (especially those who took private room accommodations), potential patients, donors and potential donors, newspaper editors, business and civic leaders, government officials, ministers and other religious leaders and any other persons who are in a position to assist the hospital in building good will. Wide distribution of this type is a strong argument in favor of brevity. A brief report is more likely to be read. Furthermore, printing and postage will be much less on a 24 or 36 page report than they will be on one of 100 or 200 pages.

In order that an annual report may be most helpful from a public relations point of view, it should be written so that it will be interesting and significant to each of the groups mentioned above. To do this effectively it should include only material that will be interesting to all or nearly all of them. Many annual reports seem to be edited on the opposite assumption, namely, that if material is of interest to any group, no matter how small, it should be included. The result is a book so full of miscellaneous statistics and lists that it is uninviting if not actually repellant.

Detailed statistics and lists have their place, of course. But tables on the nationality of patients, various classes of surgical operations and their mortality and recovery rates, minute details of accounting and lists of alumnae of the school of nursing, former interns and residents, members of the board of trustees since the founding of the hospital and other material of similar reference value could well be mimeographed and supplied only to those who would have real interest in them. Certainly such material merely clutters up a hospital's annual report. File copies of these lists and statistics should be kept in the record library or in the accounting department for historical and reference purposes. Alumnae lists might well be published as separate booklets every year or two as is done at Tacoma General Hospital.

Many annual reports lose value because of delay in publication. Statistics, like fish, do not keep. Figures on per capita costs, on surplus or deficit, on the situation in nursing, on governmental relations or on any other matters dealt with in an annual report soon become outdated. Furthermore, the public rapidly loses interest in material that is merely historical. It is important, therefore, that the annual report be published and distributed as soon as possible after the close of the calendar year or fiscal period to which it applies.

This requires planning well in advance. Prompt publication is most readily achieved if the principal types of facts that are to be presented are selected at the beginning of the fiscal period and running totals are kept on them, daily, weekly or monthly as the situation may require. Certain types of photographs that may be useful in the annual report can only be obtained at particular times, *e.g.* pictures of the hospital gardens at their best, of National Hospital Day events or of old buildings before demolition. Thus it is wise to make a tentative outline of the report at the beginning of the fiscal year.

Such a plan must not be allowed to make the report stereotyped, however. The outline must be considered as a fluid, changing organism ready to adapt to new conditions as they arise. With such an outline kept always in mind, much of the material for the annual report should be ready when the year closes. Then the person who is actually to prepare the text should set about it immedi-

ately. Charts should be drawn, layouts planned, cuts
ordered and the text carefully edited and set in type.

The report should be in the mail not later than 60 days
after the close of the year. For a hospital which follows
the calendar year this would mean that the report would
reach the friends of the hospital in February — after
they had paid their Christmas bills and before they were
being pressed by the income tax collector.* In sending
out the reports it would be well if each were accompanied
by a personal letter from a trustee asking for comment.

Annual Reports — Two Distinctive Examples

Granted that an annual report must not be tedious,
either through too great detail or the reporting of stale
facts and figures, what are some compelling features for
which it may strive? One answer to this question is to
describe examples of two distinct and effective types of
annual report that have been issued by hospitals. An
outstanding report was published by the University of
Rochester early in 1938, covering the work of Strong
Memorial Hospital and Rochester Municipal Hospital.
The complete report is only 20 pages in length, not including the cover. Almost the entire story is told in pictures
and ingenious pictorial statistics. The pictures, although
printed in one color only, are comparable in quality to
those usually found in good magazines. They are not
merely scenes in various parts of the hospital; they are
dramatic representations of the hospital's work. Each

---

*If a hospital is on a calendar year, its financial and service data
for the year, properly interpreted and related with previous years, can
well be made the basis of a preliminary informal report through the
newspapers, many of which publish a yearly summary edition on
December 31 or January 1. The service of hospitals could well be
featured. This requires prompt action and a discerning eye for news.

one conveys some thought. All reference data are relegated to the last two pages and the inside back cover.

Let us go through this report consecutively. The front cover shows a picture of the hospital entrance. Inscribed in three panels over the columns appear these words: "University of Rochester," "Strong Memorial Hospital," "Medicine, Dentistry." (Many services, such as laundry, food, heating, laboratory examinations and medical and nursing care are rendered to Rochester Municipal Hospital by the university through Strong Memorial Hospital. Essentially the two hospitals constitute one unit.)

Near the bottom of the front cover appears the following:

"Within these brick walls life begins and ends.

In this harbor, weary sea-worn ships

Drop anchor; and new-launched vessels

Start their outward trips."

The inside of the front cover shows a young child with the caption, "Look, Daddy — I can walk now."

On the fly page under the name of the Strong Memorial Hospital appears the following statement: "Few people realize the contribution made by American voluntary hospitals to public health and public welfare. This booklet offers a pictorial commentary upon the work of such an institution. Strong Memorial is a university hospital connected directly with a medical school renowned for research and teaching. The same exhaustive facilities serve the Rochester Municipal Hospital maintained by the city for those citizens who are unable to assume the cost of hospital care. In these pages one may learn of the many and varied activities of this medical center, the cost of its services and their value to all types of patients and to the community."

And that is the longest and almost the only general text statement in the whole book!

The next thirteen pages alternately show photographs of interesting hospital activities and pictorial presentations of the most significant statistics about the institutions. These pictographs deal with the following: (1) an average day at Strong Memorial and Rochester Municipal Hospitals; (2) relationship between the city of Rochester and the University of Rochester; (3) contribution of Strong Memorial Hospital to the community; (4) finances of its outpatient department; (5) cost per patient day in Rochester Municipal Hospital and how it is paid; (6) volume of outpatient services; (7) source of Strong Memorial Hospital patients; (8) agencies co-operating with the social service department, and (9) income and expenditures of Strong Memorial Hospital.

A statement of income and expense for both hospitals, comparing two fiscal years, is presented on one page. Obviously such a report gives only the most significant items. Another page is devoted to a formal statistical summary of the in-patient work in both hospitals for the two fiscal years. A third page summarizes the work of the Strong Memorial Hospital outpatient department.

The inside back cover is folded in twice and when opened equals six pages. Three pages of this cover are devoted to lists of trustees, officers of administration, department heads and assistants, medical staff, gifts during the past year and deaths of staff members. All this is set in six-point type, which is small but legible.

A bequest form appears under a photograph of a memorial tablet to the Strongs, for whom the hospital was named. An aerial view of the hospital appears on the back cover.

Dr. Basil C. MacLean, director of Strong Memorial Hospital, says that this report was influential in educating the people of Rochester to the relations between the university and the city government. This is important as Rochester Municipal Hospital is a valuable teaching unit for the university. It is operated by Strong Memorial Hospital on a contract with the city.

Quite different in character but effective in presentation is the report of Grady Hospital, Atlanta, Georgia, for 1933. This report is entirely devoid of pictures and art work. It contains nothing but text and a list of the hospital's trustees. Yet the text is written so simply, directly and briefly, the story of the hospital's year is told in such a vivid fashion that, in spite of the lack of pictures, anyone with even a slight interest in the hospital would read it through. A brief quotation will illustrate the style of writing:

The test of competent and successful management of any institution lies in its ability to render an adequate service at a reasonable cost and in such a manner that it will please the patrons and create good will for the institution.

To achieve this objective, the trustees, the administrative officers, the medical staffs and the personnel of the hospital have been striving during the past three years. That this objective may have in part been achieved may be judged from this third annual report of the trustees to the citizens of Atlanta and Fulton County.

That the cost of operating the hospital has steadily decreased is revealed by the following figures which cover the total cost of operating the hospital:

Year	Total Cost of Operating	Year	Total Cost of Operating
1928	$523,544.68	1931	$508,386.92
1929	533,914.00	1932	525,982.63
1930	532,660.09	1933	486,126.24

These reductions in the cost of operating the hospital have been made in spite of a continual increase in the number of patients treated. Much of this increase in patronage is due to the present reduced economic condition of a large percentage of our population. The following tabulation will illustrate this steadily increasing patronage:

Year	Number of Emergency Patients	Number of Clinic Patients	Number of Bed Patients	Total Number of Patients
1928	16,663	14,303	10,183	41,149
1929	18,581	15,949	11,355	45,885
1930	19,606	16,829	11,981	48,416
1931	28,343	24,554	15,578	68,475
1932	28,127	30,122	18,889	77,138
1933	32,524	38,227	20,657	91,408

These figures indicate an increase of patients, during the past three years, of 88 per cent, during which period the cost of operating the hospital and clinics has shown an 8.7 per cent reduction.

LARGER LOAD AT LOWER COST

In spite of this reduction of cost and the increase of the patient load, the service to the patients has not suffered; on the other hand it has shown a marked improvement from practically every point of view.

The service of a much larger number of persons, and at a reduced cost, has been accomplished by improvements in methods and practices that have effected substantial savings in costs of supplies, drugs, equipment, repairs, electric power, linen, laundering and the like.

The expenditures for food during 1933 were $21,361.87 less than they were in 1932, despite the 9 per cent increase in the number of bed patients. Much of this saving was the direct result of the centralization of the diet service for the entire hospital that was effected in 1932.

As a result of these economies the hospital has been enabled to handle the larger load without calling for additional appropriations.

Since Grady Hospital has been provided to care for more or less acute cases, it is not in position to accommodate chronic or incurable cases that require bed care. There is, however, a pressing need that provision should be made somewhere for the care of such cases.

The care of the numerous additional bed patients has been made possible through the increase of 12 per cent in the bed capacity of the hospital, which was incident to the better utilization of available space. In addition, a greater number of bed patients has been accommodated because of a marked decrease in the average number of days that patients now occupy beds in the hospital.

In a charity hospital it is important to see that patients do not stay in the hospital any longer than is necessary, so it remains for the management to see that they are discharged as soon as their condition will permit. The improvement that has been effected in this direction is indicated by the following figures:

Average Days of Bed Occupancy

1928	13.6	1931	10.0
1929	14.0	1932	9.0
1930	13.4	1933	8.8

At the same time that this improvement was being effected, the average stay in the white maternity ward has been increased from 3.5 days per patient to 7.9 days as a result of the doubling in size of the maternity ward during the year 1932.

In measuring the cost of operating a hospital, exclusive of attached clinics, the criterion is the total daily per patient cost. During the past three years these costs have been materially decreased, as the following table will show:

Cost per Patient per Day

1928	$2.93	1931	$2.76
1929	3.01	1932	2.42
1930	2.99	1933	2.30

The entire report is only 14 pages in length, a commendable feature.

These two reports illustrate what different methods can be followed to reach the same end, namely, a succinct, clear and understandable picture of the year's work in the hospital. Most reports will follow a middle ground between these two, combining pictures and text. Yet either extreme can be effective provided only the report is prepared intelligently and with a view to arousing and maintaining the interest of the reader from cover to cover.

Annual Reports — Suggested Outline of Contents

A model table of contents for a hospital annual report is frequently requested. Probably no one can prepare a model that will meet with universal approbation. In fact, every hospital's annual report ought to be tailor-made. But while the report should be tailored to measure, one may, perhaps, be permitted to suggest some kinds of cloth that could well be used in its manufacture and also a general style that would be acceptable. The following outline of contents should be considered as merely suggestive. Each hospital should make additions or deletions to fit its own particular circumstances.

The report might well open with a brief statement of the purpose, function and nature of a hospital. This might point out that any hospital is first of all a workshop for physicians, designed to assist them in bringing the benefits of modern medical science to the aid of patients in the most expeditious and most economical manner. The second purpose of a hospital is to serve as an educational institution to help train the oncoming generation of physicians, nurses and other workers in the health field. The third purpose followed by some hospitals is research into the causes of disease and the methods of prevention and cure.

All of the foregoing purposes, it might be pointed out in the report, are performed by both voluntary and governmental hospitals. These two groups work in partnership in most large communities, each supplementing the work of the other. The distinctive character of the true voluntary hospital is due to the fact that it enlists the voluntary efforts of a large number of public spirited citizens, gives them an effective avenue for transforming their generous impulses into action and carries on its work without direct governmental control. It might be well, at this point in the report, to state that the members of the board of any voluntary hospital and specifically of Jones Memorial Hospital not only serve entirely without pay but also, customarily, dig into their own personal funds to help meet the expenses of the institution. A recent survey of public opinion concerning hospitals revealed the rather surprising fact that a substantial percentage of people believe that the trustees are paid for attending board meetings. This statement of hospital purposes need not take more than a page of large type.

The second section of the report might deal with the financing of the hospital. Among other matters the following might well be mentioned:

1. Capital funds for voluntary hospitals are provided by members of the public without expectation of financial reward. Tax receipts or bond issues usually supply capital for governmental hospitals.

2. The voluntary hospital's income is derived from payments by patients, interest on endowment, payments from governmental agencies for care of their wards, and

gifts and donations of money, services or articles of value to the institution. Here again, the governmental hospital will rely more on tax funds.

3. The percentage of the hospital's income which came during the preceding year from each of these sources might well be compared with a similar analysis for all voluntary or governmental hospitals of the city, the state or various typical areas. (Useful data in this connection are found each year in *The Hospital Yearbook* and may be supplemented by other figures from various agencies collecting current hospital statistics, such as the U. S. Children's Bureau or local council of social agencies.)

A third and somewhat longer section of the report might well be devoted to general trends in hospital administration and operation as they affect this particular institution and its patients. If one were writing a report for the current year, for example, the following might well be mentioned:

1. Advancing Scientific Standards: Medicine, surgery, obstetrics, pediatrics, care of the newborn, pharmacy, laboratory, x-ray, medical records, etc., and their effect on Jones Memorial Hospital

2. Advancing Standards for Care of Patients: Physical facilities, nursing, housekeeping, food service, occupational therapy, social service, outpatient service, added protection to body and mind, etc.

3. Elevation of Standards for Education of Residents and Interns: Requirements of the Advisory Board for Medical Specialties; report of the Commission on Graduate Medical Education; comparison with present practices in Jones Memorial Hospital

4. Trends in Nursing Education: Revised curriculum of the National League of Nursing Education compared with the present curriculum of Jones Memorial Hospital; plans for accrediting hospital schools of nursing; effects on number of applicants to school and cost of nursing education; possible methods of financing additional costs

5. Increasing Need for Stable Support of Hospital's Free Services: Governmental agencies, community chests; larger endowments and additional current gifts

6. Growth of Hospital Care Insurance: Its present and probable future effects on Jones Memorial Hospital and its place in a national health program

7. Relations of Voluntary to Governmental Hospitals: Need for clear definition of respective functions and coordination of services

8. Emergence of Personnel Relations as a Matter of Hospital Concern: Increasing attention to wages, hours, safety, training, health conservation

9. Improvements in Business Practices: Accounting, purchasing, storage, office administration, records

10. Development of Keener Appreciation by Voluntary Hospitals of Their Public Relations Responsibilities and Opportunities: Study of community needs, planning hospital development, etc.

Other problems of a similar nature will doubtless be suggested by the hospital's own experience. This section, while constituting the main body of the report, should not be allowed to become detailed and exhaustive or the reader's interest may flag.

The effect of these various advances upon the prestige and reputation of the hospital might then be given a section of the report. The reactions of patients, employes, the medical staff, governmental agencies and the general public should all be noted.

The final textual section of the report might summarize the effect of advances in hospital practice and of general business conditions upon the financial position of the hospital. An income and expense comparison for the past several years would serve as a starting point. If the hospital has endowment, its growth or shrinkage should be noted, as well as the growth or shrinkage of the hospital's current obligations. Any unusual gifts to the hospital might be mentioned. Some indication of probable obligations of the near future might also be included. Finally, the immediate and long-time financial needs of the institution should be forecast as clearly as possible. Special features might occupy two pages, one devoted to "facts at a glance" and another to special needs of the hospital.

There are certain types of reference data that most hospitals wish to include in their annual reports. These should be critically examined to see which of them really merit a place in the report and which, as was suggested earlier, can be satisfactorily reproduced in mimeographed form for those who are especially interested. Those figures and lists which are to be included can best be put in smaller type in the back of the book where they are available to all persons who are interested but where they will not slow up rapid reading of the report by a person who wishes merely to learn the important points of the hospital's year. The names of the officers and trustees of the hospital, of the women's auxiliary officers and committee chairmen, of the administrative and educational staff and of the medical staff will ordinarily be included.* The list of donors and benefactors may be given. A necrology of those formerly connected with the hospital is often added. A list of publications of the medical and administrative staffs is frequently incorporated in the report.

Some of the human interest material that abounds in hospitals might well find its way into the annual report. Cold figures can be brought to life by telling, without false sentimentality, the actual story of what hospital care has meant in specific instances. Unusual acts of heroism, thoughtfulness or intelligence by hospital employes may deserve brief mention. Some hospitals grant awards to employes for fine service; these could be described. Occasionally a person will make a contribution to the hospital that, although small in itself, indicates keen interest and an unusual desire to help. One story of such a "widow's mite" appearing in the annual report may inspire other persons.

Good photographs, charts and diagrams should be used freely. These should be accompanied by explanatory captions which bring the significance of the picture clearly to the reader's attention. Small pen and ink sketches can also be used to advantage.

Pictorial statistics, the new technic recently brought to this country from Austria, presents certain types of facts so that their significance may be readily grasped. An excellent book on this technic has been published in this country.[1]

*Some hospitals recently have indicated in their medical staff lists those men who have been certified as specialists by their respective specialty boards.

The makeup of the report should be flexible rather than stiff and formal. It is not necessary to start each new section on a new page. Large and inviting type (10, 11, or 12 point) and good paper should be used.

At various points throughout the annual report brief quotations appropriate to the subject matter might be inserted as short boxes or panels. These should serve to indicate the spirit as well as the functioning of the hospital. Several illustrations will show what is meant:

If from one point of view the hospital may be regarded as part of a militant machine whose function it is to safeguard mankind against forces inimical to life, from another angle the hospital is disclosed as part of the educational structure of modern civilization. The hospital teaches its patients how to live, and from its laboratories, its wards, its social service department and its school of nursing it sends out into the world an endless stream of teachers to carry into the remotest hamlets the golden truths of hygiene.[2]

Persons unfamiliar with hospital management often expect more from these institutions than they can possibly render. So great is the free service they contribute to their communities and so widely has it become expanded in recent years that the public, for the most part, takes it for granted as a vested right, without asking or even wondering how it is financed or by whom the costs are ultimately paid.[3]

The hospitals of the nation constitute our most important agencies in relieving the suffering of our people incident to the ills and injuries to which they are inevitably subjected. Almost every man, woman and child in our land at one time or another must have the care and treatment hospitals afford. Our country is fortunate in having a large number of well equipped hospitals ably managed and staffed with highly efficient professional experts. The relationship between these institutions and the people should be intimate and sympathetic.[4]

Well prepared house magazines serve as monthly visits with several thousand present or potential hospital supporters.

Many [persons] badgered and burdened by the exactions of the tax collectors wonder why, when the government is expending so many billions on relief, private charity should be necessary. The simple answer is that governmental relief does not and cannot reach hundreds of thousands of helpless people. We cannot and will not transfer to the government the entire responsibility for taking care of those of our neighbors who require help.5

The quality of medical care is an index of civilization. . . . Today in American civilization, health occupies a high place among accepted social values. As we emerge from the present depression and build up a surplus of income not necessary for mere subsistence, we shall do well to realize that we can invest this surplus in no better way than in the preservation of health.6

Good physical and mental health is the bulwark of any nation. It is the foundation of wealth, strength and power. Its preservation has been one of the high objectives of the American people. The huge investment by health conservation agencies has paid increasing dividends during the past several years of great stress. The nation's death rate per thousand of population has been driven down very appreciably since 1929.7

Bulletins or House Magazines

A well prepared annual report is a good medium for low pressure publicity for a hospital, but it is most effective when it is one of a series of mailings.

A properly planned and edited bulletin or house magazine is an excellent medium for low pressure promotion, even better than an annual report. It may be sent to the same type of people who receive the annual report. If the expense is not too great, it would be highly desirable to send it to all employes of the hospital to keep them informed of current events and developments in the institution, thus helping to build a spirit of pride and loyalty.

One of the finest hospital bulletins in the United States is *The Pilot*, published by Evanston Hospital, Evanston, Illinois. This little 16 page booklet appears monthly and measures 5½ by 7½ inches. When publication was started in the summer of 1936, it had a circulation of about 2200. Now there is a print order of 4800. The costs for printing, postage, pictures, engravings, envelopes and handling now run about $2500 to $3000 a year. In addition, the editor of the magazine is paid a small weekly salary and expenses, which adds about $400 or $500 to the annual cost.

Ada Belle McCleery, administrator of Evanston Hospital, has described so admirably the principal attributes of a successful house magazine that a part of her statement may well be included here.[8]

One of the advantages of the house organ is the regularity of its appearance. It is believed that the issues should follow one another often enough to make reading a habit. A three month period between publications does not help in habit formation. The time element is too great. Publication once a month is recommended, the bulletin appearing each month at approximately the same time.

To be effective, a house organ must have a policy to which it adheres. For instance, the policy might include such things as the kind of information to be disseminated, the manner in which it is to be presented; or it might be reduced to such simple terms as not to brag and not to beg.

Certain preliminary decisions must be made in starting a house organ. It is good publicity to select a name easily pronounced and easily remembered, one that carries some meaning and is not too stereotyped.

After the name is selected the size, number of pages and the frequency of publication must be determined, all being governed somewhat by the amount of money budgeted. A house organ should not be financed by advertisements or by paid subscriptions. In a sense they defeat the purpose for which the organ is published. As far as size is concerned, large sheets do not mail flat and folding mars the appearance of the illustrations. However, small sheets do not carry large pictures.

It is believed that house organs serve their purpose best when the style is simple. They must be easy to read or they won't be read. In this connection the type is important both in style and size; neither can column arrangement or page arrangement be ignored, but these are technical details.

Illustrations should be used freely and are well worth their cost. If either patient or client is the subject for a picture, permission in writing should be obtained before the picture is released. No picture should be published if its publication would in any sense harm the persons featured. Not infrequently suitable photographs may be obtained from commercial photographers and unfortunate situations averted.

A house organ does not write itself. For that reason a salaried editor should be selected who knows how to write with sincerity, with simplicity and with sympathy. Because the publication is the "voice," as it were, of the institution sponsoring it, someone in authority, probably the administrator, should read every word before it is sent to the printer, to see that all information is accurate and that it is ethical in every respect.

The administrator should expect to share in the writing and to him falls naturally the outlining of the contents month by month. He soon learns to keep his mind attuned to the news value of everyday happenings. A house organ potentially is a great success or a great liability. The responsibility for its success or failure is shared by the editor and the administrator.

There is the danger always of becoming so absorbed in the mechanics of publishing and editing that the continuous processes of research and publicity are neglected. Both must be carried on as long as the institution functions. Each year brings changes in the people who make up the community. The new arrivals must have repeated for their benefit lessons older residents have learned. There are, in addition, new lessons to be taught because a constant change is going on in progressive hospitals. This change includes discarding the obsolete, developing new methods, adapting new discoveries to old methods and finding new uses for that which is worth preserving. It is by an uninterrupted process that the public comes to a knowledge of the hospital, and hospitals keep from becoming sterile.

Lest some readers infer from the foregoing that a house magazine cannot be started unless a hospital is prepared to spend $3000 or $4000 per year, attention should be called to some other successful hospital bulletins. The *News Bulletin* of St. Vincent's Hospital, New York City, is a 12 page letter size magazine reproduced by photographic processes from a typed original and is illustrated with pen and ink sketches. It is cleverly edited by one of the Sisters and has aroused much community and staff interest in the hospital.

The *Grace Hospital News*, New Haven, Connecticut, is a little four page monthly bulletin, which, in spite of its small size, manages to tell a good deal about the operation of the institution. One feature of this magazine is a short article headed "Need of the Month," which describes some item which the hospital especially needs and cannot buy. During 1937, $90 was contributed for pillows, $57 for bed lamps and sufficient money to buy an operating table. The public did not respond to requests for money for a meat cutter and for blankets. One unexpected result of publishing these needs was that the porters, maids and orderlies in the hospital held a benefit dance to provide certain equipment for the institution. A friend of the hospital offered to match the money they made.

In general it is not considered wise to use a house magazine to request funds directly. Continuous asking for funds is likely to become tiresome. Furthermore, it is like shooting a load of birdshot into the air on the chance that a flock of ducks may be passing over. It is usually much more effective and economical to aim directly at a particular flock. This cannot be done in a house magazine.

In spite of solicitation of funds, however, *Grace Hospital News* has proved effective in building good will for the hospital. The total cost, approximately $115 per month for a circulation of 4000 copies, is met by contributions from interested members of the board of trustees and staff. It is sent to board members, medical staff, nursing alumnae, women's auxiliary, all New Haven people who contributed $25 or more to the Community Chest, all private patients during the preceding four years and any other persons whom the administrator considers to be potential supporters.

Hospitals that desire house magazines but are deterred by the expense should investigate those put out by certain publishing firms. These bulletins are furnished in a standardized pattern. Usually most of the pages are devoted to well written material that applies to any general hospital anywhere. The front and back pages may be used for articles concerning the work and services of the particular hospital that is buying the bulletin. Material for these original stories on the outside pages is furnished by the hospital and edited and "made up" by the company's editor. The result is that a hospital can put out a creditable bulletin at a minimum of expense. While such a house magazine obviously is not as good as one that is original throughout, assuming the latter is equally well edited, it is a good avenue of public relations that is available at nominal cost.

Experience of many hospitals could be cited to indicate that a well managed house magazine is a valuable tool for hospital exposition.[9] It should not be started until a basic public relations program has been envisioned and then the house magazine should be designed so that it will take its proper place in this program and will fit in most effectively with other activities.

REFERENCES

1. Modley, Rudolph: How to Use Pictorial Statistics, Harper & Brothers, New York and London, 1937.
2. Goldwater, S. S.: The Privilege of Being a Hospital Trustee, *The Modern Hospital*, April, 1930, p. 63.
3. Lorimer, George Horace: Editorial, *The Saturday Evening Post*, March 16, 1935.
4. Roosevelt, Franklin D.: Letter to the National Hospital Day Committee, March 7, 1935, *The Bulletin of the American Hospital Association*, April, 1935.
5. Editorial, *Colliers Magazine*, Nov. 2, 1935.
6. Wilbur, Ray Lyman: The Final Report of the Committee on the Costs of Medical Care, University of Chicago Press, Chicago, 1932, p. x.
7. Ball, Otho F.: Community Assets Essential to Sustained Recovery, *Rand McNally Bankers' Monthly*, May, 1933.
8. McCleery, Ada Belle: Producing Publicity, *The Modern Hospital*, Feb., 1938, p. 59.
9. Hyde, Florence Slown: The Hospital Bulletin as a Valuable Educational Medium, *Hospitals*, Sept., 1937, p. 51.

Chapter 9

EXPOSITIONAL METHODS —
LETTERS, PAMPHLETS,
BOUND BOOKS

THE FIELD of direct mail promotion contains many technics for exposition. Each has its own distinctive function. In addition to annual reports and house magazines, which were discussed in the preceding chapter, letters, pamphlets, booklets, bound books and similar material may also be sent by direct mail.

Whether the presentation is in the form of a letter, a pamphlet or a bound book, it should be prepared with the utmost care. Before it is written there should be a clear understanding of the exact purpose for which it is designed and of the best medium for achieving this objective. It may be merely to establish a friendly interest, it may be to prepare the ground for action or it may be actually to lead to a definite and specific action. Whatever it is, the mailing piece should be designed to do just that — no more and no less. Lack of a specific objective is wasteful. Too many objectives in one particular piece are confusing. The place of each piece in the whole public relations effort should be clearly visualized and it should be constructed with that end always in view.

Letters

With the advent of stenographers, dictating equipment and other conveniences, letter writing has become something of a lost art in America. Many business letters today seem to be written without form. They do not clearly state their purpose in the beginning, proceed logically from one point to the next and then clearly come to a close as soon as the purpose has been accomplished. Letters used in a public relations program should be carefully prepared. There should be no ambiguities. Conciseness is of the first importance. Sentence structure should be simple and direct. Hyperbole and exaggeration have no place. Graciousness and courtesy should be intrinsic, yet in trying to achieve them there should be no sloppiness or verbosity.

The writer of a good letter will usually put himself in the reader's place. He will ask himself: What would I want to know about this subject? How much time would I give to reading a letter about it? Would I have any objections that are not answered by this letter?

Some social institutions rely largely upon letter appeals to raise the donations necessary for the continuance of their work. In Great Britain this is true of some voluntary hospitals;[1] in the United States hospitals have not used this technic as widely as have other types of social institutions.

Homer J. Buckley of Chicago, considered by many to be one of the leading authorities on letter writing campaigns of this type, has recently set forth some of the rules he observes. He warns that no rules should be followed blindly because each appeal is unique. With this qualification, it will be of interest to examine his 12 suggestions.

1. Great care should be expended upon the preparation of lists. If I had only one dollar to spend on a mail campaign, I'd spend twenty-five cents of it in the preparation and

checking of my list. Eliminate duplications in the list as far as possible and classify individuals into groups so that appeals to them can be personalized. Use different members of the board of trustees, women's auxiliary and others interested in the institution to sign the letters to people whom they know best.

2. Lists should be classified into (a) regular contributors and (b) prospects. The former group should be cultivated just as assiduously as the latter. They should provide 85 to 90 per cent renewals. When the percentage falls below this, it is a warning signal. Between appeals, short significant reports should be sent to regular subscribers with a brief letter calling their attention to some interesting aspect of the report. These letters should not solicit funds. It is a relief to a contributor to receive a letter occasionally that merely acts as an accounting for his gifts and doesn't ask for more.

3. Since the mortality of lists is high, they must be brought up to date and supplemented frequently. In a large city like Chicago, for example, 42 per cent of all families will change their addresses every year. This means that probably 15 to 20 per cent of the persons on an institution's mailing list will move each year. Some will leave the city; others moving within the city will not be reached by the usual forwarding procedures. Therefore, in such cities at least 10 new names must be added each year for every 100 names on the list in order to keep even.

4. When a person who previously donated to an institution does not do so for two successive years, it is advisable to make a special inquiry. A letter may tell him frankly that, because he has supported the institution in the past and is no longer doing so, officers of the institution wonder if there has come a change in his attitude or circumstances. "If so, we would appreciate knowing the facts so that we may not annoy you with unwelcome requests." Every reasonable effort should be made to conserve the interest and good will of each person who has once contributed. It should be made easy for him to reply and then his reply should receive personal attention.

5. Both home and office addresses may be used. Some types of appeal ought preferably to be sent to the office and others to the home. Sometimes the original appeal can be sent to the office and a carbon sent to the home a few days later with a flag attached, reading something as follows: "Attached is a copy of the letter I sent recently to your office. Probably you will wish to discuss this matter with your family at home where you have more leisure. I am therefore taking the liberty of sending you this copy. If you have already acted upon our invitation kindly disregard this."

6. Mailings to an office should be carefully timed to avoid the heavy Monday morning rush. It is preferable to have office mailings arrive on the first afternoon mail on Tuesday, Wednesday or Thursday. In a large city the afternoon mail will usually be caught if the mailing reaches the central post office about 10 or 11 a.m.

7. Solicitations should not be made too frequently. Every three months is the absolute maximum and usually semi-annual or annual appeals are better. But informative material should go out as often as every month or two.

8. The well written letter is the best mailing piece for appeals. It should be supplemented frequently with interesting enclosures. The text of a letter going out to a large list should first be tested out on a small representative group (500 would usually be a fair sample). If it does not pull, another letter should be tried on another representative sample. The general mailing should be postponed until a letter is finally discovered that will pull. Once such a letter is found, it may be used again and again, at yearly intervals, even on the same list. Specific statements, of course, must be brought up to date from year to year.

9. Handwritten letters photographically reproduced are a good variation from the usual typewritten letter. These can be written and signed by various persons.

10. Return envelopes should always be enclosed, usually using the business reply type on which the postage is paid by the addressee. The color and appearance of these should be changed from time to time. The address on the return

envelope may be typed or written in script to give variety from the usual printed address.

11. Letters can play an important part in cultivating bequests. For this purpose material should be sent to potential benefactors and to attorneys and trust companies. One of the important elements in stimulating bequests is to assure the potential benefactor that the institution or organization will continue to be administered intelligently and effectively and for purposes that he approves.

12. From 5 to 15 per cent of proceeds is a reasonable proportion to spend on the expenses of direct mail promotion. This will vary with the institution, however, and the character of its appeal.

Although American hospitals have not used letter campaigns extensively as a means of raising current funds, such campaigns provide a potentially useful tool which can well be given careful consideration and trial. In addition, many hospitals may use letters to promote ideas that have no immediate bearing on gifts or donations. Letters may give information about hospital services which are available but which the public has not yet learned to use; they may help to obtain a larger and better qualified group of candidates for the nursing school; they may clear up public misunderstandings about the relation of physicians and hospitals. An illustration of public misunderstanding occurred recently when a patient told a hospital administrator that she knew why her doctor brought her to his hospital instead of to another. "He would lose his commission on my bill in a hospital where he didn't have a staff appointment."

Vassar Brothers Hospital, Poughkeepsie, New York, sent out a series of five letters in the summer of 1938. These were designed to clear up false ideas about the hospital's work, especially its ambulance service, outpatient department, medical staff relations, maternity flat rates and relation to governmental agencies.

Sometimes letters may take the form of short essays expounding a particular point of view. The famous *Federalist* papers, prepared by Hamilton, Madison and Jay in support of the federal constitution, were in essence a series of letters in essay form which appeared in a newspaper and were afterward reprinted as a book. So brilliant and searching were they that they have been credited with being responsible for converting the states to the federal idea. They are still studied by historians, political scientists and constitutional lawyers and might well be studied by public relations directors.

The same plan, namely, the distribution of a series of carefully formulated and well written statements and analyses of a program, may be applied in the exposition of any idea. This writing may appear in any one of many forms. The most direct and often the most effective is a personal letter. If the letter is in danger of growing too long, some of the information may be set up as a memorandum to accompany it, possibly in the form of a printed pamphlet or booklet. Finally, for matters of real importance, a regular stiff bound book may be utilized. Each of these should be accompanied by an introductory letter.

The writing of good letters is an art. This is one of many places where an experienced public relations counsel may save much money for the hospital. Because of his training and background he will know how to create a letter that will be effective.

Pamphlets and Booklets

The preparation of pamphlets and booklets is also a technical job in which an experienced public relations counsel will be of great value. A good printer can often help with suggestions regarding the physical form such a piece should take. But only a qualified public relations man will be able to advise intelligently regarding content and style.

The same considerations regarding coherence, clarity, logical sequence, conciseness, modesty, simplicity and directness of statement apply to pamphlets and booklets as to letters. The only difference is that, since they are printed, the text may be longer and illustrations may be utilized. Also, of course, because of the variety of type sizes available there is much more opportunity for originality and individuality.

The use of illustrations is important. Nowhere does the difference between an amateur and a professional piece of work show up more quickly than in the character and quality of illustrations. For public relations work, illustrations should be so planned that they tell a definite story or make a specific impression. Amateur photographs often merely show a group of people in a hospital background. An effective photograph conveys the impression that "this hospital serves excellent food," "the nurses in this hospital are well trained and careful," or "people are kind to you in this hospital." Words should scarcely be necessary to convey the meaning to the average reader.

There is great latitude of quality in printing. The difference between a good printer and a poor one is relatively as great as the difference between a good physician and a poor one. And the results of poor printing are as often fatal to the purpose. Good printing is a basic economy. If a publicity piece is worth sending out, it merits good printing and good layout. Layout, *i.e.* the arrangement of type, illustration and white space on the page, is not ordinarily a printer's function although a competent printer will often be helpful in planning layouts. Layout work requires a combination of artistic skill and understanding of the mechanical requirements of printing.

The possibilities open to the purchaser of printing today are many times those that were available a generation ago. Offset or lithograph printing is being developed to the point where it is little if any more expensive than letter press. It opens up new vistas in printed material. Many excellent books have been written on the printing arts and the interested reader is referred to these for basic information.[2] The only reason for discussing printing in this volume is to call attention to the fact that wise choice of printing is a technical procedure calling for extensive knowledge and good artistic sense. Most hospitals will do well to seek skilled advice in the purchase of any extensive amount of printing.

Bound Books

A word should be said about the use of bound books in a hospital public relations program. There is a definite place for such apparently expensive pieces. When the hospital is out for large stakes, when it has an important, interesting and somewhat involved story to tell and when the people who should hear this story are men of substance who may be expected to contribute $10,000, $25,000, $100,000 or even more, then a bound book may be the most effective and, hence, the most economical possible method of exposition.

A recent example of excellent promotion in this form is a book entitled *So Near the Gods*, issued by the Society of the New York Hospital in 1938. This book of 120 pages is one of the finest expositional pieces that I have ever seen. It presents the work and needs of the hospital in a way that no series of letters, pamphlets or booklets could possibly do. It is written so interestingly and prepared so attractively that each recipient doubtless read it immediately and added it to his permanent library.

The book contains 14 chapters concerning the growth and work of the hospital and of Cornell Medical School with which it is affiliated. These are followed by various lists of gift opportunities, of hospital and medical school needs, of financial and service data and of officials of the two institutions. The title of the book is taken from Cicero's statement, "In no other act does man approach so near the gods as when he is restoring the sick to the blessings of health." Excellent full page illustrations are used freely throughout the book.

The text has obviously been prepared with great skill. It is as interesting to read as a novel yet every page contributes substantially to the reader's understanding of just what the hospital and medical school are trying to accomplish. A quotation will serve to illustrate the character of the writing.

The first chapter deals with the founding of the hospital. The second is as follows:

THE NEW YORK HOSPITAL TODAY

"It rises like a prayer for healing."

So said a distinguished medical visitor from Switzerland when, for the first time, he saw the soaring white structure which rises above the East River, to the north of the Queensborough Bridge.

To him this building, which houses The New York Hospital and Cornell University Medical College, seemed to symbolize the aspirations of modern medicine. That it did so was natural, for the building is the expression both of an idea and of an ideal.

To Help the Sick

Medicine is built around the idea of helping the sick. Thus, in the center of this building group is the general hospital. Its wings reach to the south in the pavilions for medical and surgical bed patients; to the north in outpatient and emergency clinics.

Great branches have grown out of medicine and surgery. Among them are the care of women, of children and of mental patients. In The New York Hospital group each of these has a special hospital, fronting on the East River but joined to and coordinated with the general hospital.

To Train Doctors and Nurses

It is not enough to provide a place for the sick. Someone must care for them, and be trained to do so. Thus it is that on the York Avenue side the general hospital is flanked by the buildings of Cornell University Medical College and The New York Hospital School of Nursing.

To Find a Better Way

Doctors and nurses will never be perfectly trained so long as there is an unsolved problem of disease. The buildings of The New York Hospital tell of this, for in the structures which join the general hospital to the medical college and the special hospitals are laboratories. In them a ceaseless search goes on to solve the problems of the individual patient and to find new and better ways to prevent and cure disease.

Care of the sick, here and now —

Teaching of doctors and nurses, to serve the community of tomorrow —

Research which aims to help everyone, everywhere and for all time —

These are the three objects of modern medicine. Each is dependent on the other. All three are brought together within The New York Hospital group.

17 OPERATIONS

3 DELIVERIES

5B X-RAY EXAMINATIONS & TREATMENTS

30 PHYSIOTHERAPEUTIC TREATMENTS

433 PATIENTS

2950 MEALS SERVED

14 TONS OF COAL

37 ADMISSIONS

36 EMERGENCY CALLS

37 CASES DISCHARGED

17 AMBULANCE CALLS

600 POUNDS OF MEAT
146 GALLONS OF MILK

3 TONS OF LAUNDRY

KITCHEN

17 SOCIAL SERVICE CASES

730 EMPLOYEES

Hospital statistics need not be dry. This represents the average day at Strong Memorial and Rochester Municipal Hospitals.

This quotation is all but one paragraph of the second chapter. The entire book can easily be read in an hour. And probably few persons would pick it up without reading it through at a sitting.

Notice how this quotation from the book points out ways in which the hospital exemplifies principles of public relations listed in Chapter 3. The hospital provides good hospital service. It seeks to adapt this service accurately to the needs of the public in its service area (which for some services is world wide). The hospital is constantly identified with progressive and important public movements, its appeal is "bigger than the institution." In this and other sections of *So Near the Gods*, data and figures are given that seem to satisfy all questions the average person would ask, yet the book does not become tiresomely statistical.

There is a strong emotional appeal in this writing yet it is constantly submerged to the rational and intellectual appeal. A hospital administrator reading this book will notice mention of many refinements of hospital service indicating good administration. The book is dignified but not ponderous. It is "prepared in terms suited to the amount of time, interest and intellect the recipient will probably give it."

There appears to be no exaggeration; certainly there is no derogation of other hospitals. In fact, in several instances other hospitals or the hospital field as a whole is praised. Throughout the book one gains the impression that the "governors" of The New York Hospital are alert to discern public needs and to utilize the public's investment in the hospital to meet those needs.

It may be said, in passing, that this book was written by a man connected with one of the country's leading

188   *Hospital Public Relations*

fund raising organizations. The basic social and scientific planning of the medical center, the philosophy of which constitutes the principal part of the volume, was done by various persons associated with The New York Hospital and with Cornell Medical College, principally by Dr. G. Canby Robinson who had previously planned the Washington University Medical School Center in St. Louis. Dr. Winford H. Smith, director of Johns Hopkins Hospital, was consultant. Assistance was also given by a number of people connected with the Columbia-Presbyterian Medical Center.

REFERENCES

1. Lloyd, Major R. M.: The Business of Appeals, *The Hospital,* Sept., 1938, p. 326, and Lloyd: Some Modern Appeal Methods, *The Hospital,* March, 1939, p. 99.
2. McMurtrie, Douglas C.: Some Elementary Principles of Typography, Transactions of the Twenty-sixth Annual Meeting of the National Tuberculosis Association, 1930, and Lopatecki, Eugene de: Typographer's Desk Manual, Ronald Press, New York City, 1937, and Lopatecki: Advertising Layout and Typography, Ronald Press, New York City, 1937, and Hoch, Fred W.: The Standard Book on Estimating for Printers, United Typothetae of America, Washington, D. C., 1936, and Birren, Faber: The Printer's Art of Color, Crimson Press, Chicago, 1936.

Chapter 10

EXPOSITIONAL METHODS — NEWSPAPERS AND MAGAZINES

THE POSITION of the newspaper in the community and its relation to social institutions are changing rapidly. To gain perspective, let us review briefly the recent changes in newspapers and their community position before we deal with their relations to hospitals.

Today's Newspaper in Society

The influence of the newspaper in society is said to be declining. Alfred M. Lee has pointed out in his brilliant book entitled *The Daily Newspaper in America* that the newspaper no longer occupies the strategic place in the formation of public opinion that it did even one generation ago. "Readers become more sophisticated and publishers, possibly, less so."[1] William Allen White of the *Emporia Gazette* declared editorially after the 1936 election, "I am not sure the press ever had any political influence; but I am sure that it has none now."[2]

William Randolph Hearst declared himself on this subject in the following words in 1924:

I rather think that the influence of the American press is on the whole declining. This, I believe, is because so many newspapers are owned or influenced by reactionary interests and predatory corporations, and are used selfishly to promote the welfare of these reactionary interests rather than the welfare of the public. This tends to weaken the confidence of the public in all newspapers. . . .[3]

189

The depreciating political influence of the daily press may be due, indirectly at least, to the enormous advance of mechanical invention. Newspapers today are physically the finest that the world has ever seen. They are printed better and faster; their news is more complete; they have better illustrations and publish them sooner; they are more rapidly distributed. But to be so excellent they have had to make enormous investments in plant, equipment and franchises and to assume the responsibility of meeting heavy pay rolls. Hence, they can be owned only by men of great wealth or by strong corporations. The day is gone in the large cities when an industrious printer could publish a daily newspaper; it is rapidly drawing to a close even in the smaller towns. Furthermore, daily newspapers are so dependent upon a large volume of advertising, upon favorable paper contracts and upon maintaining low wages that their lineup on political and economic questions is often on the opposite side from that of the great majority of the people.

But this loss of influence has been proved only regarding political and economic questions on which the newspapers have organized opposition. On nonpolitical subjects that are not being actively and aggressively pushed by organized groups through other channels of communication, the newspapers still presumably wield a large influence. This influence may be exerted through advocacy, through opposition or through a conspiracy of silence.

Newspapers and Social Institutions

It is highly desirable to obtain and retain newspaper support for social projects whenever possible. The daily newspaper is the most widely distributed medium of public information. Probably more people can be given a modicum of facts about a particular subject through newspapers than through any other single medium. The newspaper reading habit pervades all strata of the population (although all strata do not necessarily read the same newspapers). The newspaper is one of the least expensive methods of communicating with the public, if it is intelligently and skillfully used.

The opposition of newspapers can be dangerous. Not long ago in Chicago one of the hospitals which had incurred the enmity of a prominent sensational newspaper gave the paper an opportunity for attack. This hospital, after giving first aid to an injured man and ascertaining that he was unable to pay the cost of hospital care in advance, sent him to the county hospital. He had been shot while disarming and overpowering two hold-up men. The newspaper immediately labeled the man as a public hero and entered upon a campaign of vilification of the hospital, which probably helped to put it out of business. The hospital was not prepared to meet such a campaign and its answer to the attack was scarcely heard in the general tumult and shouting.

Although this hospital may have been peculiarly vulnerable, any unprepared hospital would find itself at a serious disadvantage if charged by a newspaper with refusing to care for a seriously wounded public hero because he could not pay cash on the line. It is important, therefore, not only to make every effort to avoid laying an institution open to attack but to be prepared to meet such an attack should it be made. Untoward incidents are bound to occur in any hospital, although competent and imaginative administration will keep them to a minimum.

Rather than support or oppose a hospital, a newspaper may merely ignore it completely, at least so far as the institution's constructive program is concerned. When this happens, the responsibility usually can be laid at the door of the hospital itself. Newspapers do not knowingly neglect any source of important news and a hospital can be such a source if it is engaged in a constructive and creative program.

Newspapers, of course, differ in their definition of news. Some papers, like the *New York Times* and the *Chicago Daily News* or the *Christian Science Monitor*, have a broad definition that results in considerable attention to important scientific and social trends and developments. (The *Monitor*, of course, has a somewhat restricted definition of "science" when it comes to the medical field.) Others, such as the Hearst papers and most of the tabloids, demand sensational subjects. In general, the newspaper definition of news is so narrow that the person who wants to use the papers as a means of communication regarding social matters must do so through a certain amount of ingenuity. Instead of going directly to his subject, he must find or create some event or incident on which he can hang his story. Having satisfied the rather formal requirements of the city desk, he can then frequently tack on the important part of the article.

Getting Into the Papers

In a well balanced public relations program, something between 15 and 30 per cent of the budget and effort may properly be devoted to newspaper work. This percentage will fluctuate, of course, depending upon the stage of the program and the relative importance of reaching the broad mass of people or of reaching only selected groups.

Whatever the expenditure, it ought to be made most advantageously. How can this be done?

As in any other public relations work, the obvious first step is to decide what is wanted. Does the institution wish to create merely a sympathetic public attitude? Is it interested first in attaining recognition as a scientific leader? Does it wish to be known as an educational explorer? Is it eager to be considered as a leader in social pioneering? Does it wish to obtain patronage only from the well-to-do or is it glad to serve poor as well as rich? Does it wish to obtain more governmental or charitable support, to attract better applicants to the nursing school or to improve the level of its medical staff? Perhaps the hospital wishes to strengthen its women's auxiliary.

In most institutions there will be a combination of objectives and motives. Every story prepared for the newspapers should first be examined to see whether it really contributes toward achieving one or more of the objectives. Public relations results cannot be measured in terms of column inches. Too many articles on insignificant or petty matters will tend to convince the public that the major concerns of the hospital are petty or insignificant. A hospital's own publicity would then be a boomerang. Each article prepared should make a definite and distinct contribution to the public's understanding of its hospital and an appreciation of hospital problems and aspirations. This does not mean, of course, that these problems and aspirations need be explicitly stated in each article. But the stories should build logically toward significant goals.

There is many a hurdle between the preparation of a newspaper story and its actual appearance in the morning editions. Some of these obstacles may lie in the story itself and some in the general relationship between the institution and the newspapers. The story must, as stated previously, meet the particular newspaper's definition of news. Sometimes this may mean rewriting the story for different papers to meet variations in their definitions.

The technic of writing a good newspaper story is fairly well standardized, although brains and imagination can always devise new variations on the old formula. There are so many good books on the subject that no space will be taken here to reiterate the purely technical aspects. The average administrator can hardly be expected to add this to his other duties but a public relations worker can ordinarily prepare all of the newspaper copy that will be required. His articles should, of course, be approved by the administrator before being released to the newspapers.

No matter how good the story, it will have a better chance of going into the paper if the relations between the editorial department of the newspaper and the social institution are cordial.

An illustration may indicate the need for such cordiality. An unfortunate situation arose in a mid-western town where the administrator of the only hospital could not understand the insistant prying, as he called it, of the principal reporter of the town's one newspaper. The hospital received no publicity of constructive value but was simply the background for gossipy stories on which small communities seem to thrive. The irate administrator finally barred the reporter from the grounds, whereupon the latter began paying the employes a dollar for each usable story.

One day the reporter rushed to the hospital with his young sister who had been severely burned. As he stood watching the rapid emergency treatment and begging the doctors and nurses to save her, the administrator came by. He was on the point of ordering the reporter from the building when a nurse quietly told him the situation. He at once offered his sympathy and his assurance that everything possible was being done for the girl.

In a few minutes the two men were in a heart-to-heart talk, telling each other their worries and troubles. The reporter pointed out his need for interesting local news, especially news that has names and personalities in it. The administrator, using the sister's case as an example, pointed out that the hospital's concern must always be primarily with the patient and that busy doctors and nurses should not be interrupted to answer questions and are not the proper channel for hospital news. He went on to speak of the ethical and legal restrictions on disclosing privileged information. Between them the administrator and the reporter later worked out an agreement regarding the kind of news concerning patients that could emanate from the hospital. The administrator also told the reporter about his plans for the hospital, some of the difficulties encountered and ways in which the townspeople could help. Later, the reporter prepared a series of articles on the hospital's various departments that served to interpret these to the public.

This incident illustrates a fortuitous method of achieving cordiality between hospitals and reporters. Administrators, however, should not rely upon chance to make friends with the journalists. There are a number of definite steps that can be taken to assist in developing harmonious and cooperative relations with the press.

First, and probably most important, is the adoption of a general policy that the hospital will be strictly honest with the newspapers. This does not necessarily mean that every question must be answered. Obviously, the hospital authorities are trusted with confidential information concerning patients that cannot be made public. When faced with such a situation, the hospital should state that the information it has received is privileged and cannot be revealed except with the authorization of the patient or someone empowered to speak for him.

Second, hospital officers should develop an understanding and appreciation of the requirements of reporters. Reporters are, of course, entitled to the ordinary courtesies offered to any guest. Furthermore, special attention should be given the reporter who is trying to meet a deadline. He will be particularly appreciative of such help and will show this in his handling of the news. As the hour for going to press approaches, time becomes "of the essence of the thing." Unnecessary delay puts heavy obstacles in the path of the reporter and makes it more difficult for him to do justice to the information that he receives.

Outside of the movies, most reporters are just average human beings doing their work as best they can. They live always in fear of the possibility of missing the most important aspect of some news story. John L. Given expresses the reporter's relation to the news aptly:[4]

An editor proceeds on the theory that "nothing succeeds like success" and the reporter, no matter how well he has done previously, who wakes some morning to find to his dismay that what he long feared has happened, that he failed to get the most important feature of the news while another reporter did get it, goes to his office feeling that so far as one newspaper is concerened, his time has come. . . . A reporter who has missed news which he was expected to get may be able to give 20 reasons why he failed, but he cannot do other than admit that he did not get it. The editor argues, "You got it or you did not. You did not. Therefore, you must pay the penalty." . . .

Reporters have a great deal more to say about what gets into the paper and how, and what stays out, than is generally supposed. The man who imagines that a reporter is only a messenger or an errand runner is much mistaken and the mistake may cost him dearly if, thinking himself safe from reprisal, he goes out of his way to be ugly when he is approached by a newspaper representative. . . . No first-class paper asks its reporters to accept insults in silence, and few of them will fail to support their men when they are attacked. . . .

Frequently reporters go to some pains to be helpful. Convinced that a cause is just, they keep it before the public and gain adherents for it by referring to it as if its merits were everywhere acknowledged. . . . The reporters must be first to recognize worth; if they fail to see it the editors never hear of it, as they view the world through the eyes of their representatives.

A third method of improving relations with newspapers is to give to city editors, feature writers, science editors and others who might be concerned an understanding of the institution's objectives and program. Everyone likes to be "in the know" and for newspaper people this is not only interesting but important. They are in a better position to evaluate events when they have a good understanding of their implications and direction. The hospital might well make an annual custom of inviting appropriate newspaper and magazine people to a luncheon or dinner at which the president of the board, the chairman of the public relations committee, the president of the medical staff, the administrator, the public

relations counselor or other qualified person outlines
accomplishments and proposals. If some of the material
is off the record, that should be indicated.

A hospital contains a great deal of good copy. A fourth
way of improving relationships is to assist the newspapers to find and make use of this material. Research
work that has been completed, educational developments,
vocational opportunities, economic trends, physical improvements, administrative advances all furnish possibilities for constructive stories. Historical material is
often of general interest and may fit into an exposition
of the present needs of the institution. Occasionally,
newspapers have carried series of articles on various
departments in a hospital, indicating what the departments do and how they do it. One such series on Johns
Hopkins Hospital was written by H. L. Mencken and
published in the *Baltimore Sun* during July 1937. There
were 20 articles in all, each running a column or more
in length; several of them were accompanied by representative hospital pictures.

Occasionally, also, a hospital administrator will be able
to give a reporter leads that will be beneficial to him. A
few years ago the newspapers of a large city were trying
to gather evidence against a clever racketeer who had
intimidated local officials. One reporter had a friendly
contact with a hospital administrator who was able to
give him helpful medical clues without involving his hospital or himself. Such dramatic occurrences are not frequent, of course, but other less exciting opportunities are
often at hand. A reporter is always grateful to anyone
who has helped him solve a problem. Although too much
should not be presumed on this gratitude, it, nevertheless,
oils the machinery of newspaper relations.

A fifth and final suggestion for improving such relations is to be alert in supplying the newspapers with good material for their "morgues." These newspaper reference libraries should contain a substantial body of accurate data on hospitals and social institutions. For example, the hospitals of the community could well give the newspapers information about the total number of hospitals in the United States and Canada, their total bed capacity, their distribution by type of service and by type of ownership and similar facts that may easily be obtained from the current hospital number of the *Journal of the American Medical Association*. Figures on hospital per capita costs for various types of institutions in various localities ought to be provided; some of these data can be found in the current editions of *The Hospital Yearbook*. The total capital investment of hospitals in the United States and its distribution among various types of institutions and various types of ownership would also be valuable. The latest generally available statistics are to be found in C. Rufus Rorem's *The Public's Investment in Hospitals*.[5] Since these figures apply to 1928, corrections should be made to bring the totals up to date. The growth and expansion of hospital services as well as medical service will also be of interest to newspapers and will give them perspective on current developments. Any of the several good histories of medicine may be consulted and also the silver anniversary number (September 1938) of *The Modern Hospital*. The compilation of important trends in hospital service in this anniversary number could well be made available to the newspapers. Data on the growth of hospital care insurance may be obtained from the American Hospital Association.

On the more personal side, the hospital might well make available to newspapers the important biographical data concerning national and local figures in medical news which most hospitals possess. These data are found in the *American Medical Association Directory*, the membership lists of the various specialty societies, the directory of the American College of Hospital Administrators, *American Men of Science* and other similar volumes that every hospital should have in its medical library. Certainly, the physicians on the staff of the hospital should be listed and full biographic information about each sent to the newspapers. Similar data concerning the administrator, the trustees and the important department heads and nursing school faculty members should be included. For those persons who are listed in *Who's Who*, the information given by the hospital should supplement rather than duplicate the material found there, since every newspaper may be presumed to buy the current issue of *Who's Who* as soon as it is published.

Keeping Out of the Papers

To date, hospital administrators have probably spent more time and effort trying to keep certain information out of newspapers than they have trying to get other material in. There are many occasions when the hospital wishes to keep information from the newspapers, either to protect the hospital against unfavorable publicity or to protect some patient or physician.

The occasions when the hospital wishes to protect itself usually arise when some accident has occurred within the institution: a patient has committed suicide, a nurse has given the wrong kind of injection causing the patient's death, an outbreak of impetigo or intestinal infection has struck the nursery or someone has been hurt through a fall or an elevator accident.

There is no sure method of keeping such matters out of newspapers. They are news and, if comparable occurances happened in a factory or office building, we would lose confidence in the newspaper that failed to report them. The public look to the newspapers to provide a full picture of the news of the day. In a community with more than one newspaper, moreover, each paper is afraid to suppress news that its rivals may publish.

Strenuous efforts made to conceal the facts will often make the newspapers even more avid to obtain them. They naturally go on the assumption that if a matter is worth concealing or evading it must also be worth knowing. Usually the safest and best procedure is to notify the newspapers immediately, offer to give them all the facts that they wish, tell them that a careful investigation has been started and that the causes will be removed if possible, and then inform them that you would prefer to have the story "played down" but you will leave it to their judgment. Obviously, if the hospital administrator has already established friendly relations with the reporters and editors, they are much more likely to accede to his wishes. If they are really convinced that the hospital is playing an important part in the life of the community, they will not wish to destroy public confidence in the institution.

Administrators should be careful not to be unreasonable in requesting reporters to suppress news. Given says, in speaking of the problems facing reporters:

> Harder to deal with than the man who is willing to pay for silence is the one who appeals to the reporter's generosity or sympathy. It is extremely difficult to turn a deaf

ear to the person who says: "You have my future in your hands. Tell what has happened and I am lost. Keep quiet and I am saved, and no one will suffer. Think of my family." There may be times when it is proper for a reporter to be moved by an appeal, but he should never forget that he is paid to be the eyes and ears of a newspaper and that the editors are expected to get a chance to do any suppressing that is thought necessary. The reporter who kills news on his own responsibility betrays his paper, no matter under what other designation his action falls. He becomes a false philanthropist, or worse yet, what is known as a "genial," a man who is willing to do the right thing at somebody else's expense.

Slow as he should be in making promises about his own actions, a reporter should never allow himself to assume the responsibility of making promises for his paper. It is not safe even in seemingly trivial matters; there may come a sudden change of circumstances which lifts the affair concerned into prominence, and again editors are not unlikely to make a great stir if they discover that their province has been encroached on, no matter how little the harm done. If a green reporter dared do it, he could insure orders for a long story every time he appeared in the office by saying: "I promised not to say much about this." And he could kill his gleanings just as readily by announcing: "I promised to give this in full."[6]

Given goes on to point out that it is embarrassing to a reporter to give him news and then add, "Of course, this is not for publication." The editor may sometime ask the reporter whether he ever heard the story in which case he must lie or admit that he withheld information. Some other reporter may print it and thus subject him to a scoop. Or he may later hear the same information from another source without any pledge of secrecy in which case he will, of course, offend his original informant if he uses it.

The wise and tactful administrator will avoid these pitfalls in his dealings with the press. He will be honest, frank and sincere and will try to build up friendly relationships with the newspapers by these means rather than by means of gifts or bribes. When he wishes material suppressed or played down, he will give his reasons and then permit the reporter and his editor to decide on the basis of all the facts just what should be done. He will, of course, try to protect himself, his institution, his associates and his employes from unwarranted censure. When censure is warranted, an effort at undue protection will be likely to be of more harm than good to the hospital.

If the problem involved is one of protecting patients or physicians, the matter is somewhat different. The information that the hospital has concerning its patients is, of course, confidential and privileged. The hospital has a duty to withhold such information.[7] A great deal of unnecessary harm could result, for example, if the hospital disclosed that certain patients were suffering from venereal or mental disease or drug addiction. Unless they are police cases, the hospital could properly refuse to give the diagnosis on all cases, private and ward, merely stating that the patients are in the hospital for treatment and are being studied.

There may be occasions when it would be unfortunate to have the public even know that a certain important business man is in a hospital for a serious condition. If these occasions occur with any frequency, the hospital could adopt a standing rule that such inquiries should be referred to the patient's family, business associates or physician. In order to make it effective the rule must operate uniformly. If the hospital ordinarily gives out the names of patients and then suddenly refuses to confirm or deny that a certain person is a patient, it may be far more embarrassing to him than if the hospital had acknowledged his presence. A refusal would lead the newspapers to "smell a rat" and to dig in deeply to find it.

When requested to tell the diagnosis or the present condition of a patient, the hospital should take into account all of the circumstances. Injuries resulting from crimes — shootings, stabbings, assault, attempted suicide and similar affairs — must ordinarily be reported to the police anyway. They thus become public knowledge and available to the newspapers. Hence, the hospital might as well win the reporters' good graces by giving them such information as they would otherwise obtain from police records. The same holds true for automobile accident cases.

The wisest arrangement is for the hospitals, physicians and newspapers of the community to appoint a joint committee to work out and list the items of information that the hospital can and will give on each patient on request. This has been done in Cleveland and a *Code for Giving Information to the Press*, worked out in detail, is shown in Appendix IV. Further than this, some specific person or persons in the hospital should be named to give this information. This saves the time of reporters and assures the hospital that the proper information is given out.

Since the Cleveland Hospital Council worked out its code, the same code has been adopted by many other hospital groups and individual hospitals. When it is also approved by the newspapers, it is much easier to enforce. As in disease control, prevention is better than treatment — prevention in this case being prevention of misunderstanding and antagonism arising from different concepts of what facts are properly public property.

If a hospital is carrying on a creative public relations program, the newspapers will find the hospital such a good source of constructive news that they will not feel the need of extensively playing up untoward incidents in hospital activity. The best defense against newspaper attack is an active, aggressive offense against sickness and its related conditions.

Magazines and Social Institutions

Many hospitals have relationships that make it logical for them to provide material for certain magazines. Hospitals with religious affiliations, of course, have a close connection with the religious press of their denomination.

There are in many of the larger communities various special magazines that will gladly accept interesting articles and will be good mediums for strengthening contacts with certain groups of the public. These include local society magazines, community publications, school and club publications and local trade magazines.

The hospital magazines, of course, are always eager to obtain good articles on new developments in hospital management. A hospital administrator can build a reputation for intelligent leadership most quickly by contributing thoughtful and significant articles to the hospital magazines. Often these articles can be released to local magazines and newspapers when they appear in the hospital publications. Thus, the benefits can be local as well as national in character.

Occasionally a hospital will have material that merits publication in a national magazine of general circulation. Massachusetts General Hospital, for example, was extensively discussed in national magazines at the time it opened its pavilion for patients of moderate means.

Ordinarily these magazines will only use such material when it is written about a problem of broad public concern and a hospital's experience is used merely for illustration. National agencies usually are in a better position to obtain national publicity of this kind than individual local agencies.

REFERENCES

1. Lee, Alfred M.: The Daily Newspaper in America, The MacMillan Company, New York, 1937, p. 183.
2. Lee, *op. cit.*, p. 182.
3. Hearst, William Randolph: *Editor and Publisher*, June 14, 1924, p. 3.
4. Given, John L.: Making a Newspaper, Henry Holt & Company, New York, 1907, pp. 175, 215, 217.
5. Rorem, C. Rufus: The Public's Investment in Hospitals, The University of Chicago Press, 1930.
6. Given, *op. cit.*, p. 177.
7. Bradley, F. R.: Medical Records and the Law, *The Modern Hospital*, April, 1939, p. 70.

Chapter 11

EXPOSITIONAL METHODS —
VISUAL AND AUDITORY TECHNICS

AFTER CHILDHOOD, we all learn primarily through the printed word. But the knowledge so acquired is often somewhat impersonal and even vague. It can frequently be made more living and vivid if it is dramatized for us by other technics. There are various such technics available: exhibits, motion pictures, slidefilms, dramas, pageants, public meetings, radio broadcasts and special events.

Exhibits and Motion Pictures

A Chinese proverb says that one picture is worth a thousand words. Within limitations, this is certainly true. It is especially true of emotional and sensory as distinguished from intellectual appeals. This does not mean that intellectual and rational material should be omitted entirely from an exhibit or a motion picture, but rather that in general these technics are better adapted to arousing emotions, while the strictly rational appeals are usually better made in some other way.

An exhibit, of course, is obviously a form of low pressure exposition. It does not force one who looks at it to do anything. It must invite his attention and hold it by intrinsic interest. Exhibits are particularly useful in hospital exposition to show comparisons. One can illustrate progress in medicine by comparing the old and the new. One can account for the present level of hospital costs by comparing the scope of service in hospitals and hotels. One can show graphically the difference between present facilities and facilities planned for the future. Exhibits can dramatize the advancing educational work of an institution by indicating the present content of courses, nature and quantity of equipment and extent of faculty preparation as compared with that of twenty-five or fifty years ago.

One of the many places in which an exhibit can be used logically and successfully is in the lobby or waiting room of the hospital. An interesting and attractive exhibit there will help patients and visitors to pass the time cheerfully and will give them significant information about the institution. This plan has been followed with considerable success at Tacoma General Hospital, among others. The food clinic of the Boston Dispensary has developed an extensive series of food exhibits which are placed at various points throughout the building and are found to aid effectively in teaching food values to patients.

Stores and office buildings also will often cooperate by providing space for an attractive and interesting exhibit. Hospitals have been particularly successful in obtaining such space for National Hospital Day but there is no reason why it cannot also be obtained at other times during the year if the exhibit is of such character as to reflect credit upon the donor of space.[1]

Hospitals have recently found themselves to be a favored locale for motion pictures. A score or more of successful Hollywood films have used a hospital setting. The fact that many of these gave a somewhat garbled impression of what actually goes on in a hospital is of less significance to our present discussion than the equally obvious fact that hospital life contains many elements of drama. If Hollywood thinks that it can be made interesting and good "box office," why cannot hospitals themselves use motion pictures to tell their story?

The obvious answer is that they can. The American College of Surgeons, the Duke Endowment, the United Hospital Fund of New York and the Minnesota Hospital Service Association are among the hospital agencies that have used motion pictures successfully in their promotional work. Several individual hospitals have also made motion pictures for public consumption but most of these have been too amateurish to be very effective.

One of the outstanding hospital motion pictures that has appeared to date, in my opinion, was prepared by George U. Wood of Peralta Hospital, Oakland, California. This picture is made without a sound track so that it may be used anywhere that a simple projector is available. It shows the entire course of an actual patient's sojourn in a hospital. A maternity case requiring a cesarean section was chosen as best illustrative of the whole range of hospital care. Although the actors are all amateurs, they take their real life parts so well that they give the impression of professionals. The photography has been done in color with a great deal of artistry and imagination. The film is so planned that it can be used by nearly any hospital to illustrate the character and content of good hospital care today. It is sufficiently interesting to hold the attention of a nonhospital audience. The use of color makes the film far more vivid than a black and white presentation.[2]

Films of this kind will ordinarily be shown to audiences outside of commercial theaters. Men's and women's clubs, parent-teacher associations, neighborhood groups,

church audiences, college and university groups, high
school pupils, cooperative societies, granges and dozens
of similar organizations provide audiences before which
such films may be shown.

It would be ideal, of course, if each hospital could have
a film made particularly for its own use. It could then
stress its own program of service. As a practical matter,
however, this would be out of the question as a good film
costs from $2000 to $5000 to produce, even if all services
are donated. It is usually better, therefore, to purchase
or rent one of the many films for hospital public relations
that have been approved by the American College of
Surgeons. A list of these approved films is given as
Appendix V.

Slidefilms

A new medium of communication is being used with
considerable success by scores of industries in their
advertising, dealer sales promotion and public relations
activities. This new technic, called the slidefilm (or if
made with a sound accompaniment, the sound slidefilm),
has increased in popularity during the last six or eight
years.

The sound slidefilm consists of a coordinated series of
still pictures, in black and white or in color, which are
processed on 35 mm. film strip and run through an
especially designed projector. The sound story is on a
record and it is synchronized exactly with the pictures.
Reliable producers of slidefilms recommend a fast tempo
to the illustrations so that each one remains on the screen
for a few seconds only, thus actually creating an interest-
sustaining illusion of motion. The preparation of the
script or scenario is handled by men who are skilled in

writing for the particular medium. The organization purchasing a slidefilm supplies the script writer with the required data for the story and then cooperates with him until the script has been prepared exactly as desired. Such a script contains the sound story in one column and the picture directions in a parallel column.

The advantages of such a presentation are obvious, particularly when there are a number of people with different backgrounds, training and understanding who are to present a subject to various audiences at different times and under widely varying conditions. The sound slidefilm makes sure that each presentation gives the exact story in a clear and convincing manner since every point is visualized on the screen. Attention is fixed on the screen and the usual distractions are eliminated. It is easy to hold the concentrated interest of an audience of any size up to 300 or even more people when an intriguing, well executed sound slidefilm is being exhibited.

The production of a sound slidefilm of from fifteen to twenty minutes in length, if done by professionals, usually costs between $1000 and $2500, depending upon the difficulties inherent in its manufacture. Color films increase the cost by about 50 per cent. Duplicate copies of the film and record are quite inexpensive, a set (one print and record) usually costing about $3.50.

Most individual hospitals could not, of course, afford to pay the entire production cost except during a fund raising campaign or in other similar periods of intense activity. But local, state and national hospital associations and hospital care insurance organizations could well consider the wide possibilities of this interesting new medium.

Better than a verbal description of a slidefilm is an actual sample of the type of script that could be worked out for such a film. The following excerpts from a script, written at my request by a professional script writer, will show how it is prepared. In presenting this partial sample, no particular effort is made to tell a complete story. The purpose is only to illustrate how a sound slidefilm could be handled.

PICTURES	SOUND
1. Main title: "Hospitals — Then and Now" Hand lettered over interesting background of two-panel frame showing (1) an old time hospital scene contrasted with (2) a modern hospital scene.	A few seconds of appropriate music followed by voice of narrator. *Narrator*: Hospitals — Then and Now. Even the past quarter of a century has produced such amazing changes in hospital science, care and equipment that the story of the advance becomes one of the dramas of present day civilization. But just suppose —
2. Exterior or interior view of "Old Bethlehem" Hospital in London. (If not available, the scene may be staged and photographed.)	— you had been unfortunate enough to require surgical treatment in a great hospital such as historic "Old Bethlehem" of London. The year, let us say, is 1839, just one century ago.
3. Interior scene revealing overcrowded conditions in early hospitals of date about 1830-1840.	You would have been crowded into a place like this where often as many as three or four persons occupied one bed. The food was coarse and monotonous and the sanitary facilities were wholly inadequate.

4. Long shot view of hospital ward about 1830-1840 showing very large room and beds around the entire wall space.

The condition in the wards was most unpleasant. Often a ward occupied an entire floor and had 50 or more beds. The problem of heating such a large space was obviously a serious one.

5. Medium closeup of surgery before anesthesia. Patient held down by strong-armed men.

Then came the ordeal of surgery which the patient had to endure without the benefit of modern anesthesia. Small wonder that the chance for life was less than 50 per cent.

6. Another surgery about 1860 showing doctors in frock coats. (Administrator should seek other environmental data.)

Even as late at 1860 it was common practice in many hospitals for the doctors to operate in frock coats and they went from one case to another without even washing their hands.

Thus the story might proceed following the outstanding developments up to the present day. A major part of the film could deal with the extraordinary facilities and improvements that have been added to hospital service within the last twenty or twenty-five years.

61. Attractive view of interior of patient's room in modern hospital.

The old iron beds and hard mattresses have given way to attractive wood and metal beds and comfortable inner spring mattresses. Upholstered chairs, a convenient bedside table, carpeting, attractive draperies and soft colored walls are in keeping with a restful homelike atmosphere.

62. Closeup to show patient on bed, which is being wheeled into corridor.

The patient's bed is on large casters so that, without painfully disturbing him, he may be moved to surgery, x-ray, physical therapy —

63. Long shot to show patients in attractive solarium.

— or to the solarium, perhaps, where an environment of cheerful character contributes both to his mental and physical well-being.

64. Composite to show specially designed beds in use. Type of beds should be that used in cardiac or asthmatic cases or other types which hospitals use.

Special types of beds are available which permit patients to sit or lie in positions most favorable to the treatment of their particular illnesses. Such beds are used in treating cardiac and asthmatic patients, as well as many others.

65. Full-room view of modern operating suite being made ready for surgery.

A trip to an air conditioned operating room in a modern hospital is an amazing revelation of the intrepid genius which has, even within the last twenty years, produced scientific marvels in the care and treatment of surgical cases.

66. Closeup at angle to show surgical area and bring out fact that no shadows cross.

The surgical area is lighted so that no shadows can possibly interfere with the work of surgeons and their various assistants.

67. Closeup of anesthesia machine being used.

Anesthesia machines are used which permit a precise flow of each gas at any rate that may be desired.

68. Closeup as nurse demonstrates the adjustable operating table.

The operating table is adjustable to any desired position. This contributes greatly to successful surgery.

The film could continue with a general trip through the hospital to inspect and discuss facilities, such as the x-ray, physical therapy, laboratory, dietary and other departments.

85. Composite of equipment given in text and any other suggested by hospital staff.

Of course, such apparatus as the electrocardiograph and the anesthesia machine, the equipment used in physical therapy and in obtaining and storing normal and convalescent human serums, —

86. Composite of additional equipment.

— the indispensable x-ray machine so greatly advanced even within the past five years, sterilizing equipment and other facilities that create maximum safety or comfort, —

87. Closeup composite of equipment given in text.

— the extensive and intricate outlay of laboratory equipment, such as the autotechnicon, lyophile apparatus, Van Slyke apparatus for the analysis of blood gases, basal metabolism apparatus and numerous others, —

88. Long shot interior of modern hospital kitchen.

— the maintenance of staffs of trained dietitians, the purchase, maintenance and use of modern sanitary and scientific kitchen equipment — all of these up-to-date methods of hospitalization —

89. Picture of person at cashier's window paying bill.

— are expensive to buy and maintain. Constant improvements and new discoveries make frequent replacements necessary, but all are essential to the saving of human life, the prevention of suffering and the adequate safeguarding against future complications. The values received are worth the cost. Consider, for example, improvements in maternity service.

90. Over background picture of old hospital, superimpose in titles the words of the text.

"In April and May, 1856, nearly all of the 347 women who had been confined in the Paris Maternity Hospital died of childbed fever."

91. Long shot of modern hospital nursery.

Today many hospitals have maternal death rates as low as 2.7 per thousand cases!

92. Graph or bar chart to illustrate statistics given in text.

Just a generation ago the average stay of a hospital patient was from twenty to thirty days. Today the average is about ten days.

93. Closeup of patient receiving x-ray examination.

Yes, scientific care and scientific equipment are expensive to maintain, but saving life is worth all it costs! Today—

94. Closeup of pamphlet describing hospital care insurance plan.

— there are plans for hospital care insurance that bring the benefits and security of hospitalization within the reach of the majority of our self-supporting citizens.

An appropriate ending would be used to close the presentation and to sum up the points which the sponsoring organization wished to emphasize.

Dramas and Pageants

Because medical service has moments of high drama, because it has an ancient and interesting history, it is possible and sometimes appropriate to present in the form of a drama or a pageant some aspects of hospital development or present day service. Dramas and pageants, like motion pictures, are designed to appeal primarily to the emotions. Hence, they should not play too important a part in hospital public relations. But, if used with other forms of exposition, if written with sincerity and candor and if effectively acted and staged, they can contribute appreciably to the total effect of a public relations program.

Moving pictures, dramas and pageants, all are better suited to a general mass appeal than to an appeal to the discriminating minority. Few hospitals have sufficiently skillful actors and dramatic coaches to present a play that would stand even lenient comparison with the offerings of the legitimate theater. But mass appeals are frequently desirable, particularly when the hospital needs to awaken interest and to improve its general reputation and standing in a community.

In the past few years there has been such a wide increase in the number of "little theaters" and of W.P.A. theaters that an enterprising hospital might easily find it possible to enlist skilled aid in its theatrical ventures. Certainly this would be desirable, if possible.

Like most aspects of public relations, this relationship might easily be beneficial to both parties. The alert hospital administrator can be of real assistance to the dramatic group. Recently, for example, one of the administrators in Grand Rapids, Michigan, acted as technical adviser to a local little theater group in its presentation of *Men in White*. He coached the actors in operating room technic and provided them with needed hospital equipment, including an operating table, instruments and gowns. He was billed in their program as the technical adviser.

Unfortunately, there are few good plays or pageants available for hospital use. This is an almost untilled field and one that calls for good writers. Perhaps with the increasing growth of hospital interest in public relations, some worth-while material may be written for this use.

Public Meetings

When a hospital is engaged in a serious effort to develop its services in line with the needs of its service area, the data collected make excellent material for presentation at meetings concerned with the hospital's program. As mentioned in Chapter 8, special meetings may be arranged for the presentation of the principal results of the study to the leading citizens of the community. Frequently, outstanding leaders in medical and hospital work can be obtained to address such meetings. If the objectives of the institution are "in line with broad social trends" and "larger than the institution," a meeting of this kind can take on an historic significance. Properly planned and well staged, it can be a forceful method of enlisting interest and developing support.

Such a meeting, of course, is one method of high-spotting the work of the institution. It should, if possible, be supplemented by a number of additional meet-

As yet the potentialities of radio as a medium of public education have scarcely been tapped by hospitals or other agencies.

ings at which the data are presented to various other groups concerned: labor unions, church groups, women's clubs and similar organizations.

Another type of meeting is also useful in a hospital's public relations program. This is the health lecture.[3] An interesting example of what may be done effectively along this line is furnished by the Salem Hospital, Salem, Massachusetts. A series of eight such health lectures was given on Sunday afternoons during January and February 1938. It covered the following topics: "The Functions of the General Hospital," "The Public Health Problems of the Community," "Appendicitis and Other Abdominal Emergencies," "Associated Hospitals Group Insurance," "High Blood Pressure," "The Common Cold and Its Complications," "Tuberculosis and Advances in Treatment," "Home Use of Drugs and the Family Medicine Chest." Although the hospital is on the outskirts of the city and one of the talks was given on the day of a blizzard, there was an average attendance at the eight lectures of 112.

Salem Hospital is so firmly convinced of the value of the health talks that a new series was given in 1939. The hospital's dermatologist gave a talk on the effect of cosmetics on the skin and the pathologist and radiologist were included in the program.

Health meetings need not always be in straight lecture form. The first in the 1938 series at Salem Hospital was not a lecture but a little play. With the scene laid in a patient's room, her questions of various people who came in gave an excellent opportunity to convey a broad picture of the educational work of a community hospital. Round table discussions and panel discussions are also popular. If these are carefully planned, they can bring out all aspects of a subject effectively. Audience participation can well be invited.

A series of health lectures can, if funds permit, be printed individually or in a booklet for distribution to the hospital's constituents. Or they can be shortened somewhat and appear as articles in the monthly house magazine. Copies can be given in advance to the newspapers. Especially in small towns, the papers might use such lectures extensively.

The hospital administrator, various of the department heads and some members of the board of trustees and the women's auxiliary can aid hospital public relations work by accepting invitations to address community groups of various sorts concerning the hospital's work and objectives. They also can talk about subjects on which they have special knowledge. The superintendent of nurses, for example, can discuss home nursing; the dietitian should be a most welcome speaker before women's groups on various aspects of food purchase, preparation, combination and decoration. The hospital housekeeper can readily work up valuable material concerning the care of floors, rugs and furniture, problems of interior decoration and similar topics. Each of these persons will naturally make occasional references to the work of the hospital. Even if this is not done, the mere fact that an expert from the hospital is helpful will in itself indicate that the hospital desires to serve the community. As mentioned in Chapter 7, the administrator himself can often be effective in work of this kind.

Radio

The possibilities of radio as a public educational medium for both children and adults have only been scratched. No one knows how far it may go in this direction. Enough has been done already, however, to indicate that the potentialities are large if they are intelligently used.[4] As Walter Damrosch points out, printing has made us eye-minded but the radio may again make us ear-minded as were the disciples of Socrates.

National radio broadcasting began as pure entertainment designed for the purpose of selling radio sets. Entertainment is still the prime function of radio today.* But the number of wave lengths available is limited. Hence regulation is essential.

Regulation inevitably involves a direct or indirect censorship over programs. Obviously, when only a few stations in any area can be permitted to broadcast programs at a particular time, the Federal Communications Commission must decide which are to broadcast and which are to remain silent or to go out of business. In doing so, the commission takes account of the character of the programs broadcast. Stations that provide programs that the commissioners believe are "in the public

*As long ago as 1931, however, Dr. Henry Adams Bellows, vice president of the Columbia Broadcasting System, Inc., and a former member of the Federal Radio Commission, declared that not a single station "has built up and maintained a dependable listening audience by providing merely entertainment and amusement. The listeners themselves have seen to this; they insist on being interested as well as entertained. Run over the daily operating schedule of any broadcasting station which puts forth even the slightest claim to good standing. A full half of it makes no effort to furnish entertainment or amusement; it is designed solely to arouse and hold public interest. Its features may be well done, or ill; they may show a fine perception of the relationship between public interest and public service, or they may not; in any event, the very fact that they are there is in itself a recognition of the necessity for creating and continuing an interest that is quite independent of entertainment." (Radio and Education, 1931, Proceedings of the First Assembly of the National Advisory Council on Radio in Education, the University of Chicago Press, Chicago, 1931, p. 43.)

interest" are more likely to be the ones whose permits are readily extended. Those that present material believed to be worthless or positively harmful may find it more difficult to remain in operation. Whether it is desirable to put so much power into the hands of a few men and whether there are any practical alternatives are involved questions, too complex for discussion here.

Over against this pressure from governmental bodies is another pressure that is even more direct and powerful. It is the pressure of the listener. It is the simplest thing in the world to turn off a radio or to switch to another station. Once that is done, nothing which comes subsequently on that period can wean the listener back (unless, perchance, he finds programs on other stations that are even less inviting to him and returns to give the first station another try).

Every program carries with it the possibility of alienating listeners, an alienation that the station executives may discover only as it eventually shows up in permanent loss of listeners. In spite of this danger, radio executives have shown a commendable willingness to experiment with new types of program.

Hospitals and other social institutions have a peculiar opportunity in radio. If they can create types of program that will increase the number of a radio station's listeners and at the same time will be "in the public interest," radio stations will give favorable attention to their requests for free time on the air.

What types of program will meet these two requirements? This is difficult to say dogmatically. Perhaps it will be easier to make suggestions if first we describe and eliminate certain types of program that are not desirable.

It now appears to be the consensus of publicity experts and radio directors that the day of the straight radio talk is about over. President Roosevelt, Herbert Hoover, Boake Carter, H. V. Kaltenborn and certain other persons have either such important positions (national or local) or such excellent radio personalities that a straight talk is widely heard. The same is true of other popular celebrities, from Shirley Temple and the quintuplets to the latest aviation idol. But the average person making a radio address is largely wasting his and the station's time. Radio stations are increasingly unwilling to allow their free time to be thus used.

The broadcasting of banquet addresses is no longer considered a great novelty. Unless the speaker is a person of great importance addressing a significant public meeting, stations are not likely to be tempted by such an offer. Even if the event is important, it is probable that it can be recorded or recreated for radio use more successfully than it can be broadcast at the time of occurrence.

A straight musical program given by the nurses' chorus or the hospital's music guild will attract a considerable audience only if it is of good quality. One radio program using the musical talents of regular employes is the *Musical Steelmakers* half hour on Sunday afternoons. This is reported to be not only popular with the public but also a potent force for better personnel relations. A program that is exclusively musical is more effective in building good will and general interest than in educating the community concerning the hospital.

Some of the most successful radio programs of the educational type have been *The March of Time*, an expertly prepared dramatic presentation of the highlights of the news; *University of Chicago Round Table* and

Northwestern Reviewing Stand, both informal discussions by groups of experts on leading questions of the day; *Town Meeting of the Air,* a cleverly staged public debate between experts on important questions; *One Man's Family,* an excellent dramatic serial; *Information, Please,* an amusing and informative quizzing of the experts, and Alexander Woollcott's *Town Crier,* a dramatic one-man show strongly flavored with sentiment (not on the air at the present time).

When a program or a series of programs for hospitals is to be prepared, the script writer should realize that it will be judged by the radio station on the following points: (1) Is it sufficiently interesting and entertaining to attract new listeners and hold old ones? Dullness is the implacable foe of all program builders. Is it of real merit or merely a publicity stunt? (2) Will it be considered by the Federal Communications Commission as "in the public interest"? (3) Will any listeners be shocked or alienated by material to appear on the program? The station, of course, will delete any such material but it is preferable for the author to exercise good taste himself. (4) Will the material be of general benefit to hospitals or will it benefit one particular hospital only? (5) If it is presented, will other groups demand that they, too, be given free time?

These are the hurdles the program must meet in the radio studio; in addition, it must be examined from certain hospital angles, particularly when it deals with specific aspects of hospital work or life: (1) Does this program give a true and accurate picture of best current hospital practice? Is the material honest and sincere or has it been slanted to give a biased picture? (2) Will it arouse in listeners a feeling of security and confidence in the character of work done in hospitals? (3) Will it at the same time give a fair picture of the handicaps to good hospital service resulting from limitations of funds? (4) Will it create in the minds of listeners a reasonably accurate picture of the life of nurses, physicians and others engaged in hospital service? (5) Will it fit into the hospital public relations program and coordinate well with other public relations work that has been done or is contemplated? Obviously, some of these questions may not be pertinent to particular programs.

If physicians are asked to participate in radio programs, each script must be carefully examined in the light of the physicians' ethical obligations. In its recently revised code, The Canadian Medical Association states the ethics involved as follows:

It is legitimate and even desirable that topics relating both to medical science and policy and to public health and welfare should be discussed by physicians who can speak with authority on the question at issue. In any medium of discussion, but especially in radio broadcasting because of its vast range, it is essential that the physician who takes part should avoid methods which tend to his personal professional advantage. Not only should he personally observe this rule, but he should take care that the announcer in introducing him makes no laudatory comments and no unnecessary display of the physician's medical qualifications and appointments. . . . A physician serving in a public capacity is in a different position but even he should see to it that it is his office, rather than himself, that is exalted.

To arouse and maintain interest in the type of subjects that will most likely fit into the public relations program of a hospital, recourse may be had to some of the technics that have proved most effective in other types of program. These include round table discussions, debates, interviews, tours combined with interviews, and, probably the most successful of all, dramatizations. The important thing is to develop personality in a program, the type of personality that is welcome in the family circle. Consideration should be given to the effective use of music for the introduction and conclusion of the broadcast. Many hospitals have some kind of musical organization, either among the nurses, the employes or the women's auxiliary, that can be used for this purpose. Of course, the music must be of high quality; otherwise it would be far better omitted.

Hospitals deal in dramatic materials — life, death and the struggle of man against his most persistent enemy, disease. That these materials are full of potentialities for radio use is indicated by the large number of commercial programs using the hospital as a background for a serial. Most of these serials are only moderately good as drama and often are far from authentic pictures of hospital life. But the fact that they are continued on the air and are increasing in number shows the possibilities open to hospitals. The time is ripe for some strong hospital group to ascertain what can be done with a well written, absorbing, dramatic script, carefully edited to assure authenticity and prepared so as to give the public a true picture of what the best hospitals are and what they are trying to do. This would require a writer who can make effective drama out of the simple elements of life common to all of us. Styles of writing might be as varied as those found in the stories of O. Henry, Christopher Morley, Sir James Barrie or Carlton E. Morse, author of *One Man's Family*. Such a drama should be presented by professional actors so as to make it convincing.

A word should be said concerning the use of recordings in radio broadcasting. Recording instruments are now available that can be transported almost anywhere. With these, a radio tour of a hospital can be arranged, with visits to various departments and with interviews of patients, physicians and department heads, as may be desired. Properly planned, such interviews can be interesting and educational. The records can be transported anywhere for use at any time for radio broadcasts. A new technic, extensively used in England but only recently brought to this country, employs a substance analogous to a motion picture film for the record. This record can be played back as soon as the program has been recorded. There is no time lost in a developing process such as is used for ordinary films or for a duplicating process like that needed for regular phonograph records.

The use of radio in schools is increasing. There are important aspects of this development that hospitals should consider. In Chicago in the fall of 1938 and spring of 1939, for example, several series of dramatizations were prepared by the vocational guidance officials of the Chicago public schools. One series depicted, particularly to high school pupils, the various vocational opportunities in hospitals. The radio dramatizations were supplemented by extensive mimeographed material giving more specific information about hospital vocations, such as administration, nursing, dietetics, medical record librarianship, anesthesia and laboratory technology.

Radio programs sponsored by hospitals should help to break down the fear and dislike which some people feel toward hospitals and to substitute feelings of confidence, friendliness and respect. The most effective use of radio requires that it be fitted into a general public relations plan. Persons whose interest is aroused by broadcasts should be able to do something about it: write for further information, contribute to certain hospital activities or in some other way convert their impulses into action.

The use of radio on a regular schedule involves substantial responsibilities. One institution, Deaconess Hospital, Evansville, Indiana, has a radio program, the Sunshine Hour, that has been broadcast from the hospital every day except Saturday and Sunday since September 1925. (During the 1937 Ohio River flood which inundated most of Evansville, this program was off the air for a little more than a week but was among the first resumed, as the Red Cross felt it would be an aid in maintaining morale.) The program was started as a morning family religious service but, as radio progressed, Albert G. Hahn, administrator of the hospital, became convinced that it would reach a larger number of listeners, especially among the aged, sick and shut-ins, if given in the afternoon. Surveys, made by the Evansville Trade Extension Bureau among the 3½ million persons living within 200 miles of Evansville, indicate that the program is heard by at least 200,000 listeners daily. Letters about the program come to the hospital from as far away as Montana and Texas. Ministers of all denominations from Evansville and surrounding territory take turns in arranging and conducting the Sunshine Hour program. It usually consists of two or three songs, a prayer and a talk lasting about twelve minutes. The ministers are requested to avoid controversial subjects. Mr. Hahn usually acts as the announcer.

Several other programs are broadcast weekly from Deaconess Hospital. The Sunset Hour is conducted in

German for elderly persons each Wednesday afternoon. The Friendship Hour is a musical program presented by the younger musicians of Evansville. Health talks are given weekly. The musical and health talks are broadcast during only part of the year. While the hospital is mentioned on these programs merely as sponsor, this activity is building up a friendly feeling toward Evansville Deaconess Hospital.

Hospitals and hospital associations might well study the radio series sponsored by the Million Unit Fellowship movement of the Methodist Episcopal Church. As part of a national program, a series of radio dramas has been prepared under the title, *Heralds of Destiny*. These dramatize outstanding and heroic events in the lives of various Methodist leaders, many of them in the missionary field. Episode No. 1, for example, is entitled *Thoburn of India*. Its synopsis reads as follows:

The young missionary and his wife stationed in a far outpost of India awake suddenly in the night. Brilliant moonlight pooled upon their bed reveals a deadly cobra at their feet. The native servant is summoned but refuses to kill the snake — his religion forbids it. The young man risks his life and kills it. Later he defies other native superstitions successfully. Mohammedans try to frame him, but he escapes miraculously. Thoburn of India, in another exploit, appears in the front trenches in the Philippines while Insurrectios, led by Aguinaldo, rain shells on Manila.

Each of these dramatic episodes is introduced by a short musical prologue. Only the briefest mention is made of the sponsor. The episodes are recorded and furnished without charge to radio stations in various parts of the country. At present, more than 150 stations are using the programs on a regular weekly schedule during the winter and early spring. The entire cost for the

preparation of the script, the employment of experienced
radio actors, the making of the master record and a sufficient number of copies and the necessary promotion and
mailing activities comes to approximately $6000 for a
series of 18 weekly programs. The programs are well
publicized by the national sponsors through newspaper
releases and material sent directly to ministers for announcement on bulletin boards, from pulpits and in
church calendars. The series has aroused widespread
interest and hundreds of letters of commendation have
been received by the stations and the national head-
quarters from ministers and from other listeners in all
parts of the country.

The same amounts of money, effort and imagination
devoted to a hospital radio series would doubtless produce one of even higher dramatic qualities since there is
a larger store of material on which to draw. The *Heralds
of Destiny* program is broadcast mainly by stations in
the smaller cities. A comparable hospital program would
probably be used in the larger cities also. Even in large
cities the competition for radio time is not so intense that
hospitals will find it impossible to obtain a period. Radio
stations the country over now are able to sell only from
30 to 40 per cent of the total time they have available.
Since they wish to fill all the hours allotted to them, they
must create sustaining programs if they do not have good
programs offered to them. But a program must be good
to be given a period on the schedule. A united hospital
fund, an active and well administered hospital council or
a successful hospital care insurance plan will ordinarily
be better prepared than will most individual hospitals
to sponsor radio programs which will merit time on a
regular schedule. Furthermore, the station will be more

inclined to give time to a cooperative group of hospitals than to a single institution.

Special Events

A variety of special events may be used to bring a closer relationship between the public and the hospital. National Hospital Day, Hospital Sunday, commencement exercises of the nursing school and certain traditional holidays offer possibilities to the alert hospital.

The observance of National Hospital Day has increased year by year since it was first proposed in 1921 by the late Matthew O. Foley. Prizes are now offered for the best general program and the best publicity program in each of two classes — hospitals in cities of more than 15,000 population and in cities under this figure. To some extent the observance is still confined to hospitals in smaller communities. During recent years, however, some of the larger metropolitan hospitals have found that they can create a type of event which is suitable to the larger institution and of distinct value in increasing prestige in the eyes of the public and of the employes. The prize winning program arranged at Cleveland City Hospital in 1938 by James A. Hamilton and his associates is ample evidence. This was characterized by a great deal of originality in both concept and execution.

The publicity program which preceded the observance of National Hospital Day in Cleveland was unusually thorough. A special proclamation was issued by the mayor upon authorization of the city council. Nearly 50,000 invitation folders and 14,000 announcements were distributed among employes and hospital visitors and enclosed with bills sent out by wholesale drug houses. A thousand posters were displayed in schools, stores, theaters and public buildings. Several billboards were posted at important locations. Signs were used in taxis and on buses; bumper signs were placed on 500 automobiles. Movie trailers were shown in the theaters. Press publicity in Cleveland newspapers totaled 300 column inches. A total of 125,000 pamphlets of the Cleveland Railway Company, distributed in their street cars, buses and stations, carried announcement of the open house. Various other local magazines and bulletins published announcements.

The four Cleveland broadcasting stations gave a total of 144 minutes of radio time. In addition, floater announcements were made on the radio from May 9 to 12, inclusive. Five different radio talks were given on May 12 over local stations and two of these were on national hook-ups. The work of hospitals was discussed in the history and civics classes of the junior and senior high schools. These classes have an enrollment of approximately 30,000 students. Letters of invitation went to all civic organizations and churches. Nurses in uniform made three-minute talks to four civic clubs.

Perhaps the most spectacular publicity of all was provided by a squadron of three Ohio National Guard airplanes that flew over the city in various formations from 11:30 to 12:30 on May 12. On the underside of the planes were large signs inviting observers to visit City Hospital. The planes completed their flying with special stunts over the hospital.

The result of all this publicity was that a total of 25,000 persons visited Cleveland City Hospital on National Hospital Day. What did the hospital do to make their visits worth while? Each person was given a six page folder describing the work of the institution. A series of

23 exhibits were set up in the nurses' auditorium to depict the work of various departments of the hospital. At each exhibit there were mimeographed sheets outlining the work of that particular department, showing its function and its volume. Several of the exhibits had actual demonstrations. The exhibits were open from 9:30 a.m. to 7:00 p.m. but the demonstrations were given only in the afternoon. Tours of the hospital were conducted by members of the Junior League at half hour intervals from 9:30 a.m. to 6:30 p.m. During the afternoon five different moving pictures on health and hospital topics were shown. Talks, demonstrations and moving pictures depicted nursing as a vocation and girls considering this field had an excellent opportunity to gain an understanding of just what it involves.

A luncheon for civic and professional leaders was given at the hospital on May 12 by the city's director of public health and welfare. At this luncheon certificates and pins were presented to all employes who had served the hospital continuously for twenty years and they were made members of the Twenty Year Service Club. The luncheon guests were also given tickets admitting them to the Ohio premiére of *The Birth of a Baby* which was shown in one of the hospital's auditoriums early in the afternoon. Another important feature of the luncheon was the award of the Burri plaque to the department "which has done most during the year to stimulate public interest in City Hospital, to strengthen public confidence in the institution, and otherwise to improve public and community relations with the hospital through the dissemination of reliable information pertaining to the department and the display of its functions and significance in the operation of the hospital." A committee of citizens acted as judges and awarded the plaque to the dietary department. Following the observance, letters of appreciation were sent to every person or group that aided in the celebration of National Hospital Day.

In 1939, a similar program brought 30,000 people to Cleveland City Hospital.

Cleveland City Hospital is a vast institution of more than 1500 beds. In sharp contrast is Paradise Valley Sanitarium and Hospital at National City, California, a small community health center of only 150 beds. In 1938 it won both prizes in its class for its National Hospital Day observance. This program has been fully described in the hospital magazines, so a detailed description need not be repeated here.[5] One of the outstanding features was the cleverness used in building up many significant educational exhibits depicting the advances in surgery, nursing, first aid treatment, diet, radiology, animal experimentation, anesthesia, infant identification and other aspects of medical practice. Widespread public interest was aroused as was clearly evidenced by the participation of Governor Frank F. Merriam of California and Governor Rudolfo Sanchez Taboada of the adjoining state in Mexico. Part of the proceedings were broadcast on a Pacific Coast radio network of 25 stations reaching from the Mexican border to British Columbia. Between 8000 and 9000 people attended.

Over the course of the past nineteen years, hundreds of articles about National Hospital Day have appeared in the various hospital magazines.[6] Both the magazines and the hospital associations have probably focused relatively too much attention on this event and not enough on the desirability of a well rounded complete public relations program carried on every week during the year.

National Hospital Day should be one feature of such a program but not, by any means, considered as an entire program. The objectives of National Hospital Day in a particular institution should be made to coincide with the objectives of the public relations program as a whole; the methods used to set up avenues of communication between the public and the hospital should harmonize with and supplement the methods of the larger program.

Hospital Sunday has been observed for many years by certain institutions. On this day contributions for the benefit of the hospital are received in the various churches of the community. Ministers, priests and rabbis are asked to mention the work of the hospital in their sermons. Preceding Hospital Sunday, local papers carry extensive reports on the work and financial position of the hospital and its place and function in the community.

In Evanston, Illinois, the Evanston Hospital has conducted a Hospital Sunday observance for 41 years. The money actually contributed to the hospital on this occasion is of less importance than the good will and understanding which result from better knowledge of the hospital and an awakened interest in its activities. A large percentage of the people who have made substantial contributions to the hospital's endowment fund have first evidenced interest in the hospital by giving small sums in response to annual Hospital Sunday appeals. Those who contribute $10 or more for Hospital Sunday are automatically put upon the mailing list to receive *The Pilot*, the hospital's house magazine mentioned in Chapter 8. Thus, their interest is cultivated through the monthly visits of this informative magazine.

A successful observance of Hospital Sunday requires careful organization and planning. All of the significant data for a recent period must be available and prepared in form that will be of real interest to the public. This must be given to the local press well in advance and can be incorporated in straight news stories, in signed articles by officers of the hospital, in interviews and in feature stories. Good photographs of hospital activities and of community leaders taking part in the observance of Hospital Sunday should be available to the papers. The ministers, priests and rabbis should all be seen and provided with full information. To avoid monotony, the story of the hospital's work must be given some new slant or interpretation each year. Arrangements must be made for collecting and acknowledging the gifts. While the actual cash returns may seem too small to justify such effort, the indirect long-time benefits should be given due weight in assessing the worth of this undertaking.

Commencement time offers another opportunity to build wider community understanding of the hospital. There is no difficulty in obtaining a large attendance at the hospital's commencement exercises. The important problem is to have ceremonies that will convey to the audience a better idea of the hospital's aims and achievements. Grant Hospital, Chicago, has widened its commencement program to include not only nurses but also record librarians and interns and residents who are concluding their educational work in the hospital. This furnishes an excellent opportunity to discuss the hospital as an educational center and to depict the need for higher standards of medical, nursing and technical education to meet the demands of medical practice and scientific investigation as they exist today.

Another commencement innovation that has proved to be of value is a joint commencement service for all the hospitals of the community. Such a program has been arranged by the hospitals of Charleston, West Virinia. Exercises are held in one of the largest auditoriums in the city and are attended by several thousand people. Because of the impressiveness and community importance of the occasion, it has been possible to obtain speakers of national reputation. The exercises have a dignity that comes to be associated with the hospitals.

A new type of commencement program is now being presented by many progressive public schools. Schools of nursing might well study this program, which is described as follows by Arthur B. Moehlman, editor of *The Nation's Schools.*[7]

The activity type of commencement program, now rapidly growing in favor, is functional in character and indicates a return to the original theory of "commencement" as a time for youth to prove itself. The participants are the graduates themselves and the theme they present is frequently an excellent symbolization of the meaning of the educational process. It may take the form of a pageant, a series of tableaux, vignettes of everyday school activity, a ritualization of themselves to the adult world before them or straight dramatization of youth problems and achievements. When carefully staged and well timed, these amateur presentations have all the freshness, vitality and appeal that make youth so interesting to people over 40. Their interpretation of the school and of its work and value is immeasurably more effective than the well-paid, well-fed, if not always well-polished "big-name" speaker.

Either this new type of program or the conventional type may be supplemented by postprogram meetings between teachers and parents, by attractive exhibits of school work so carefully staged that they have a drawing power of their own and by other social activities. The school building should be made as attractive to the eye as possible and its facilities available and understandable to visitors.

Special attention is given by most hospitals to patients
who are in the institution on holidays. All of the national holidays are usually observed, with particular
attention to Christmas and Thanksgiving. Some institutions take the trouble to keep the dietitian informed of
the birthdays of all patients. In one hospital the patient
is requested to invite one or two relatives or friends to
celebrate his birthday with him, as guests of the hospital.
This is possible, of course, only if the patient's condition
is sufficiently good to stand the extra excitement. Such
a custom is naturally pleasing to patients who are unfortunate enough to be hospitalized at the time of their
birthday.

Summary of Expositional Methods
  (Chapters 8, 9, 10 and 11)

Exposition is the function of defining, explaining,
analyzing and interpreting those aspects of the hospital
and its work that are of concern to the public. Clear
exposition is desirable for three reasons: (1) to test the
soundness of the ideas that make up a hospital's service
program, (2) to create acceptance of the ideas once they
have been proved sound and (3) to win the moral and
financial support that may be required to carry any
significant service program into effect.

There are various ways to achieve sound exposition.
All of them involve skill and sincerity to be effective. A
complete public relations program will utilize most of
the accepted avenues of communication from time to
time, selecting for each task the avenue that leads most
directly to the desired goal. Insofar as possible all
avenues of communication should be made two-way so
that the hospital may benefit by the advice, suggestions

and criticism of the public. Only in that manner can it obtain the full measure of value from its exposition.

The preceding chapters have described a variety of expositional technics. For purposes of summary these will merely be given here in check list fashion.

1. Annual Reports
2. House Magazines
3. Letters
4. Pamphlets and Booklets
5. Bound Books
6. Newspapers
7. Magazines
8. Exhibits: Still or moving, silent or sound
9. Motion Pictures
10. Slidefilms
11. Dramas and Pageants
12. Public Meetings
13. Radio
14. Special Events: National Hospital Day, Hospital Sunday, commencement, holidays

Probably any idea that a hospital or group of hospitals might wish to present to the public for consideration, amendment and adoption can be presented through one of the many existing avenues of communication.

Advances in expositional technics are going forward at a rapid rate. Intelligent use of these mediums demands that the public relations officer be constantly abreast of the latest advances in technic. Many of the available tools have never been utilized to the full. Radio is an outstanding example. The past decade has witnessed remarkable developments in the quality of radio broadcasting. Probably, before we have completely mastered this tool, television will be opening up and will require still different technics.

The four preceding chapters have not attempted to present a technical guide to the use of expositional means. To do that adequately would require a full volume on each medium. Rather, there has been an attempt to give a nontechnical description of the various mediums and to indicate in broad outline how and where they may be utilized in a complete public relations program. There is always a temptation to devote too much emphasis to the discussion of mediums and not enough to the consideration of basic objectives. The medium is important only as it is appropriate to effectuate a sound basic objective. It is much easier to obtain the services of a person who is reasonably skillful in the use of the mediums than it is to find one who can help the hospital to create a true public relations program.

REFERENCES

1. Mayer, Raymond C.: How to Do Publicity, Harper & Brothers, New York, 1937, Chapter 20, and Turner, Pearl: Learning Through Looking, *Public Health Nursing*, June, 1939, p. 315.
2. Wood, George U.: Movie Portrays Patient's Progress, *The Modern Hospital*, Jan., 1939, p. 56.
3. Morrill, Donald M.: The Community Hospital and the Next Generation, *Hospitals*, March, 1937, p. 11, and Dunstan, E. M.: The Hospital and Health Education, *Hospitals*, Oct., 1938, p. 84.
4. Much important material on the educational possibilities of radio has appeared in the publications of the National Advisory Council on Radio in Education published by the University of Chicago Press.
5. Rice, Helen N.: Hospital Day in Paradise Valley, *The Modern Hospital*, Feb., 1939, p. 52.
6. Unsigned: Bibliography of National Hospital Day Literature — 1921-1937, *Hospital Management*, April, 1938, p. 24.
7. Moehlman, Arthur B.: Preparing for 1939 Commencements, *The Nation's Schools*, April, 1939, p. 33.

Chapter 12

FUND RAISING CAMPAIGNS

THE HOSPITALS of America, with minor exceptions, were built and are supported by the public without expectation of direct financial returns. The physical plants have been erected and equipped with funds from taxes or from gifts. Ordinarily hospitals do not compute the cost of depreciation, of interest on invested capital or of replacement of capital (a sinking fund) when they are figuring the cost per patient day. It is assumed as a matter of public policy that the original plant shall be provided to patients without cost. It is further assumed that pay patients as a group may be expected to meet the cost of their own maintenance and perhaps part or all of the cost of care for free patients. But patients' fees are not expected to provide for replacement of buildings. A hospital that is doing a large amount of free service does not ask its pay patients to meet the entire cost of caring for free patients.

Need for a Fund Raising Campaign

But even though patients are not charged for the costs of depreciation and replacement, the fact remains that buildings do wear out, become obsolete or are outgrown and equipment must frequently be supplemented or replaced. Furthermore, the demand for hospital service is constantly rising, thus forcing hospitals to expand their facilities.[1] In spite of the reduction in the average length of stay and in the number of patients suffering from smallpox, measles, diphtheria, whooping cough, scarlet fever and similar diseases, the wider public understanding and acceptance of hospitals as almost indispensable agencies in both the diagnosis and the treatment of disease have caused a much freer use of their facilities and have raised the total hospitalization rate per thousand persons.

Moreover, every year hospitals find new fields that call for additional operating and endowment funds. In the past decade, the need for money with which to care for the growing influx of free patients in clinics and wards has created the most prominent demands. This is but one of many needs. As was mentioned in Chapter 4, additional funds are required to raise the level of nursing education to that recently established by the National League of Nursing Education and now attained by leading hospitals. Endowment should be provided in certain of the better equipped hospitals to permit the encouragement of research. The education of interns and residents is becoming more costly and the forthcoming recommendations of the Commission on Graduate Medical Education may somewhat accelerate this tendency. This activity, too, might well be endowed to assure that it is maintained on the plane that advancing standards require. A small endowment for the medical and nursing library would give some leeway for the purchase of needed books and scientific journals. One of the most useful small endowments of which I have learned is a fund left to a California hospital, the income from which is to be used to help pay the expenses of the administrator and his department heads when they attend professional meetings and educational courses or institutes. That endowment may, in fact, be one of several contributing reasons for the progressive leadership that this hospital has shown for a decade or more. An endowment or special funds could well be sought to finance some new activity which seems to be definitely needed, possibly a mother's milk bureau, a serum center or a physical therapy department.

Whatever the specific need may be, from time to time every voluntary and governmental hospital will find it necessary to raise capital funds. The latter, of course, will appeal to the taxing body which controls it, whether this is the city, county, state or federal government. If a clear need can be established and if there are not too many competing demands upon the source of funds, the tax-supported hospital will obtain all or a substantial percentage of the money it needs. It will be much easier to convince the public officials that the hospital should have additional funds, however, if it has carried on a sound and effective public relations program. It takes no great astuteness to realize that legislative bodies can appropriate money to popular causes with less reluctance or political risk than they can to unpopular or unknown ones.

The voluntary hospital cannot ordinarily turn to tax funds for its needed capital. The only other source is the beneficence of individuals who are or may become interested in the hospital and its work. Usually the only way to obtain a large amount of money from them is through a fund raising campaign. The ability of a voluntary hospital to raise capital funds when these are needed will in the long run determine whether the hospital can continue. Hospitals cannot live forever upon earned income and previously acquired capital. Since most hospital capital is invested in buildings and equipment which wear out or become obsolete, eventually the capital is exhausted.

Place of a Campaign in a Public Relations Program

The experienced mountaineer does not expect to climb a high peak without preparation. He first conditions himself by less vigorous exercise. He accustoms his back and legs to the loads they must carry by carrying lesser loads. He asks a physician to test his heart and lungs to be sure that they are equal to the strain he will put upon them. He studies the terrain in detail and estimates carefully what his progress should be for each section of the trip. When he is going to make an assault upon a high peak, he first gets onto the plateau at its base. Even when there, he waits for favorable weather conditions before beginning his climb.

So it is with the attempt to raise funds. A sound public relations program is the plateau from which should rise the peak of the fund raising campaign. The campaign should be tackled only after a considerable period of special conditioning. The administrator and all the personnel of the hospital should have become public relations conscious. They should have engaged actively in building and maintaining channels of communication with the public so that the public, too, is conditioned to the needs and objectives of the hospital. Both parties should have become accustomed to the load of mutual responsibilities. If they have been thinking and acting in these terms for months or years, they will come to regard their mutual responsibilities as a normal part of civilized living, just as the mountaineer is thoroughly accustomed to his heavy boots, knapsack, his alpenstock and rope.

To be sure that their position is sound, the hospital authorities should call in a qualified hospital consultant to check over all phases of their service. They should prepare a detailed plan of the campaign, built around a carefully arranged time schedule. Even when the time schedule has been agreed upon, the plan should not be actually launched if business conditions have suddenly turned adverse.

Ideally, a hospital should never need to engage in a fund raising campaign. Its public relations program should attract a constant flow of gifts which increase in volume as the needs of the hospital and of the community increase. Actually, very few hospitals have yet reached this happy situation.

The early chapters of this book give, in general terms, a statement of the preparation required for a fund raising campaign. Expressed in few words, it consists of three steps. First comes study of the hospital from every angle to be sure its service is the best that present financial limitations permit. Second is study of the public's needs from every angle to be sure that the hospital is meeting them insofar as it possibly can. Finally, the hospital sets up or clears two-way avenues of communication between itself and the public so as to be sure that each party is developing mutual understanding, good will and respect for the other.

This formalized statement of the preparation for a campaign might be taken to imply that all philanthropic gifts are made as a result of such a program. This conclusion, of course, would be untrue and misleading. One nationally known eastern hospital, for example, received a gift of nearly one million dollars from an obscure man whose aid had never been requested by anyone representing the hospital. To this day, it is not known what prompted him to make the gift to this particular institution although he undoubtedly had heard of the fine quality of its work. There is now and probably always will continue to be a considerable amount of spontaneous, instinctive and emotional giving, often based largely upon personal experiences. A few such givers will be quite uncritical in reaching their decisions. They give to satisfy their own ethical concepts or to attain mental and emotional peace. Probably even they, however, as well as most other donors would prefer to give to an institution that keeps itself informed about public needs and conscientiously endeavors to fill them, as does the large eastern hospital just mentioned. The expositional technics of a public relations program, however, should not be so obvious or so wholesale in character that the benefactors feel robbed of personal satisfaction in their gifts. Philanthropy is essentially individualistic and often has religious motivations. The philanthropist does not like to be told that there is a technic for getting his money, no matter how noble the object may be.

For the benefit of persons who are in search of worthy charities to which they can donate, it would be wise for all well directed hospitals to furnish information about themselves and their work to trust companies, to the trust departments of banks and to attorneys.

Conditions That Should Precede a Campaign

A successful fund raising campaign is rarely a happy accident. Almost without exception, it is the result of careful planning and diligent application. One of the most important parts of the plan is the time schedule. It is not a simple matter to decide when to make an appeal for funds. No specific rule can be laid down for all cases, yet, even when there has been a history of good rapport between the hospital and the community, several conditions should be met before a campaign is set under way.

First, there should be a clearly defined need for the additional funds. A hospital should not appeal for money to construct a doctors' office building, for example, unless it has first ascertained that the new building will conserve the time of physicians and patients, that it will enable the doctors to give more effective treatment to their patients or will reduce the cost of such treatment and that it will enable the hospital to make better use of its x-ray and pathologic laboratories, its occupational and physical therapy departments and its other special services. More than this, there should be careful study to determine whether the same objectives could be accomplished by using space available in the present buildings.

Even when all of these questions are answered favorably, the hospital should clearly demonstrate why a fund raising campaign is better than floating a bond issue and why it is better to have the facilities provided by the hospital than by commercial or governmental interests. It should be possible to prove the need for a campaign to the satisfaction of any unbiased person. In other words, all the reasonable alternatives to the fund raising campaign should have been fully explored and found to be definitely less satisfactory.

Second, it should be shown that the remedy proposed to meet the need will actually meet it and is possible of fulfillment. In the instance cited above, the hospital should have ascertained that the doctors will actually use the facilities if they are erected. It should show that there is parking space sufficient to accommodate the additional people who will be coming to the hospital. Enough study of the plans should have been made to show that the sum sought is sufficient to construct and equip the building and, if additional operating income is necessary, to provide endowment for that purpose. The study should be as keenly critical as that which an intelligent business man gives to a comparably large investment.

Third, the board of trustees should be representative and should inspire confidence.[2] Occasionally, a group of men or women constituting a board will gradually come to look upon themselves as though they were members of a private club. They become so interested in themselves and their own small group that they do not realize that they no longer are truly representative of the community which the hospital is supposed to serve. Sometimes this is because all the board members are of advanced age and have lost the ability to look at hospital problems with the progressive vision of middle age or youth. Sometimes it is due to the fact that they have all been drawn from one small social clique with little contact or understanding of the viewpoints and interests of other large segments of the population. Quite frequently, a hospital board will believe that it can appeal to the general public for support and yet keep exclusive control of the hospital in the hands of a religious sect representing only part of the supporting population.

In such circumstances, it is often essential that a reorganization of the board of trustees precede any public appeal for funds. If Catholics, Jews and those without religious affiliations are to be asked to contribute to a Methodist hospital, for example, it is usually wise to ask the ablest Catholic layman and the most influential Jew in the community to take a place on the board. If the laboring people of the community are to be solicited, why should they not have a representative among the trustees? The same considerations apply to the various racial groups that are to be enlisted. Too high a percentage of ministers on a hospital board is likely to cause business men to fear that the business management of the hospital may not be efficient. On the other hand, a board composed exclusively of business men may be lacking in social consciousness. Occasionally, the members of a board of trustees are so well known for their probity, intelligence, disinterestedness and social consciousness that these factors overcome any possible criticism due to the board being drawn from only one religiou or economic group.

Fourth, in addition to being representative and confidence inspiring, the board of trustees should be united in support of the development before they ask for public support. If the hospital's appeal is not strong enough to win the board, how can it be expected to be sufficiently strong to persuade persons who are less intimately associated with the institution? Not only moral but financial support is required. The scale of contributions set by the trustees will often determine the scale to be followed by the community as a whole. Frequently, potential subscribers will wish to know what other persons of the same means are giving and they will scale their contributions up or down accordingly.

A recent campaign for $650,000 in an eastern hospital failed miserably. The hospital is a good institution and it has a legitimate need of the funds requested. But apparently the board of trustees itself was not convinced of the merit of the appeal. One of the members, who had recently inherited two million dollars, gave $5000 to the hospital's campaign. Another who has large means gave $6000 but most of it was in the form of hospital bonds. Even the president of the board, who had insisted upon being general chairman of the campaign, gave a small sum himself and solicited contributions from four persons only.

The administrator of this hospital had planned to give $2000 to the campaign out of his own limited means. But when he saw that the wealthy men on his board were satisfied to give small sums he scaled his own contribution down to the proportion of his board members. It was $25. The hospital received a total of $75,000 in pledges. But $16,000 had to be paid to the fund raising counsel and $19,000 was in hospital bonds, which the hospital could retire but did not wish to sell again.

Counterbalancing this example, many campaigns could be cited where wisely guided hospitals with enthusiastic and united boards of trustees have received subscriptions well above their quotas. One recent example that has been described in hospital literature is the campaign of the Ellis Hospital, Schenectady, New York. The hospital had literally outgrown its clothes. In 1929, a competent consultant made a careful study of the hospital's needs and recommended a progressive expansion program. Then the depression brought some relief of the overcrowding and the expansion program was postponed. By 1935, however, the upward trend had carried the hospital's occupancy above the 1929 level. The next two years saw even worse crowding. The x-ray and laboratory departments were particularly overtaxed. The trustees then revived the expansion program and engaged an able firm of fund raising counsel to direct a campaign for $700,000. The campaign was conducted

It may be necessary to raise special funds for nursing education and for proper provision for the welfare of hospital workers.

with low pressure promotion as much as possible but approximately 1200 volunteer workers were enrolled in the effort. A total of $850,000 was actually subscribed by 25,000 people. This number was the equivalent of one subscription from every family in the county. Of the total subscribed, $525,000 was obtained by the special gifts committee from 194 large donors. This campaign had the largest number of subscriptions and the largest total receipts ever recorded for any campaign in Schenectady and its environs. The campaign well illustrates the value of careful planning and strong informed trustee leadership.[1]

The fifth requirement to be met before undertaking a fund raising campaign is competent hospital administration. Sometimes a good board is handicapped in its appeal for funds because the quality of administration is not as high as the community has a right to expect. This is less likely to be true today than it was in the past because boards of trustees are increasingly realizing that the task of administering a hospital is one that calls for high abilities and sound judgment. The assumption that anyone who has failed as a business man, a minister or a school teacher is, nevertheless, qualified to direct a hospital is giving way to a realization that this complex task calls for actual training and good experience. Today one frequently finds as hospital administrators men who have already demonstrated high abilities in the ministry, in business, in teaching, in medicine or in other lines. Such men are usually the first to admit any gaps in their knowledge of hospital work and are the most diligent in filling these gaps through study and attendance at conventions and institutes. Furthermore, there is a growing number of men and women who enter hospital administration only after careful training either through a graduate course in hospital administration or through a long apprenticeship to a competent administrator.[3]

The sixth prerequisite for a successful fund raising campaign is a qualified medical staff, democratically organized and representing younger as well as older physicians. Less often than formerly but still often enough to be significant, one finds hospitals where some one particular physician or small clique seems to have entire dominance. This clique or individual rules the medical staff and the administration like an autocrat, while other physicians of equal ability but less domineering character are neglected. When this happens it tends to make a mockery of any nonprofit claims of the hospital. Actually, whether it is admitted or not, such a hospital is run for the profit of the dominant physicians on the staff. This situation is not conducive to public support, even though the physicians in question may be men of high attainment and popularity. Equally bad is a situation in which the lay trustees allow their own personal ties and friendships to influence staff appointments and promotions. There must be equity among the physicians of the community, each receiving hospital privileges in accordance with his ability and none having privileges beyond those to which his competence, diligence and ethics entitle him.

Another variation of this difficulty arises when the medical staff of a hospital is distinctly third-rate in character. Obviously, in a metropolitan community, every hospital cannot have on its staff all the men of national reputation in that city. But unless a hospital has a fair proportion of the really good physicians it is not in a strong position to appeal to the public.

Some hospital medical staffs, although containing competent men, fail to achieve the excellence they should because of unwillingness of the physicians to assume their proper obligations. When a physician accepts membership on a medical staff he enters into a contract, expressed or implied, to carry his fair share of the indigent service of the institution, to cooperate with the governing body and with the administration for the development of the hospital and to safeguard and advance its reputation. He further agrees to carry his share of the load of teaching medical students, interns, residents and nurses, to assist in the self-discipline exercised by the medical staff and to submit to it when he is at fault.[4]

Another possible weakness in the staff setup is comparable to one suggested concerning the trustees. A medical staff may carry on its work through the years without sufficient additions of younger men. Today the men finishing internships and residencies are often so excellently trained that a hospital should be alert to enlist them on its staff and give them responsibilities in accordance with their capacities. This requires a retirement age at which older physicians will assume a consulting or emeritus status and a ladder of promotion up which the younger men can climb. People are unlikely to give generously to a hospital if their own personal physicians are unable to use the hospital's facilities. This is another reason for enlisting the most promising younger doctors of the community. Of course, as mentioned earlier, these younger physicians, as well as all others on the staff, should undertake only those procedures for which they are competent.

A seventh requirement that should precede a financial campaign is adequate conditioning of the hospital and the public, as mentioned in a previous section. It is difficult enough today to raise funds for voluntary social effort without taking on the unnecessary burden of trying to do so too rapidly and consequently building up unnecessary resistances. From three to six months should be considered as the minimum time necessary for preparation, even when a hospital has carried on a continuous public relations program of good quality. One or two years is usually essential if there has been no adequate public relations program.

An eighth prerequisite to a campaign is the existence of reasonably favorable business conditions. Potentially large campaign givers are often greatly influenced by the economic situation. When a man is deeply worried over the continuance of his own livelihood, he is not likely to respond generously to appeals to safeguard the future of a social institution, no matter how much he approves of it. The jitters are not conducive to generosity.

On the other hand, hospitals and other social institutions should not wait indefinitely for the return of "prosperity." The flush feeling of the twenties may never come again. In 1937 and the early part of 1938 a considerable number of fund raising campaigns were successful. Some others were successful in the latter half of 1938 but the number of failures was greater in this period.

Testing Public Opinion

Even the examination of the hospital on the foregoing points may not reveal all causes of lack of public enthusiasm. A public opinion poll might well be undertaken to ascertain whether such additional causes exist and, if so, why.

The technic of testing public opinion has been rather fully developed in recent years. Dr. George Gallup and Dr. Claude E. Robinson of the American Institute of Public Opinion, Elmo Roper of *Fortune* magazine surveys, Henry G. Weaver of General Motors, Daniel Starch and others have taken the well known statistical principles of sampling and used them to determine the position of advertised products in the public mind and the effectiveness of advertising. From this it was a short step to using these technics to measure the broad outlines and movements of public opinion on matters of general policy.

Public opinion polls have now been refined to the point where they can measure fine gradations in shifting popular favor, at least insofar as political questions are concerned. It is assumed, probably with considerable justification, that the technics that have proved successful in the measurement of political opinion are equally valid in the measurement of other subjects.

These technics have already been applied by at least one hospital as a part of its investigation and conditioning prior to undertaking a fund raising campaign. Some of the results of the poll were startling. Although less than 7 per cent of the people were expecting to require hospital care themselves during the subsequent twelve months, practically everyone agreed that the presence of the hospital was worth something. Seventy-five per cent of those replying stated they would be able, without sacrifice, to pay a hospital bill of $65. On the other hand, more than one third of those responding stated that they considered special charges too high. Thirty per cent wanted compulsory health insurance immediately and 47 per cent wanted it eventually. More than 18 per cent of those replying thought the trustees were compensated for their services! About 10 per cent thought that the hospital's school of nursing aimed to take advantage of apprentice labor. Two thirds of those replying would, if they managed the hospital, extend credit as does a "normal" business and sue patients who failed to pay. The trustees were considered as ultimately responsible for the quality and quantity of hospital service by nearly twice as many people as considered that this duty fell on the public or on individual citizens. A small number felt that governmental agencies should be responsible. Nearly three fourths of those replying would, if wealthy, leave something to the hospital and nearly one fourth would, they said, make a large bequest. Less than 5 per cent would leave nothing.

This questionnaire, which drew a 17 per cent response, was mailed to a picked list of well-to-do persons. Hence, it is not representative of the community as a whole but probably is representative of the selected group composed of persons best able to subscribe capital funds to the hospital.

Certain general rules can be given for conducting a significant test of public opinion. The first rule is that careful study must be given to the subjects upon which information is desired. These subjects should concern matters upon which the public is likely to have opinions. It is of little value to take a poll if a majority of the answers are going to be noncommittal. On the other hand, it should not be assumed that the public will be devoid of opinions merely because the facts upon which those opinions ought to be based are complex and not generally available to the public. It is a difficult matter, for example, to determine whether one hospital offers better

service than another. Yet in all except the large cities
most people will have definite opinions on this subject
and these opinions can be measured by proper technics.
Whether these opinions are sound or not, their mere
existence is a matter of importance. The first rule, therefore, is to define clearly the subjects to be investigated.

The second rule is closely related to the first. This is
to formulate questions the answers to which can be accurately tabulated. The questions, if possible, should be
phrased so that a clear "yes" or "no" answer can be
given. Even more important, the questions must elicit
the true opinions of those interviewed. It is easy, especially for persons who are emotionally interested in the
results of a poll, to allow bias to enter into the formulation of questions. Even Doctor Gallup and the *Fortune*
survey have been accused of occasionally using questions
that were not entirely devoid of slanting.[5] Both groups
spend a great deal of thought in trying to avoid such bias.
But it is hard for most of us to be objective about our-
selves and to realize and discount our own biases and
predilections. One technic recently adopted to try to
counteract this tendency has been to use two sets of
questions with slightly different phrasing and then to
compare the results.

The third requirement in a procedure of testing public
opinion is to define the group from which we wish
answers. For a political question this would mean the
voters of a city, county, state or nation. For a hospital
inquiry, it would perhaps mean all of the people in the
service area of the hospital who are old enough to have
opinions about the institution. Detailed information
must then be collected about this population so that it
may be broken down into its component units. From the

federal census or other sources, there should be full information on distribution according to age, sex, economic group, racial group, urban and rural groupings and any other significant differences. For example, the population might be divided into two sex groups, four age groups (20 to 29, 30 to 44, 45 to 64, 65 and over), three racial groups (white, Negro and other), six income groups (under $750, $750 to $1250, $1250 to $2000, $2000 to $3000, $3000 to $5000 and over $5000) and three urban-rural classifications (metropolitan areas, suburban or satellite areas and smaller towns and rural areas). Such a breakdown would give 432 possible different classifications ($2\times4\times3\times6\times3=432$). Of course, many of the theoretically possible classes might not actually have any people in them, as, for example, the classification of female Negroes with incomes of $5000 or more, over 65 years of age and living on farms.

If the data on the whole population were available in sufficient detail so that it could be broken down into all of these various classes then it would be easy to see just what percentage of the population falls into each class. The sample to be polled could then be set at some arbitrary multiple of this percentage. For example, if the hospital's service area contains 150,000 people, a sample of 1 per cent of the total population would probably be a reliable basis for judgment. This would involve a total poll of 1500 persons, selected so that all groups are proportionally represented. The only precise and absolutely accurate method of determining the size of the sample to be taken in each group is to tabulate the returns as they are received and to continue interviewing until the additional interviews do not change the results in the particular subdivision. As soon as this point is reached there is no need to make additional inquiries.

For practical purposes, however, it is not usually possible to divide the entire population into all of the possible groups simultaneously. Instead, the sample can be compared with the total population for each characteristic separately rather than for all characteristics simultaneously. For example, the sample could be tested first according to age classifications, then according to economic classifications and so on. If on each of these tests the sample has almost precisely the same percentage distribution as the whole population, it can be assumed to be representative and reliable.

The next principle is to employ interviewers who are sufficiently intelligent and objective so that they can obtain a true picture of the opinions of the sample population interviewed. The canvasser must be careful not to interject his own point of view. The Gallup poll employs more than 600 interviewers over the country. Most of them are college graduates and many are young married women. The *Fortune* survey uses 48 interviewers who are carefully supervised. A hospital poll would not require even this number of interviewers.

When the returns are in and have been tested for representativeness, as outlined above, the answers to the questions can be tabulated. This can usually be done more quickly and economically on punch cards than by any manual system.

Careful study should be given to the results of such a poll. If it has been properly conceived and executed, it should give to the hospital administrator and trustees a revealing and significant picture of the attitude of the public toward the hospital. The executives would see just where their public relations have been weak, what needs the public believes are not being fulfilled by the hospital at present and where services are offered that do not meet public needs or fulfill public demands. Conversely, they would discover those activities which the public feels are of real worth and would draw new inspiration to carry these on and to develop them to their full possibilities. This reassurance is often valuable in giving new courage and a broader vision of their function to a board that is irresolute.

Hospital executives should not hesitate to undertake a public opinion poll for fear people will not talk freely. Once they have been assured of anonymity, they will answer readily. In fact, they feel complimented to be asked.

Such a poll is necessarily rather expensive. It would probably be too costly for a single hospital to undertake, unless it did so as a preliminary to a fund raising campaign. A hospital council, however, might readily undertake such a program, carrying it forward from year to year to discover trends and to cover somewhat different subjects.

Eventually, hospitals will probably not attempt large fund raising campaigns until they have made such a test and have adjusted their present and future programs to take account of the opinions revealed. Fund raising counsel will probably qualify themselves to undertake the direction of such surveys.

If the comprehensive type of poll here outlined is more expensive than an individual hospital feels is justified even in preparation for a fund raising campaign, a cheaper although less accurate poll may be undertaken by using mail questionnaires and sending them only to the better educated group in the population. Such a poll obviously will not provide a true and complete cross index of the opinions of the entire community, although if there are genuine criticisms of the hospital's service to those people who are not covered in the poll, these probably will be known and mentioned by those who do reply. Those who have used such partial tests believe that they are valuable (1) to indicate to the responsible people in the community the hospital's eagerness to improve its service, (2) to discover and answer latent criticism among the people who might later use this criticism as an alibi for not subscribing and (3) to create occasions for commenting in the public press upon misconceptions and for presenting straight exposition of the hospital's problems which otherwise would hardly be suitable for newspaper copy.

Need for Expert Guidance

The technic of raising funds through campaigns has been worked out with great care by keen, imaginative men who devote their lives to this work. It is obviously impossible, within the limits of this book, even to attempt to detail this technic as it is practiced by the leaders in the field.[6]

As a result of careful study of hundreds of campaigns, the leading campaign specialists have developed and codified hundreds of "standard practices," which answer practically every question of detail that will come up in the course of conducting a campaign. But, even if one could obtain a copy of these closely guarded books, he would not be equipped to run a campaign successfully. In addition to written statements, one needs considerable experience in the application of the technics to particular situations. One must develop a "feel" of a campaign so that he can accurately gauge the tempo, enthusiasm and determination of the workers.

Except when an institution happens to have an experienced campaign manager on its staff, it is wise and economical to employ a competent firm of fund raising counsel to manage and direct any important appeal for funds. There is greater assurance of reaching the goal, the total campaign costs will constitute a smaller percentage of the money actually raised and the psychological reaction of the community will be better if the campaign is competently directed.

How to Select a Fund Raising Counsel

The field of financial campaign management has suffered greatly from the incompetent, if not actually dishonest, work of some individuals and firms. Fortunately, today, most of the incompetent and dishonest ones have been driven out of the business. However, the firms that remain vary widely in ability, understanding and skill.

An American Association of Fund Raising Counsel has been formed with nine member firms. These are the leaders in the field. This association has adopted a statement of qualifications for membership that represents a minimal standard.

1. The active executive head of the member organization shall have had a continuous experience of at least ten years as professional counsel in the fund raising field.
2. The members must have a record of consistently successful work and repeated calls to serve the same clients or others involving the same constituency.

3. They must show satisfactory references, both from clients and from one or more banks or trust companies.

4. They must assign as executives-in-charge only those members of their staffs who have served as associates on six or more campaigns or who have been continuously employed as staff members for a period of at least one year.

5. Membership in this association shall be confined to those organizations which do business on a fee basis only and which make no profit, directly or indirectly, from disbursements for the account of clients.

These criteria are interesting minimum requirements but they are not sufficiently definitive to be of much real meaning. Such vague terms as "consistently successful work" are not of help to the board of trustees actually concerned with the problem of choosing a firm of fund raising counsel. What type of work is "successful"? Any firm that was ever in the business would be able to show letters of recommendation from former clients indicating its success. In the flush of victory when a campaign has apparently gone over the top, it is all too easy to obtain such recommendations. But the careful board of trustees will wish to know more. It will want detailed answers to a variety of questions concerning specific campaigns carried on within recent years.

First, does the firm adhere to sound principles of public relations? Principles for a sound public relations program were given in Chapter 3. The actual work of the firm ought to be checked carefully against each of these principles to see whether it helped its clients to build soundly for the future. It is not always easy to judge whether a particular act or series of acts was done in accordance with sound principles but insofar as possible this ought to be investigated.

Second, what has been the firm's actual record of quota achievement? How often has it reached or exceeded the set quota? How often has it fallen more than 10 per cent below it? Were the quotas set in accordance with the true needs of the institution and the potential resources of the population or in accord with the amounts of the gifts already assured? Obviously it is no great credit to a firm to reach a quota of $500,000 if it knows before it starts the campaign that two or three large donors have already pledged $350,000. On the other hand, even under such circumstances, a properly managed campaign is an asset to the hospital since it assists the public relations program and makes the entire community feel a sense of participation. This discussion should not be interpreted to mean that every campaign should strive for the highest possible quota. It is unfair to the donors and to other social agencies to ask for more money than the hospital really needs.

Third, what percentage of the pledges have been collected and at what expense? There is obviously a considerable difference between the amount pledged and the net amount the hospital actually receives, even disregarding for the moment the direct costs of the campaign. This shrinkage is composed of three items: (1) interest on the deferred payments (a dollar in hand is obviously worth more than one that is promised for three years hence), (2) nonpayment of pledges and (3) the cost of collection procedures. If the campaign was so conducted that there were relatively few deferred pledges and these were of short duration, if low pressure methods were used so that there was a relatively small shrinkage from nonpayment and the costs of collection were low, the campaign was obviously of more benefit to the hospital and, therefore, more of a credit to the fund raising counsel than if the opposite conditions were true. The difference between the total of pledges and the actual net present cash value of the campaign may amount to as much as from 5 to 10 per cent on a well run campaign; on one that is not well directed, the difference is likely to reach much higher figures.[7]

Fourth, for what period were pledges given? In general, it is easier to obtain a pledge payable in 10 semi-annual installments of $500 each than it is to obtain $5000 payable in two semiannual installments. The latter pledge is worth somewhat more to the institution. In evaluating the relative success of various firms of fund raising counsel, therefore, consideration should be given to the length of the period of the pledges obtained.

Fifth, what has been the effect of the campaign on the hospital's prestige? A firm that conducts a campaign in such a way that the institution has heightened prestige after the campaign is obviously preferable to one that impairs prestige. Frequently, the difference between the two results is governed, in considerable part at least, by the breadth of the approach. A good firm of fund raising counsel should insist that the hospital approach its problems of development and support from the community-wide point of view. An institution that takes the attitude that it will do just as it pleases regardless of the effect on other hospitals or the community's general hospital and social system loses position and prestige.

Sixth, how thorough was the preparatory work? One simple and reasonably accurate way to test the caliber of a fund raising firm is to find out how long a time it thinks will be required for preliminary investigation and preparation of the public mind before a campaign is launched. In general, as was mentioned earlier, the more time it requires for preliminary work, the better campaign it will stage. Even today some firms are still advocating only the briefest preparatory periods, *e.g.* from three to six weeks. Under the difficult conditions now prevailing, probably from three to six months is the minimum for adequate preparation and from nine to eighteen months would be decidedly preferable. A four months' campaign would probably be successful only for an institution that had been doing an excellent piece of public relations work before the campaign organization was employed.

Seventh, how much specialized hospital experience has the firm had? Other things being equal, a firm that has had extensive experience in raising funds for hospitals can do a better piece of work for other hospitals while one experienced in college campaigns can be more valuable to a college. The same thing, of course, holds for churches, orphanages, community chests, chambers of commerce and any other particular types of effort. A few of the firms specialize in certain types of campaigns; others are general firms taking any type of campaign but trying to develop certain specialists on their staffs. Either plan is acceptable if the men in charge are thoroughly familiar with the specific field for which they are employed.

Eighth, does the firm give honest reports of results? Perhaps a note of warning should be sounded against those firms that claim suspiciously uniform results, that say they have never failed and that mention the amount pledged but are hazy on the matter of quotas and the amount actually paid. Every good firm as well as the

In fund raising campaigns, attractive leaflets are prepared by
skilled counsel who direct and coordinate the entire program.

poor ones has had some failures, particularly in recent years. The ups and downs of the business cycle have come so rapidly that even the best laid plans have sometimes gone astray because of general business conditions, a result that cannot be chalked entirely against the firm. The dates of the successful and the unsuccessful campaigns should be studied with care in relation to the fluctuations of the economic cycle.

Ninth, what men are suggested as directors of the campaign? Not all campaign directors are of equal ability. The trustes should interview each man who is proposed and should scrutinize his individual record with great care. It may be more important to employ the right campaign director than to employ the right firm.

Hospital trustees and administrators who are faced with the responsibility of selecting a fund raising counsel will be interested in reading the histories of the members of the American Association of Fund Raising Counsel that appear in Chapter 12 of the recent book by Irene Hazard Gerlinger entitled *Money Raising, How to Do It*.[8] Mrs. Gerlinger prints in this book a series of statements concerning each of the firms, prepared by the firms themselves. She makes no attempt to discriminate between the various firms on the basis of their competence or their experience. A careful selection cannot be made relying solely upon the thumbnail histories that Mrs. Gerlinger presents but they may constitute for some readers an interesting introduction to the firms.

Follow-Up of a Fund Raising Campaign

Just as the fund raising campaign should not start without previous public relations work, so its close should not mark the end of public relations efforts. House magazines should still be published, annual reports should be as carefully prepared and as widely distributed, public health lectures should be as frequent and as valuable, the hospital administration should be as eager to discern and to meet new public needs after the campaign as before. The efforts to improve the hospital's service and its relations to physicians, employes, students, neighbors, visitors and potential benefactors should not be relaxed.

There are several concrete reasons, with definite bearing on the campaign, for thus continuing the public relations work. One is that this will make the collection of pledges easier and will lower the amount of shrinkage on them. A second is that the necessary effort for collection of pledges can easily be incorporated in the organization that carries on the continuing public relations work. A third reason is that additional gifts will probably continue to come to the hospital if it carries on its public relations work without intermission. Furthermore, as has been emphasized continually, the hospital has other objectives to achieve in its public relations activities besides the raising of funds in a campaign. It must mantain and enhance its prestige with patients and physicians; it must continue to attract a high type of student to its nursing school and a fine quality of intern and resident; it must continue to develop support among federal, state and local governmental bodies, and it must earn and receive the loyal service of devoted employes.

A second item in the follow-up of the fund raising campaign should be actual delivery of the results promised in the campaign. If the hospital promised that it would build certain buildings, they should be built within a reasonable time; if it agreed to increase its care of free patients, such additional number should be accepted; if it stated that the standards of nursing or medical education would be improved, these standards should be advanced as promptly as possible; if it declared that employes would receive better pay and working conditions, these promises should be faithfully executed. A hospital must never put itself in a position where it can, with reasonable justice, be charged with failing to carry out the promises made during a campaign. Of course, Rome was not built in a day and it may take time to work out the necessary details. But reasonable progress should be made toward fulfilling the various obligations undertaken.

A third part of the follow-up of a campaign should be periodic reports to donors and the general public of the progress made in achieving the results for which the campaign was undertaken. Through personal letters, the annual report, the house magazine and newspaper articles, the hospital should give an accounting of its stewardship. Such reports should be issued with reasonable regularity and promptness and should be prepared in an attractive manner so that they will be read.

Finally, if any weaknesses in the hospital's organization or program are discovered during the fund raising campaign, they should be corrected at the earliest possible moment. Such weak spots may come to light anywhere in the organization: in the board of trustees, in the administrative office, among the department heads, in the medical staff, among the auxiliary members, in the service program of the institution, in its financial policies or in any of scores of other places. Most of them, of course, should have been discovered and corrected before the campaign was begun. But sometimes they may elude detection and definition until after the campaign is started and then it may be unwise to make changes during the midst of this special effort.

Summary

The task of raising funds for a hospital is a specialized aspect of a whole public relations program. When viewed as a part of the well rounded program advocated in this book, it is easy to see why the evangelistic type of appeal is outmoded and why the factual analytical approach is more successful. The same reasoning applies to the fund raising campaign that applies to the public relations program as a whole. The appeal to reason is more powerful in the long run, raises less antipathy and helps to create a sounder and more lasting structure than the appeal to emotion.

The principal conclusions of this survey of fund raising campaigns may be stated rather simply.

1. By and large, hospitals that attempt to provide a well rounded community service, to care for all economic groups, to keep abreast of medical and educational advances and to make adequate provisions to meet the increasing demands of the public cannot expect to do all this out of earnings from patients. They must obtain capital funds, and often operating funds also, from the general public. To obtain needed capital funds, whether for physical replacement and expansion or for endowment, usually requires a fund raising campaign. The governmental hospital may turn to the taxing body but the voluntary hospital must turn to the generosity of the public.

2. The fund raising campaign will stand much greater chance of success if it has been preceded by a soundly planned and executed public relations program. The

longer the public relations program has been under way, the better.

3. Before launching a fund raising campaign, certain conditions that are almost prerequisites to success must be fulfilled. There may be many such conditions and only careful and critical examination will reveal them all. Among those most frequently discovered are the following:

a. There should be a clearly defined need with substantial evidence that, until it is met, the hospital, its physicians or its patients will be handicapped in their desire for the best health service.

b. Convincing evidence should be presented that the remedy proposed will actually meet the need in large measure, that the sum sought in the campaign is sufficient to attain the objective and that there are no other alternatives to a fund raising campaign that hold equal promise of success in solving the problem.

c. The board of trustees should be a representative and confidence-inspiring group.

d. The members of the board of trustees should be substantially united behind the proposed development and willing to back it in generous fashion with their own funds in proportion to their means, as well as with time and effort.

e. The hospital should have competent administration that will arouse confidence in the public that the money will be expended wisely and effectively.

f. The medical staff should be of good quality, should be democratically organized, granting privileges to each man in strict accord with his competence and integrity, and should be representative of the younger as well as the older physicians.

g. The campaign should be preceded by a sufficient period of preparation so that all aspects of the plan have been thoroughly explored and so that the hospital and the public have both been conditioned.

h. Ordinarily a campaign should not be started when general business conditions are adverse. Some campaigns have been successful in spite of unfavorable general conditions but it is more difficult to succeed in such circumstances.

4. The new technic of testing public opinion can well be used to determine whether the public is favorably inclined toward a hospital and whether any additional problems need to be solved before a fund raising campaign is launched.

5. Unless a campaign is quite small, it is wise to employ competent experts to direct it. The uninformed trustee, who would never for a moment consider himself qualified to compound a prescription or to perform a surgical operation, nevertheless, often thinks that he can direct a fund raising campaign. This is usually found to be a costly mistake. Campaign direction is a specialty just as complicated and requiring as much technical knowledge, skill and judgment as does removing an appendix.

6. Not all persons who claim to be experts in fund raising merit such rating, although the situation is now far better than it was a decade or two ago. The conscientious board of trustees will wish to ask certain significant questions before it decides upon its fund raising counsel. Among these questions the following may well be mentioned:

a. Does the firm adhere to sound principles of public relations?

b. What has been the firm's actual record of quota achievement in other campaigns?

c. What percentage of the pledges obtained have been collected and at what expense?

d. For what period were these pledges given?

e. What has been the effect of the campaign on the prestige and community standing of the hospital?

f. How thorough was the preparatory work in past campaigns and what length of preparation is suggested for the coming campaign?

g. How much specialized hospital experience has the firm had?

h. Does the firm give honest and complete reports of its results?

i. What man will be sent out as compaign director and what has been his individual record? He should be interviewed by the board.

7. The follow-up period of a fund raising campaign is as important as the preparation period. Good follow-up involves the following:

a. Public relations work should not only precede and accompany the campaign but should continue after its close. This will make for prompter collection of pledges and will reduce the expense of collection. It will stimulate further gifts and will aid in achieving the nonpecuniary objectives of the hospital.

b. The hospital should carry out as promptly as it reasonably can the promises that were made during the campaign.

c. Periodic reports to donors and the general public should inform them of the progress made in achieving the results for which the campaign was originally undertaken.

d. Any weaknesses in the hospital's organization or service program discovered during the campaign should be corrected.

The days when slipshod methods could achieve a campaign goal are gone, probably forever. But in spite of increasing governmental financing of social enterprises and increased taxation, campaigns for voluntary social institutions are achieving success with reasonable frequency. To avoid disappointment, they should be prepared with the greatest of care and thoughtfulness.

REFERENCES

1. Lang, Chester H.: History of a Hospital Campaign, *The Modern Hospital*, May, 1939, p. 58.
2. Bachmeyer, A. C.: Qualifications for Trusteeship, *The Modern Hospital*, April, 1939, p. 77.
3. Hamilton, James A.: Need for Adequate Education and Training for Hospital Executives, *Hospitals*, Jan., 1938, p. 11.
4. Ponton, T. R.: Medical Staff in the Hospital, Physicians' Record Company, 1939.
5. Spingarn, Jerome H.: These Public-Opinion Polls, *Harpers Magazine*, Dec., 1938, p. 97.
6. Stone, J. E.: Appeals for Funds and Hospital Publicity, Birbeck & Sons, Birmingham, England, 1934.
7. Addleman, Perry: Pledged But Not Paid, *The Modern Hospital*, Feb., 1935, p. 77.
8. Gerlinger, Irene Hazard: Money Raising, How to Do It, Suttonhouse, Los Angeles, 1938.

Chapter 13

JOINT PUBLIC
RELATIONS PROGRAMS

MOST OF the preceding chapters have dealt with the problems and programs of an individual hospital. Perhaps for some years to come such programs will be the most significant in the development of hospital public relations. There is, however, a growing amount of joint effort being undertaken by hospitals. This is carried on by local hospital councils, councils of social agencies in which hospitals are represented, community chests, health councils, district hospital associations, state hospital associations, hospital care insurance plans and national agencies serving the hospital field.

Unquestionably, the trend is toward joint effort. Many of the important problems facing hospitals today cannot be solved on an individual basis. To an increasing extent this is true of hospitals' relations to governmental agencies, to labor groups, to organized groups of contributors (community chests, for example) and even to the general public from which they draw their patients.

Local and District Agencies

Local organization of hospitals has proceded apace during the past five years. In some areas this has been effected through hospital councils which bring together the administrators and the representatives of boards of trustees and of medical staffs. This is undoubtedly the preferred method of organization when there are suffi-

cient hospitals to make it effective. Where there are
fewer hospitals, however, district organization is an
acceptable alternative. Under the latter plan, a state is
divided into compact and reasonably homogeneous districts. Each district holds meetings at frequent intervals
with the officers of the state association in attendance so
as to coordinate state and local activities. Most district
organizations have not yet brought trustees and medical
staff members into constant and direct relationship with
administrators. There appears to be no reason why this
cannot be done, however.

Health councils and councils of social agencies can also
aid in coordinating the work of local hospitals, provided
the circumstances are favorable. In some communities
these organizations have taken a narrow point of view
that has made it difficult for hospitals to work with them.
In other instances, however, hospitals have been integral
and important members of local health councils or councils of social agencies.

What functions which have a direct bearing on hospital
public relations should be performed by these local agencies? The first and most obvious, of course, is that of
research and study. An outstanding example of this
activity is the *Hospital Survey for New York*, planned
and executed by the United Hospital Fund of that city
with aid from various philanthropic foundations and
individuals and from other agencies. Excellent work of
the same general type, although on a much more restricted scale, has been done by the Cleveland and Chicago
hospital councils. Hospital and health surveys have been
made also in Philadelphia, Louisville (Kentucky), San
Francisco and certain other communities. Only the New
York survey, however, is recent and up to date.

But a survey is only one of many services of benefit to the public that hospital councils can perform. The better councils are constantly engaged in research upon a variety of problems for the purpose of improving the quality of administration and filling gaps in the hospitals' service to the community. The United Hospital Fund of New York has a special department known as the Hospital Information and Service Bureau, which collects current statistics and conducts studies. In Cleveland and Chicago, work is going forward continuously upon important problems of community interest, such as standards for maternity and infant care, labor relations and improved personnel practices, emergency ambulance service, inclusive rate plans and hospital charges in general. The Chicago council publishes a 24 page printed bulletin which is sent each month to 4,000 of the leading citizens of the community, including hospital trustees, medical staff members, politicians, newspapers and others. This is a distinct public relations aid.

The public relations significance of a hospital council lies first of all in its very membership. Any program that will bring about better understanding and cooperation among trustees, medical staff members and administrators is, by that fact alone, an important step in proper public relations. But an active and intelligently directed hospital council goes far beyond this. It shows by its principal actions that hospitals are true community institutions devoted to aiding the people to obtain the best possible grade of hospital service at the least possible cost consistent with such quality. It is sometimes difficult for hospital administrators and trustees to realize that this is the true function of hospital councils. Sometimes they seem to assume that the council is in existence pri-

marily to enable their hospitals to show a surplus at the
end of the year. While it is one of the functions of a
council to aid hospitals in their financial problems by
improved administration and other means, this should
not be considered as the primary objective. Such a limit-
ing concept tends to defeat the council in its efforts to
improve the hospital's public relations.

Hospital councils are usually restricted in the action
they can take by the fact that they can exercise only a
moral influence over their members. Frequently, for
example, the best interests of the community dictate the
consolidation of several hospitals so as to form strong
well administered units in place of poorly run and poorly
financed institutions. A hospital council, because of the
combined wisdom and judgment of its members, should
be the best qualified agency to arrange this type of consolidation. Actually, however, it often finds itself blocked
by the local pride and jealousies of those in control of
existing institutions. A council that is expected to defend
and advance the interests of member hospitals is seriously
weakened if these institutions persist in practices that
are no longer sound from the community point of view.

Some councils have a certain power of the purse which
enables them to exert a more significant pressure upon
their members. The United Hospital Fund, for example,
has raised about $2,000,000 annually for its member hos-
pitals in recent years. The Cleveland Hospital Council
raises no money directly but it acts as the advisory body
to the community chest of Cleveland concerning the distribution of funds to hospitals for the care which they
provide to the indigent. Other hospital councils will
doubtless in the future play a more important part in
raising funds for hospital operating expenses. Whether

this is done independently or in conjunction with a general appeal for all types of welfare agencies will depend in large measure upon the situation in each community. If all hospitals could be as fairly treated by their community chests as have been those of Cleveland, there is no doubt that a joint appeal would be preferable.[1]

Up to this point the discussion about the joint raising of money has dealt only with current operating funds. What is the situation when it comes to capital funds? Here the problem is somewhat different. Payments to hospitals for current operating expenses can be made on the basis of average or individual per capita costs. But capital extensions cannot be allocated among different hospitals so easily. On what basis can we decide that Hospital A needs $150,000 for additional semiprivate beds, Hospital B needs $30,000 for a new tumor clinic and Hospital C, $250,000 for a new nurses' home? Will the friends of Hospital B give generously to a joint campaign for these three institutions when they know that most of the money is going to be given to Hospitals A and C?

Those who have had extensive experience in raising funds for capital purposes have generally come to the conclusion that this activity can be most successful when each institution makes a separate appeal. But the cooperative idea should be retained even here. Each hospital should lay its cards on the table with the others. There should be an opportunity for each hospital to suggest amendments that would be in the community's interest. If Hospital A starts its campaign first, it should be able to publish written endorsements of the need for the additional facilities from prominent members of the boards of trustees of Hospitals B and C. If possible, members of the boards of the latter hospitals should accept membership on the campaign committee for Hospital A. When the tables are reversed and one of the other two hospitals is engaged in raising its needed funds for expansion, Hospital A should, of course, extend equal cooperation. Where a hospital council exists, campaign plans should be submitted to and approved by the council.

As was stated in the previous chapter, the actual conduct of a fund raising campaign should be designed to aid the public standing of all the hospitals in the community. The public should learn to consider the entire group of hospitals as one of its chief bulwarks against the onslaughts of disease. Statements about the campaign should be made in such a manner that people will see that agreements among the different hospitals enable them to complement rather than to compete with one another's services.

An example of the community-wide approach is given in the recent campaign conducted by the Toronto Western Hospital with the professional advice of one of the leading firms of fund raising counsel. In the *Toronto Star* for February 11, 1939, appeared the second of a series of articles on the work of modern hospitals. A brief introduction read as follows:

Following is the second of a series of articles describing modern hospital practice, elements of its evolution and the indispensable rôle it plays in modern life. Although numerous references are made to the Toronto Western Hospital, because of the current undertaking by representative citizens to complete its building fund, most general statements apply equally to other large public hospitals in the city and province.

Then follow nearly two and one-half columns concerning hospitals and their services with only one reference to the Toronto Western Hospital in this article. The following quotation will show how the material is presented so as to be of general benefit to all hospitals in the province.

Laughs, shudders and thrills are closely packed in the last several decades of the history of medical science and the evolution of the modern hospital.

In 1582 the celebrated French surgeon, Ambrose Paré, declared that "excepting unimportant details, nothing more is to be added to the science of surgery." As late as 1882, Samuel D. Gross, then president of the American Surgical Society, echoed similar reassurances in stating, "All avenues of approach to surgery have been investigated."

Yet in 1882, the antiseptic surgical technic of Lord Lister was still stoutly resisted by a skeptical profession, bacteriology was but a point of the compass — a direction in which to explore; radioactivity, x-rays and radium were unthought of; the existence of vitamins and hormones was not even suspected, and nothing even faintly resembling a modern hospital was in existence. If the self-complacency of these old-time surgeons is amusing, there was equal, or greater, horror in certain conditions accompanying the ignorance of those same years.

Puerperal fever—child-bed fever—was a typical monster. In the hospital of the University of Jena, for example, from 1860 to 1863, no lying-in patient left the hospital alive. All died.

Epochal discoveries, however, were just over the horizon of time-to-come. A Frenchman, a German and an Englishman—Pasteur, Koch, Lister—were destined to turn the latter part of the nineteenth century into one of the most significant chapters of medical history. And stemming from their contributions was to come a period of medical discovery, and a movement toward the application of these advances to the relief of suffering human beings of which only the most visionary could have dared to dream.

Presently, it was as though a fire burned on every hill, as though the greatest of all crusades was being organized. There was a renaissance of interest in medical subjects which, for sheer intensity, outmatched the renaissance of classical culture following the Dark Ages. The fervent curiosity about the causes of life and death, health and disease, which had burned like a coal in man's mind since the dawn of consciousness, now leaped forth in flame, and the flame burst quickly, almost like an explosion. . . .

While the bacteriologists, under the leadership of Pasteur and Koch, and the new-era surgeons following Lord Lister, were revolutionizing the known world of medical science and altering the entire map which their predecessors had so erroneously drawn, a "new world" was being discovered. It was the world of radioactivity.

At Wurzburg in 1895, the physics professor Wilhelm Konrad Roentgen discovered, almost accidentally, what he named "x-rays." Scarcely three years later, in Paris, Marie and Pierre Curie announced the discovery of radium. . . .

With this attention-commanding introduction, the article proceeds to tell of the significance in medical practice of these discoveries. The discussion builds public confidence in all well equipped hospitals, not merely in the Toronto Western Hospital.

State and Regional Public Relations Work

A few of the state hospital associations have developed extensive public relations programs. Outstanding is the work of the Pennsylvania Hospital Association.[2] In 1932 the Commonwealth of Pennsylvania threatened to cut off 25 per cent of the state aid that it was giving to hospitals. Through a state-wide distribution of press releases, a few radio talks, some meetings and a limited amount of printed matter, the hospitals were able to arouse public

THE HOSPITAL AND INTERRELATED SERVICES OF THE FUTURE

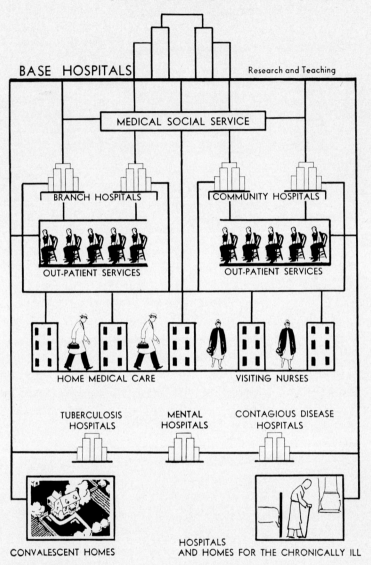

BASE HOSPITALS   Research and Teaching

MEDICAL SOCIAL SERVICE

BRANCH HOSPITALS   COMMUNITY HOSPITALS

OUT-PATIENT SERVICES   OUT-PATIENT SERVICES

HOME MEDICAL CARE   VISITING NURSES

TUBERCULOSIS HOSPITALS   MENTAL HOSPITALS   CONTAGIOUS DISEASE HOSPITALS

CONVALESCENT HOMES   HOSPITALS AND HOMES FOR THE CHRONICALLY ILL

A community plan of complete hospital service for all who need it is the best basis for a sound public relations program.

opinion to the dangers of this move so that it was averted
in 1932 and again in two succeeding bienniums when the
threat was renewed.

The program planned for the year beginning on June
1, 1938 was outlined by the chairman of the public relations committee of the Pennsylvania association as
follows:

1. To effect a closer contact with all regional groups for
   the stimulation of publicity in each region
2. To plan a sustained radio program over every station
   in the state that will work with the local hospitals
3. To stimulate and as far as possible to assist in arrangements for talks before clubs and other organizations
4. To initiate in printed form a series of educational leaflets dramatically portraying hospital services, these to
   be offered to interested hospitals at the lowest possible
   pro rata cost for wide distribution
5. To induce additional newspapers to use the association's *It's a Fact* series
6. To prepare publicity for specific groups the support of
   which the hospitals need and which should be told the
   story of what the hospitals are doing
7. To bring home to members of the legislature, among
   other groups, the problems of hospitals even when no
   emergencies are present
8. To assist in obtaining passage of a law reimbursing
   hospitals for losses resulting from automobile accident
   cases
9. To effect better understanding between hospitals and
   their medical and surgical staffs in educating and
   serving the public

Such a program has been carried on for six years at a
cost ranging from $6000 to $10,000 per year, most of
the money having been contributed by supporting hos-

pitals according to their bed capacity and also according to whether they have participated in state aid.

The *It's a Fact* series, mentioned in the list of objectives, consists of short articles about hospital activities sent to local papers at regular intervals.

The program of the association, as outlined by the chairman, does not meet the standards set up in this book for a public relations program. No mention is made of any attempt to inquire into the needs of the people of Pennsylvania for hospital service and the best methods of meeting these needs. However, it may be taken for granted that the various committees and councils of the association are carrying on this work continuously, although no mention is made of a definite and direct hook-up between the work of such bodies and the public relations committee. The excellent work of the state association in cooperation with local hospital councils in Philadelphia and Pittsburgh in establishing hospital care insurance plans in the state is one evidence of its concern for public welfare.

Conventions of medical associations can be used as occasions for public education. The community health meetings, held by the American College of Surgeons in connection with its national and regional hospital standardization conferences, set an excellent pattern for one aspect of this work. At these public meetings, speakers of national reputation present significant up-to-date information on cancer, heart disease and other subjects of direct interest to laymen. To be successful, such meetings should have a carefully prepared program on subjects that are of distinct public interest and invitations to attend the meetings should be widely disseminated well in advance.

State and regional hospital meetings can also be effectively used as focal points of certain types of hospital publicity. Usually a regional meeting embracing several states will offer more opportunities than the meeting of a single state. A regional group attracts a larger attendance, it usually commands more prominent speakers and can afford to devote more time and effort to the preparation of a publicity program. Most associations have, to date, given little real thought or effort to the possibilities that are offered by such meetings.

The following publicity program for the meeting of the Tri-State Hospital Assembly in Chicago in May 1938, while far from perfect, indicates some of the possibilities. A schedule of newspaper stories was drawn up about three months in advance of the meeting. The first story went out to the newspapers of the three participating states (Indiana, Illinois and Wisconsin) about March 10. This told of the meeting, the attendance expected, gave a broad outline of the program and some indication of the major problems to be discussed. There were two purposes of this release: one to call to the attention of the public and of hospital people the place and date of the meeting, the other to notify editors so that they would place the meeting on their calendars.

A second release went out on April 10. This listed for each state the people from that state who were to appear on the program as well as some of the nationally known figures that would be in attendance. A few days later stories were also sent to the press services which provide news to the rural papers. Special stories about the place that women occupy in hospital work were prepared for the women's editors of the metropolitan papers in the three states. An article on the advancing standards of

nursing education was prepared for the education page
of one of the Chicago dailies.

The speakers were asked to send in their papers three
weeks in advance of the meeting. As rapidly as these
arrived they were read and, if found to contain material
that would be of public interest, releases were prepared
covering the newsworthy statements. Unfortunately,
many speakers were slow in sending in their speeches
and hence this work piled up heavily in the last few days.
Each of the stories was given a release date and sufficient
copies made for all of the Chicago papers and the press
services.

Final general releases were sent out for the Saturday
and Sunday papers before the convention opened. Those
going to the smaller papers were sent out well in advance
and it was suggested to the editors that they check with
their local hospitals to determine who was planning to
attend. A memorandum pointing out good picture possibilities was sent to the picture editors three days before
the convention opened. Glossy print photos of leading
participants were also sent out with the news releases to
the larger papers.

The public relations committee decided to put special
emphasis on advances in (1) obstetric and infant care,
(2) standards for hospital personnel, (3) nursing education and service, (4) rural hospitalization and (5) hospital economic problems. Some of these subjects were
well covered by sessions of the convention. For others,
interviews with prominent persons were prepared and
submitted to them in advance for approval. These were
then released at various times during the convention.

A press room was established in the convention hotel
in a location well removed from the exhibit and other

distractions. One or more members of the publicity committee were always on duty there to answer questions and to assist reporters to obtain interviews or special information. There were typewriters, telephones and similar conveniences. When reporters arrived on the opening morning they were supplied with a general release giving basic information about the assembly as a whole, copies of the program and releases covering all the speeches of the morning session. In addition to the prepared releases, full copies of the speeches were available for them to consult so that they could write their own articles if they preferred or if they thought that the releases were inaccurate or incomplete in any way.

Likewise at the beginning of each succeeding session, releases were available to all the reporters. Thus, although there were 20 meetings going on simultaneously in the afternoons, (including sessions for nurses, dietitians, pharmacists, engineers and other allied groups) the reporters could, in a few minutes in the press room, obtain the gist of all the papers being presented.

Three radio dialogs were arranged for presentation at the time of the convention. Scripts for these were prepared in advance by members of the publicity committee.

A newspaper article, summarizing the outstanding events and principal ideas brought forth during the convention, was given to each administrator in attendance on the final day. This was prepared so that the administrator could insert his name, make any changes that he wished and, on his return home, send it to his local newspaper for publication. This proved to be a valuable and popular feature of the publicity committee's work.

A woman with considerable newspaper experience was employed part time to aid in the Tri-State publicity program. The entire cost for salaries, postage, mimeographing, typing, reproduction of pictures, entertainment and other incidentals was less than $400. Members of the publicity committee, of course, were glad to donate their services.

Hospital Care Insurance Organizations

The most important opportunity for improving hospital public relations on a broad scale is through a hospital care insurance organization.[3] Chapter 5 pointed out that hospital costs are a source of irritation and real hardship to many patients. The mere inauguration of a sound and well conceived hospital care insurance plan is in itself an earnest to the people of the community that the hospitals are alert to meet their needs and are willing to put time, thought and money into a program that gives promise of helping the public.

Once a hospital care insurance plan is under way, however, it is far more than a gesture of good will. It is an active potent force bringing hospitals to the favorable attention of the public day after day. Every one of the large hospital care insurance organizations puts out hundreds of thousands of pieces of literature telling about the plan and about the services of hospitals. Each has representatives constantly meeting small and large groups telling why hospital service is essential to the public and why good hospitals are essential to the kind of hospital service the people need.

Insurance plans are constantly sending articles to newspapers, preparing radio presentations of various kinds, designing and distributing posters, car cards and window displays. The aggressive plans use all of the important technics of exposition to bring their story to the attention of the public. And their story is the hospital's story. They can have no other.

Plans have reached a position of such financial importance in this country that they can employ competent public relations counsel and invest sums of money in their programs that individual hospitals have rarely been able to afford.

Not only have plans aided hospitals by their own publicity but often they have also turned their resources over to the hospitals to carry on special publicity activities for hospitals. Many plans, for example, have outlined and executed the entire publicity program accompanying a city-wide or regional observance of National Hospital Day. St. Louis, Chicago and the Twin Cities come to mind especially in this connection. Some plans have also handled convention publicity for state or regional hospital meetings.

The following report on publicity work of the Duluth branch of the Minnesota Hospital Service Association indicates what can be done by an aggressive, intelligently directed plan. The benefits to hospitals are obvious. The report covers the publicity work undertaken when the association opened its office in Duluth and is for a period of 2½ months from June 1, 1938 to August 20, 1938. The following statement is an abbreviation of one prepared by Miss Katherine Regan who has subsequently become public relations director of the Associated Hospital Service of Philadelphia.

The most valuable single source of publicity was, of course, the *Duluth Herald and News Tribune,* whose city editors have constantly cooperated with the association and whose help has been invaluable. The papers printed every story submitted. The *Duluth Herald and News Tribune* used

52 news stories with a total of 240¾ column inches and 8 news pictures (2 or 3 column width). Histories of St. Luke's and St. Mary's, Duluth's two voluntary hospitals, and an advertisement for the association (all paid for) appeared in the tabloid section arranged by the paper for the state medical association meeting.

There is no accurate check on the amount of publicity in Duluth weekly newspapers since several stories were said to have appeared in Finnish and Swedish, both languages unknown to the publicity director. In two weeklies there were five articles with a total of 28½ inches. These smaller papers seem to be willing to use anything sent them and should be good for additional summary releases from time to time.

Like the newspapers, the radio stations have been of great help in building public interest. As a result of a meeting with local hospital administrators and some subsequent meetings with other persons, WEBC donated a fifteen minute program on Friday afternoons from July 1 through August 19 and would have continued the program had the association so wished. Eight programs were presented with the emphasis always on St. Luke's and St. Mary's rather than on the Minnesota Hospital Service Association. The broadcasts presented the following subjects: "What Is a Hospital?" "Doctors, Patients, Hospitals," "Hospital Costs," "Hospital Housekeeping," "The Hospital and the Community Health Problem," "Great Battles in Medicine," "Child Care in the Hospital," "Group Hospitalization." Music for these programs was furnished by the string ensemble of WEBC whose director was most helpful. The ensemble was used because the hospitals did not have talent available during the summer.

The other station, KDAL, used spot announcements and would have welcomed a regular program, which had to be foregone because of the limited staff available to prepare such a program.

On June 8 the presidents of all Duluth clubs and organizations received a letter from either Sister Patricia or Mr. McNee [administrators of the two local voluntary hospi-

tals—Ed.] asking them to give program time during their
meetings for presentation of the movie, "How Pennies and
Seconds Count," and the Minnesota Hospital Service Association's plan. About ten clubs responded to this letter and
heard details of the plan. Several clubs are inactive during
the summer and have expressed a wish to have such a program sometime during the fall.

Window displays were arranged in five stores on Superior
Street, the hospitals themselves requesting the cooperation
of the stores. These exhibits were as follows:

1. An entire small window which included a doll house
    showing a hospital library, pictures of the records
    department of St. Mary's Hospital, a loom lent by the
    occupational therapy department and handicraft of
    patients of this department.

2. A front window in which were arranged old pictures
    of St. Luke's nurses' graduating classes.

3. Old medical equipment including a valuable collection
    of surgical, medical and obstetrical instruments lent
    by Dr. C. W. Taylor of Duluth, an old microscope and
    other old instruments lent by St. Mary's.

4. Equipment for both hospital pharmacies and hospital
    laboratories including a test tube rack of body fluids
    and a chart showing how blood is matched for trans-
    fusions.

5. A reproduction of an operating room of 50 years ago
    and in contrast such modern equipment as an inhalator
    and a stomach pump.

These displays, as far as people in the association office
were able to observe, were successful; they attracted a great
deal of attention even though they were left in for at least
a week. The stores themselves seemed well satisfied with
the response and with the display. However, there is not
enough material available in Duluth to do much in the way
of displays. The hospitals dispose of old equipment as fast
as it is outmoded and cannot spare much of their modern
equipment. There are no hospital supply houses or historical
societies that can provide equipment.

In August, to mark the end of the association's second month in Duluth and to report its progress during that time to the community through its civic and business leaders, two luncheons and two dinners were held in St. Mary's and St. Luke's. The response to these was disappointing. In answer to approximately 325 invitations, all of which contained stamped reply cards, 127 replies were received — 66 acceptances and 61 regrets. The four functions received four pictures and ten stories in the newspapers, so were adequately publicized. A prominent doctor spoke briefly at each meeting, Mr. Klein, manager of the Duluth office, reported the progress of the association and the association's movie, previously mentioned, was shown. Apparently the meetings were held too early in the season to attract a good crowd. However, the association received plenty of publicity from them and those who attended seemed to have a good time.

Another feature of the publicity program which should be mentioned was the fine response of the clergy to a letter asking them to mention the coming of the plan to Duluth. The Bishop of Duluth requested all the priests to announce this, and sermons were preached on group hospitalization in many of the Protestant churches.

All in all, the publicity campaign seems to have accomplished something toward the enrollment of members and toward the general education of Duluth people regarding the value of hospitals. The hospitals themselves, especially St. Mary's, expressed satisfaction with the various promotional activities.

Although this intensive campaign was carried on for less than three months, the association has a permanent low pressure educational program which keeps before the public the benefits of group hospitalization and the indispensable service of hospitals.

National Agencies Serving the Hospital Field

The American Hospital Association is, of course, the logical agency to direct and stimulate a national public relations effort in behalf of hospitals. This it has done in many ways through the work of its study groups, particularly since the formation of the council on community relations and administrative practice (later divided into seven councils). But the work has had only a partial effect since the results of the studies have usually not been used in a comprehensive and effective program of public exposition. Some excellent work has been done by the committee on public education, particularly during the years when this was headed by Dr. Malcolm T. MacEachern. This work, however, was directed primarily toward aiding individual hospitals to carry on their own public relations work. At no time has the American Hospital Association itself had a sound and well integrated program of public relations which was carried forward without interruption.

The time is rapidly coming when the association can no longer afford to overlook the important values which such a program would have for American hospitals. Recently the trustees of the association have given some consideration to the subject and have appropriated to the council on public education a small sum for exploratory work. The trustees are wise in moving slowly in this matter. Real progress will not be possible until there is a general meeting of minds among the officials and committee leaders of the association on all important matters affecting hospital policy. These include such subjects as the relations of hospitals to federal, state and local governmental units, to social legislation and to present day personnel problems including unionization of employes. Furthermore, these hospital leaders should reach substantial agreement on such matters as the proper responsibilities of hospitals in the care of the indigent and the attitude of hospitals to hospital care insurance plans, to the National Health Program and to the medical profession.

The most important forward step to date in the development of hospital public relations on a national scale is the decision of the hospital care insurance plans to assess themselves pro rata for the support of a national program of social and actuarial research and public education. While this program will concentrate attention primarily upon the problems that relate specifically to hospital care insurance plans, it will indirectly be of great benefit to hospitals. It is impossible to draw a hard and fast line between the field of hospital care insurance and that of the hospitals themselves. Plans are necessarily interested in the quality and scope of service provided by their member hospitals and, of course, in its cost. Hospitals are vitally interested in the soundness of the plans from the standpoint of finances and of public policies. The recent experience of the Associated Hospital Service of New York serves as a dramatic demonstration of the community of interest between the hospitals and the plans.

Plan executives have decided that attention will be given first to the research aspects of this national program and that no expositional work will be undertaken until it can be done on the basis of comprehensive and precise knowledge of the facts. Thus the program can move forward steadily without the necessity of retracing steps inadvisedly taken.

The American College of Surgeons also has played an important part in hospital public relations. Its standardization program has helped the public differentiate between the good hospitals and those whose service is either of indifferent quality or incomplete in important respects. During the past twenty years, the standardization program of the college has tended to stimulate hundreds of hospitals to higher levels of performance.

When the program was started, the college was the only national organization that was systematically inspecting and rating hospitals. Today many organizations are concerned with the problem or with certain aspects of it. Under these circumstances, the college program must be distinctly forward-looking and progressive if it is to continue to exercise major influence in this field. Officials of the college appear to be aware of this requirement and are constantly advancing the interpretation of the minimum standard. As indicated previously, however, the time may rapidly be approaching when the college should give higher gradings to hospitals that have gone far beyond the minimum standard.

The standardization program of the college has not only helped the public differentiate among hospitals, but has also helped to eliminate or drive underground the vicious practice of fee splitting. Recently the college has given a good deal of attention to the important problem of better training for surgeons. As the country comes to be supplied with a sufficient number of well trained, ethical specialists and the public becomes fully aware of the significance of certification by the specialty boards, the fee splitting specialist will probably find it increasingly difficult, if not impossible, to continue in practice. Thus, one of the objectives for which the college has been striving for the past two decades is being achieved. The abolition of fee splitting will advance the prestige of doctors and hospitals with the better informed members of the public.

The college has also taken certain direct steps to assist in hospital public relations work. It has prepared moving pictures designed to educate the public concerning hospitals, it has set up a system of approving films prepared by other organizations, it regularly conducts health education meetings in connection with its national and regional conventions, it has maintained a good publicity department for its conventions so that the important material there available is given wide public dissemination.

The American Medical Association has also carried on certain activities that are of distinct benefit to hospitals. One of the most significant has been the annual compilation of hospital statistics by the council on medical education and hospitals. Over the course of the past two decades, these figures have become increasingly reliable and useful. The work of the council in setting standards for hospitals approved for internship and residency has been of great significance. At the present time, this subject is a live one and it now appears that the council will revise its standards so that they comport with the best current thinking of medical educators and of the leading specialists. If so, the influence of the association on hospitals will become even more important.

Commendation to the American Medical Association should be given for its work in approving schools of occupational therapy, physical therapy and similar educational organizations connected with hospitals. This work has helped to raise educational standards of such institutions and to aid prospective technicians to select a school that gives proper training. The publication of *Hygeia*, the regular weekly radio broadcasts by the association and the numerous public talks and books presented by officials of the association also contribute to public understanding of medical and hospital service. The work of the council on pharmacy and chemistry, the council on physical therapy and the committee on foods has often served to protect the public from frauds and waste.

One of the youngest of the national organizations, the American College of Hospital Administrators, has already made an important niche for itself in the field of hospital activities.[4] The college is devoted primarily to improving the quality of hospital administration. Hence, it has an important bearing on hospital public relations, since sound public relations can be created and maintained most easily when hospitals are intelligently administered. The college is interested in improving the educational equipment of administrators already in practice and of the young people who are planning to devote their lives to this field. For the former, it is assisting in the formation, on a sound educational basis, of institutes for hospital administrators and of evening courses in hospital administration. At hospital conventions it is also sponsoring meetings devoted to the subject of education for administrators. For those who are coming into the field, the college is cooperating in the conduct of the course in hospital administration at the University of Chicago and is planning with other universities for the creation of similar courses when the occasion is ripe.

Other national groups have also played a part in hospital public relations. In certain instances religious organizations have promoted the welfare of the hospitals of their denominations. Some effective work has also been done by community chests and councils, through the annual national Mobilization for Human Needs cam-

paign. Such religious and social agencies cooperate
willingly with hospitals and stand ready to assist in
planning and carrying out public relations programs.

Summary

Increasingly hospitals are finding it desirable to pool
their public relations work. Many organized commercial
groups in the country have already seen the wisdom of
collaboration on an industry-wide basis in public relations efforts. In some areas hospitals have carried on
joint activities for many years. Surveying the country
as a whole, however, it is apparent that the surface has
just been scratched. Much more remains to be done than
has been accomplished to date.

Nevertheless, a summary of existing ventures in this
direction will serve to indicate some of the possibilities
that may be more fully used.

1. Local agencies that may play important rôles in
hospital public relations include local hospital councils,
district hospital associations, health councils and councils
of social agencies and informal cooperative efforts among
two or more hospitals. These groups may be effective in
a variety of ways, the most important being in cooperative study of common problems, cooperative fund raising
campaigns and cooperative publicity programs. Even
individual efforts on the part of single hospitals ought to
be so guided that they redound to the benefit of all hospitals of the area.

2. State-wide public relations work usually centers
in the state hospital association. The Pennsylvania Hospital Association has been the most active and effective
organization in the field to date. Other state hospital
associations will doubtless wish to profit by Pennsyl-

Alert, sympathetic, complete and courteous nursing service for every patient is the backbone of modern scientific hospital care.

vania's example. If such programs are based on sufficient and sound research and study they can be of major significance. Regional groups can also be effective, especially in connection with their conventions.

3. Most hospital care insurance plans began as local organizations but are tending to become at least state-wide in scope. They already constitute one of the most significant vehicles for improving hospital public relations that have yet appeared. In the future, their value in this respect will undoubtedly increase, provided only that they are soundly managed and ably guided. The work of the Commission on Hospital Service and the steps now being taken to set up a comprehensive research and public relations program on a national scale give an earnest that they will have such guidance and management.

4. Various national agencies serving the hospital field have taken important parts in hospital public relations work in the past and probably will do so increasingly in the future. The American Hospital Association is the logical organization to take major responsibility in this work. So far the association has been very cautious in the steps taken toward the creation of a true public relations program. Most of its effort has been concentrated in its convention and the work of its committees and councils. As the activities of these groups become better unified and the outlines of a public relations plan become more clearly defined, the association will doubtless spend more effort in making this program effective through well considered avenues of public exposition. As it does so, its influence both with member hospitals and with the public should wax.

The national program of research and public education authorized by the hospital care insurance organizations bids fair to become the most important national effort yet undertaken in this field.

The American College of Surgeons, through its standardization program and other activities, has contributed substantially to public understanding and confidence in hospitals. Its program also is increasing in scope and value. Likewise, the American Medical Association has done much to aid hospitals, directly and indirectly.

The American College of Hospital Administrators is making a fundamental contribution to the advancement of hospital service through its efforts to assist present administrators to improve their educational preparation and to train new administrators who shall be competent to direct the complex activities that constitute the work of a modern hospital. To date, the college has made no strenuous efforts to tell the general public about its work. A beginning in this field has, however, been made in connection with some of the institutes for hospital administrators held under the joint sponsorship of the college and of local educational and hospital organizations.

Church and community chest organizations have carried on some national hospital educational work. More may be done in this respect in the future.

No one can predict accurately the extent to which joint efforts of the type described in this chapter will increase in the future. However, there is every indication today that they will grow rapidly in number and strength.

REFERENCES

1. Street, Elwood: Joint Hospital Fund Raising, *Hospitals*, June, 1936, p. 17.
2. Eichenlaub, M. H.: Six Years in Public Relations, *The Modern Hospital*, Aug., 1938, p. 43.
3. McCarthy, Ray F.: Educational Value of Hospital Service Plans, *Hospitals*, Aug., 1936, p. 85.
4. Hamilton, James A.: The College of Hospital Administrators — Its Significance, *Hospitals*, Aug., 1938, p. 43.

Chapter 14

THE FINANCES OF A
PUBLIC RELATIONS PROGRAM

THE PRECEDING chapters have outlined, in rather broad strokes, a philosophy of public relations. While this has been done primarily in terms suitable to hospital conditions, the same general requirements would apply to any other social agency or to a business. The program suggested is comprehensive in scope, embracing a wide variety of important matters; it is not the type of thing that should be turned over to some mediocre person.

Industry is beginning to appreciate the vital need of sound public relations. Hospitals may learn certain lessons from the experience of the more progressive industries. Two lessons of particular importance stand out: first, that a public relations program costs time and money; second, that it merits the attention of the top executives. Intelligent industries do not hire some ex-newspaper man otherwise inexperienced and expect him to plan and direct a public relations program. They employ the ablest analyst and publicist they can find, pay him a salary appropriate to his ability and make him a vice president!

What Will It Cost?

Just how much a hospital should spend for its public relations program cannot be determined by any simple rule of thumb. Before attempting to give a more specific answer, let us look at some figures for industry.

The National Industrial Advertisers Association of Chicago recently compiled data on the advertising and other selling costs of a group of large companies. They found that for the five years, 1934 to 1938 inclusive, the average percentage spent for advertising by 164 companies was 2.45 per cent of their gross sales. In addition to this, an average of 13.8 per cent of gross sales was spent for other selling costs excluding advertising. (Only 103 companies gave data on this latter point.) Thus these firms, which were considered representative by the association, spent about 16 per cent of their total income from sales to create those sales.

But perhaps these figures include a large number of firms, like patent medicine concerns, which use advertising to force people to buy poor products at a high price. Let us take a look at some figures broken down by industries. These were furnished to me by *Advertising Age*. In 1935, the latest year for which the data were available, industries spent for advertising alone the following percentages of their net sales volumes: textiles, 1.8; office equipment, 2.6; hardware, 2.7; travel and transportation, 4.0; clothing, 4.5; service organizations, such as insurance and finance companies, 5.0; petroleum products, 5.7; auto accessories, 5.9; silverware and clocks, 9.3, and soft drinks, 15.2. Thus, most of these industries spent from 2 to 6 per cent of their net sales incomes on advertising. And advertising, for them, was only part of their public relations programs.

Perhaps some of these industries or units of these industries are not efficiently run. Such criticism, however, probably would not apply to General Motors Corporation. In 1937 this outstanding company spent $10,500,000 for newspaper advertising, $5,746,000 for magazine advertising and $1,818,000 for radio advertising. In addition it spent substantial amounts for direct mail promotion, billboards and many other forms of advertising. Furthermore, approximately $500,000 is spent annually for customer research. Since General Motors had a total sales in 1937 of $1,606,789,000, at least 1.25 per cent of its total budget went into advertising and customer research. If other types of public relations work, such as the personnel relations program and community activities, were included, this percentage would be somewhat higher.

General Foods is another nationally known concern. In 1937 this company had total gross sales of $133,127,000. The principal advertising expenditures were as follows: newspapers, $2,800,000; magazines, $1,336,000, and radio, $2,765,000. Thus in these three mediums alone this company spent more than 5 per cent of its total income from sales.

It is obvious, of course, that hospitals and other social institutions need not spend as much proportionately to win and conserve public support as most industries must to keep their customers. Industries must pay for nearly everything that they do to gain public respect, confidence and approval. Social institutions can obtain a great deal of publicity and assistance without cost, if they know how to ask for it and how to utilize it effectively.

No public relations program can be significant and broadly effective unless it has enough financial support to do a real job. Certain parts of a broad public relations program can well be carried on by any intelligent and aggressive hospital administrator. Other parts require a great deal of specialized knowledge. Rarely is such knowledge possessed by an administrator and when it must be purchased it is costly. The crucial point in setting up a public relations program comes when the administrator and trustees decide what kind of brains they want to hire. If they are interested merely in employing some inexperienced young man or woman with a pleasant personality, they should not expect to obtain the kind of public relations program described in this book. If they wish to have such a comprehensive program, they must be ready to pay a substantial amount for brains and experience.

Certain of the fund raising concerns are now developing a public relations counseling service. Such firms would probably be glad to accept employment on a reasonable annual retainer fee. The right kind of firm would render a valuable service for a fee of from $5000 to $15,000 a year, depending upon the complexity of the work to be undertaken. In addition, of course, there would need to be a budget for clerical and stenographic services and for printing, postage, stationery and similar expenses.

A hospital might well spend for its public relations program between 1 and 2 per cent of its total budget. Many institutions might prefer to start out on an even more modest scale, with perhaps 0.5 per cent. This is acceptable, provided the reduction is done in the quantity of work undertaken and not in its quality. If a hospital attempts to spread a small budget over a large program, the results are almost sure to be disappointing.

Whence Should the Money Come?

Should the trustees raise a special fund to finance the public relations program or is this expense a legitimate charge against the operating budget?

If the program outlined in this book has any validity, the answer to this question should be perfectly clear. A public relations program is not something separate and apart from other types of hospital service. It is not a luxury to be indulged in when there is plenty of money. It is a basic concept of public service and a group of technics for making that concept effective. It affects the very warp and woof of hospital service. It is of aid to the public as well as the hospital.

Since this is so, the cost of the public relations program is just as much a legitimate part of hospital operating expense as is the cost of heating the building, providing drugs or running the accounting department. As such it ought to appear in the hospital budget. It is designed to aid patients and the community at large as much as any of the other multifarious activities that go on under the roof of an institution. Since trustees and others often give to set an example, however, there may be circumstances when the cost of a public relations program may be carried as an extra-budgetary expense. This has the advantage of permitting the hospital to state that all funds received will go for routine hospital activities and none for public relations. As a permanent policy, however, public relations costs should probably appear in the budget.

What Dividends Will This Investment Bring?

Suppose a hospital with a $500,000 budget sets aside $10,000 for a public relations program. What benefits will this bring that will justify such an expenditure? Many of these benefits were either stated or implied in Chapter 1. Now they can be given somewhat more fully and positively.

Much benefit will accrue to patients. Probably 60 per cent of the effort put forth by the public relations staff will be directed toward improving the quality of care—physically, scientifically, psychologically or spiritually. Some persons may state that the hospital administrator is already doing everything that can be done to accomplish this very end. This should be true and in many cases it undoubtedly is, but the administrator ordinarily has scores of different responsibilities pressing on him all the time. The public relations officer can concentrate a large part of his attention on his major job: to represent and to speak for the interests of patients and potential patients.

Improved relations with the medical profession and with other related groups should be another important dividend of a sound public relations program. The more intelligent physicians will appreciate and support any efforts to help them render better care to patients. They are eager to use to the full their talents for the alleviation of pain and the cure of disease. A progressive alert hospital is of much more aid to them in this endeavor than is an institution that pays little or no attention to changing needs and advancing standards of medical and hospital service.

A further dividend should be a better understanding by hospital employes of the institution's purposes and functions. They should develop an increased sense of partnership in a vital community service. As a result they should serve the hospital more loyally and more intelligently and the hospital should, therefore, be able to pay better wages and to provide better working conditions while still obtaining the same or a larger service for each pay roll dollar.

Perhaps the most important dividend of all is wider public understanding and appreciation. This is the open sesame to many of the major objectives of hospitals. Without attempting a complete catalog, it may be well to repeat some of the results that should accrue from such broadened public understanding.

First, the hospital will almost inevitably find that its patronage increases, a benefit for both the hospital and the public. Patients will naturally be more readily persuaded by their physicians to go to a hospital in which they have confidence and in whose development they are interested than they will to go to an institution which has not earned such confidence and interest. Furthermore, as the public becomes better acquainted with the facilities which hospitals provide, it will be better able to use them intelligently. Many people have little idea of the valuable aid which hospitals can give in diagnosis and even in therapy to ambulatory private patients.

Second, the public will more readily rally to the support of hospitals in their legitimate legislative ambitions and in the entire scope of their relations with governmental bodies. Legitimate legislative programs include such things as proper licensing laws for hospitals, exemption of true voluntary hospitals from taxation and appropriate modifications of social legislation to take account of the fact that hospitals must be open twenty-four hours a day and every day in the year. Several states have achieved or are working toward legislation to compensate hospitals, at least in part, for the care of the indigent and of those injured in highway accidents who are unable to pay for the cost of their care. Hospitals need to be protected from ill-considered or crank legislation that is introduced from time to time. Among the types of bills that sometimes come perilously near enactment are those that would cripple all animal experimentation, those that would heavily tax all hospitals whether proprietary or truly voluntary, those that would break down the staff restrictions that are necessary to maintaining high standards of service and those that would inaugurate systems of governmental health service without allowing due consideration to the proper place of existing hospitals.

Third, the public will be more readily persuaded to provide the funds that are necessary to enable a hospital to maintain high standards. The public relations program should stimulate among large numbers of people a feeling of participation and partnership. They will then be ready to help the hospital in whatever ways are appropriate to their circumstances, through gifts of money or of service. They will understand why a hospital of high standards cannot be expected to charge fees high enough to meet all the costs of operating and of expanding the hospital to meet growing needs. They will appreciate what high standards mean in improved service to patients, in the saving of lives, in remedying the physical defects that sap the strength or impair the efficiency of the nation's people. They will grasp the vital need for the educational work of hospitals, a work designed to prepare new generations of nurses, physicians and other workers in the health fields who will be even more effective than their predecessors in preventing disease or alleviating its consequences.

With a public thoroughly convinced of the importance of hospitals in the nation's economy, there can be no doubt of the future of these institutions. In one way or another, means will be found to finance their continued development. Their growth to date has made our best hospitals the envy of the world. The extent to which they adopt intelligent long-range public relations programs may determine the degree to which they continue this leadership. The cost of a good program may be the price of continued growth and development.

APPENDICES

Appendix I

ONE HUNDRED UNITS OF MEASURE IN EVALUATING QUALITY IN HOSPITALS*

Governing Board

1. Qualifications for appointment (and continuance in office) of members of the governing board of the hospital.

2. Ability and willingness of the governing body to promote the interests of the hospital as a communal institution, including the fruitful participation of its officers in various enterprises for the promotion of the public welfare.

3. Ability of the governing board, the administration and the staff generally to make patients comfortable, under the circumstances of their illnesses.

4. Ability and willingness to obtain money for essential hospital purposes; ability to safeguard the investments for the hospital.

5. Relation of the governing board to the administration of the hospital:
   (a) Presence or absence of interference in administrative routine.
   (b) Relation between power and responsibility and their distribution.

6. Rules governing cooperation between the governing board, the administration and the medical board of the hospital.

*By E. M. Bluestone, M.D., administrator, Montefiore Hospital for Chronic Diseases, New York City. The material in this appendix was originally prepared as notes on a lecture given before the New York Institute for Hospital Administrators, 1939. It is here reprinted in revised form with the permission of the author.

7. Interest of the governing board in the commercial factors of medical practice and their influence on the work of the hospital.

8. Interest of the governing board in legislation affecting hospitals.

9. Interest of the hospital in the development of the younger members of the staff (including opportunities for such development and the degree of its encouragement).

10. Character of the periodic report to the contributing public (including publicity methods generally).

Hospital

11. Medical and social traditions of the hospital.

12. Standing and reputation of the hospital in the community.

13. Extent, importance, accuracy and honesty of the scientific output of the hospital.

14. Protection of hospital property against misuse and loss.

15. Location of the hospital and its accessibility.

16. Hospital layout (ease of getting around).

17. Adequacy of the number of free beds in proportion to the total bed capacity of the hospital and the needs of the community.

18. Flexibility of the hospital plan, in all respects, to accommodate essential changes.

19. Availability of separation rooms in the hospital.

20. Number and placement of beds in wards.

21. Adequacy of sanitary facilities of all kinds.

22. Interest in and facilities for the pre- and post-hospital care of the poor patient.

23. Availability and utilization of convalescent facilities.

24. Emergency facilities available for the handling of non-acceptable cases and hospitalized cases with secondary complications.

25. Availability of adequate library facilities for (a) medical staff, (b) patients and (c) employees generally.

26. Atmosphere of the hospital as to (a) sight, including color and arrangement, (b) sound, (c) odor, (d) touch, (e) temperature, (f) humidity, (g) fresh air and (h) sunshine.

27. Cleanliness of the hospital.

28. Absence of undesirable designations, such as "incurable," "cancer," "consumptive."

Policies

29. Readiness to care for all elements of the population on a basis of absolute impartiality.

30. Policies of the hospital governing the admission of patients as to (a) age, (b) sect, (c) clinical condition, (d) economic condition, (e) duration of illness, (f) prognosis and (g) curability.

31. Policies of the hospital governing the discharge of patients: (a) criteria for discharge, (b) preparation for discharge and (c) arrangements for after care.

32. Cooperativeness of the hospital with other institutions and social agencies, particularly in the matter of (a) policies and (b) exchange of useful and comparable information.

33. Policies governing appointments, promotions and discharges in the professional and nonprofessional staffs (methods of selection, criteria for advancement and measures in use for discovering deterioration in the staff).

34. Progressive character of the policies which govern the various activities of the hospital.

35. Ability to attract an efficient, faithful, humane and progressive staff of professional and nonprofessional workers; the ability of the hospital to obtain the best talent for specialized tasks in the hospital on a pay or voluntary basis.

36. Attitude of the hospital toward an operating deficit:
    (a) Exclusion or limitation of patients as the result of an operating deficit or a threatened decrease of income.
    (b) Influence of the finances of the hospital on the care of the admitted patient (transfusions, special nursing, radiology, expensive medication, eye glasses, mechanical appliances, dental service).

37. Attitude of the hospital toward its moral as compared to its legal obligations (how much further does the hospital go beyond its legal obligations to serve the sick?).

38. Distribution of budgetary items from the comparative point of view (as reflected, for example, by tendencies to build up facilities that may be out of proportion to other hospital activities).

39. Policy of the hospital toward the support of useful activities not directly required in the routine care of the individual patient (provision for extra-budgetary needs and for education and research).

40. Policies of the hospital toward (a) medical social service and (b) relief.

41. Ability and willingness of the hospital to make and to share gains in education and investigation.

42. Policies of the hospital governing surgical patients with reference to (a) consent for operation, (b) preparation (mental and physical) for operation, (c) promptness of operation and (d) post-operative care.

43. Extent, if any, of competition with the private practice of medicine.

44. Interest of the hospital in preventive medicine.

45. Adequacy and use of statistics concerning rejected applicants for admission.

46. Extent of transfer of patients, who still require hospitalization, to other institutions and the policies govern-

ing such transfer; limitation of responsibility for care, if any, (character of illness, duration of the illness and secondary complications).

47. Moral influence of private pavilion care on the treatment of ward patient.

Administration

48. Character of administrative leadership in the hospital.

49. Rules and regulations of the hospital with reference to the frequency of adjustments to meet exceptional situations; freedom from mechanical routine and government by precedent.

50. Proportionate time spent by the supervising staff at the desk and in the field; the proportion of "paper work" in the executive offices and its relation to adequate administration.

51. Extent of coordination of the in- and outpatient departments.

52. Quantity and quality of social, financial and vital statistics and the uses to which they are put.

53. Extent to which the hospital is guided by recognized standardizing bodies; the compliance of the hospital with standard definitions and terminology.

54. Attitude of the hospital toward complaints from all sources and methods of dealing with them.

55. Attitude of the patients toward the hospital as determined without direct questioning.

56. Degree of impartiality toward any list of waiting patients.

57. Adequacy of plans for the transmission of administrative policies and orders throughout the hospital.

58. Principles underlying the purchase of supplies for the hospital; business principles; economy; honesty; adequacy of the record.

59. Relative value placed on clinical time and clerical time; the conservation of valuable hospital energy.

60. Methods and regularity of auditing medical charts of patients.

61. Adequacy of the clinical record: fullness of entries; handwriting; identification (of patient and recorder) ; ease of access; scientific value; responsibility.

62. Number of patients leaving against the advice of the visiting staff and the reasons therefor.

63. Policies and rules of the hospital governing patients' visitors.

64. Facilities for the care of such property of patients as cannot be left at home.

65. Control of waste generally in the hospital.

66. Ready availability of all technics and materials for the best hospital service.

Professional and Nonprofessional Staff

67. Division of labor within the hospital; the plan of organization.

68. Availability and accessibility of the staff at all times.

69. Attitude of the working staff toward the sick and toward each other.

70. Intensity and duration of interest of the medical staff in the patient.

71. Judicial attitude toward employe discipline; premiums for originality, long service, superior qualifications and devotion to duty.

72. Presence or absence of overwork in the staff.

73. Methods of systematic supervision of members of the subordinate staff by their seniors; the extent of automatic checks in supervision.

74. Extent of interest in the welfare of the working staff of the hospital.

75. Ability of the staff to think quickly and effectively and to act without help in emergencies.

76. Character of volunteer service rendered in the hospital.

77. Appearance of the working staff (cleanliness, dress, uniform).

Care of Patients

78. Protection of the patient against malpractice.

79. Adequacy and immediate availability of all facilities (staff and equipment) for diagnosis and therapy.

80. Frequency and thoroughness of medical rounds for all patients; consultations.

81. Adequacy of the signal system for patients who must summon employes on short notice.

82. Interest in the social history of the patient by the medical staff; the use made of the social history.

83. Extent of interest in early treatment and in remote results of treatment inside and outside of the hospital.

84. Promptness and adequacy of hospital service generally; promptness of the workup and the application of therapeutic procedures.

85. Establishment of acceptable standards of service for individual clinical conditions.

86. Average length of stay of patients in relation to their clinical condition.

87. Quality of food purchases, storage, preparation and service; the ready availability of special diets when necessary.

88. Safeguards in the preparation, administration and supervision of medication.

89. Character of scientific work:
    (a) Adequacy and availability of scientific analyses and reports.
    (b) Facilities for scientific investigation.
    (c) Presence of experimental equipment, apart from a formal research program.

90. Methods in use to safeguard patients and employes
    (a) Against complicating disease and accidents.
    (b) Against fire and smoke.
91. Methods of ordering service for patients; attitude of
    the hospital toward "telephone orders" and "standing
    orders" (which are not reviewed at short intervals).
92. Protection of the confidence of the patient and his
    privacy.
93. Interest of the hospital in the individualization of all
    patients; methods in vogue for identifying them at all
    times.
94. Care of patients during transportation inside and out-
    side of the hospital; availability of portable equipment
    (diagnostic and therapeutic).
95. Character of the reception of the patient in the admit-
    ting office.
96. Arrangements for the entertainment, diversion and
    occupation of the patient.
97. Arrangements for keeping the patient in touch with
    his family.
98. Extent of clinical waste and the use made of by-
    products in the care of patients.
99. Presence or absence of exploitation of patients for
    various purposes.
100. Interest in post-mortem examinations on all patients
    dying in the hospital; percentage of such examinations;
    use made of this material.

Appendix II

CHECK LIST OF POSSIBLE
FUNCTIONS OF A WOMEN'S AUXILIARY*

ANY HOSPITAL TODAY which is functioning without the aid of a women's auxiliary is operating under a handicap. The service which these organizations are rendering throughout the country is of inestimable value. Part of their accomplishments can be measured in financial terms, but a larger part is in the form of intangible services for which there is no monetary equivalent.

The ideal women's auxiliary is a group of women of serious purpose and good standing in a community who are organized by the authority of the governing body of a hospital to work for the benefit of the hospital patients in harmony with the governing body and under the guidance of the hospital administrator.

Such an auxiliary has its own constitution and by-laws which are subject to the approval of the governing body of the hospital. It has full authority over its own internal affairs but does not attempt in any way to exercise authority in connection with the administration of the hospital. All its contacts with the hospital are made through the administrator. A women's auxiliary is a collaborating organization in the sense that the medical staff is a collaborating organization and has the same purpose, namely, the advancement of the interests of the hospital and the patient. It may often work with other lay organizations in the community.

Work of Hospital Guilds

Women's auxiliaries differ with the size of the hospital and the community. Their work may be an activity of a church, society or special club group. In large cities, women's

*Reprinted from 14th edition of The Hospital Yearbook.

auxiliaries may be composed of different groups organized
on the basis of age, such as school children, junior or "teen
age" girls, débutantes, young married women and seniors,
each of which devotes itself to some special department of
the hospital or some special service. Groups may also be
formed on the basis of type of services rendered. Such
groups are often called guilds—music guilds, flower guilds,
jelly guilds, library guilds, sewing guilds.

Some auxiliaries have city and county branches. In
Indiana there is a state organization of White Cross guilds
which are women's auxiliaries. Groups of church women,
club women, college alumnæ or junior league girls may act
as women's auxiliaries in certain other communities or
districts.

The general purpose of all, regardless of the name under
which they function, is the same. It is that of service to the
hospital and the hospital patient, part of which is rendered
in an intermediary capacity between the hospital and the
community and part of which is in direct contact with the
hospital itself. More concretely, they undertake to furnish
funds, or services, or both. Their field of activity is practically unlimited. In large hospitals they may supplement
and contribute to the work of the social service department
but do not duplicate or take the place of the trained department personnel.

Methods of Raising Funds

Dues	Fashion shows
Pledges	Charity balls
Contributions	Minstrel shows
Associate memberships	Musical revues
Membership campaigns	Amateur theatricals
Life annuity contracts	Dance recitals
Legacies	Magazine subscription sales
Endowments	Sale of cook books
Tag days	Sale of menu books
Donation days	Apron sales
Card parties	"Bake" sales
Luncheons	Candy sales
Silver teas	Horse shows

Benefit performances
  Concerts
  Drama
  Moving pictures
  Lectures
Thrift shops
Garden parties
Table setting competitions
"Half Mile of Pennies"
Penny banks
Mite boxes

Sunshine bags
Old book sales
Rummage sales
Exhibition of Colleen Moore's doll house or similar attractions
Christmas bazaars
Tea rooms
Guessing contests
River or lake boat excursions
Hospital Sundays (in churches)

Methods of Obtaining Goods in Kind

Donation days (participated in by department stores as well as individuals)
Collecting soap wrappers which are exchanged for flat silver
Every-member-bring-a-book
Egg showers
Fruit showers

Vegetable showers
Pickle and jam showers
Thanksgiving donations of food
Baby clothes donations
Needlework Guild contributions
Solicitation of books
Solicitation of material for sheets and pillow cases

Purposes for Which Money Is Raised

EQUIPMENT

Furnishings of private rooms
Oxygen tents
Linen supplies
Bassinets
Libraries
  Reference
  Circulating
Furnishings of playrooms for visiting children
Furnishings of nurseries
Radios
Invalid trays
Stretchers
Awnings
Screens
Paint
Curtains
Children's tables and chairs
Furnishings of diet kitchens

Furnishings of sterilizing rooms
X-ray machines
Moving picture projectors and screens
Baptismal fonts
Communion sets
Furnishings of roof gardens
Sand piles for children
Slabs for morgues
Ambulance entrance
Blood transfusion equipment
Diathermy equipment
Radiothermy equipment
Book cases
Book carts
Rubber gloves
Electric refrigerators, sewing machines, mangles, blankets, pads
Occupational therapy supplies

PATIENTS' NEEDS

Maintaining free beds in wards, in maternity departments, in children's departments
Maintaining private rooms
Maintaining "Tiny Tim" beds for crippled children
Providing goats' milk for babies
Layettes
Bathrobes
Establishing and maintaining cancer clinics, heart clinics, tuberculosis hospitals, outdoor clinics, fresh air camps
Fresh fruit fund
Paying salary of occupational therapist, kindergarten teacher, teacher for convalescent children, supervisor of volunteer workers, social service worker,

helper in the home where mother has to be taken to the hospital, wet nurse in infants' department when needed
Maintaining oxygen service
Flower fund
Ice cream fund
Trays and vases
Daily papers
Valentine, Easter and Christmas toys for children
Writing materials and stamps
Special dainties
Taxi service for patients on discharge or for social service workers
Circulating library
Puzzles
Playing cards

NURSES' NEEDS

Radio, piano or phonograph for nurses' home
Reference library
Fiction library
Graduation pins and bouquets for graduating nurses
Linen supplies

Building, furnishing and maintaining nurses' home
Furnishing and decorating special rooms
Scholarship funds
Loan funds
Endowments for nursing school

Types of Services Rendered by Women's Auxiliaries

CLERICAL SERVICES

Maintaining card system for visiting public wards
Maintaining card system for follow-up work after patients leave hospital
Acknowledging gifts of flowers, candy, scrap books and toys made to hospital
Addressing envelopes
Addressing bulletins
Taking messages for doctors, nurses and patients

Writing letters for patients
Writing Santa Claus letters for children
Acknowledging Santa Claus letters
Registering patients in dispensary
Supplementing work of the information office
Answering visitors' questions
Interpreting hospital rules to foreigners

Procuring special passes for old people and those not in good physical condition during non-visiting hours

Keeping track of books in circulating libraries

Guiding salesmen to purchasing agent's office

ASSISTANCE TO PATIENTS

Reading to and amusing children

Reading to older patients

Visiting wards

Feeding patients who are unable to feed themselves

Caring for patients' flowers

Running errands to the pharmacy, pathology department, record room

Helping prepare trays for patients returning late from x-ray or physical therapy departments

Preparing afternoon nourishment

Seeing that special delivery letters, telegrams, messages and packages are delivered promptly

Performing any small services which are not actually essential but add to the comfort of the patient's day

Delivering newspapers

Running elevators (in small hospitals)

Taking wheel chair patients about

Distributing books and magazines

ASSISTANCE TO SOCIAL SERVICE DEPARTMENT

Aid in household inspection

Volunteer case work

Follow-up work

Provide motor transportation to and from hospital for patients unable to pay for taxi service

Distribute health literature

Send booklets on baby care to mothers of babies born in hospital

Visit patients occupying free beds

Register new cases

See that dispensary patients and charts reach the proper clinics

Take and record weights

Drive social workers on their visits

Assist in health crusades

Assist public health nurses at clinics

Prepare holiday baskets

SEWING

Hem sheets and pillow cases

Repair linens

Binders

Screen covers

Lap towels

Baby bands and gowns

Pillow bags

Mend and patch gowns

Bedpan covers

Treatment sheets

Pitcher towels

Solution table covers

Hospital gowns

Wrappers

Layettes

Washcloths

Table covers

Nurses' uniforms and dresses

Cut garments to be sewn by church and missionary societies

Stuff animal toys

Surgical dressings

ASSISTANCE WITH AND ARRANGEMENT FOR
SOCIAL ACTIVITIES

Recruit musical and dramatic talent from theaters and broadcasting stations

Give monthly teas in nurses' home

Provide music in all forms for nurses and patients on special holidays

Dramatic readings for nurses and patients

Parties for nurses in training

Birthday parties for all babies born in hospital during year

Baby picture contests

Foster dramatic clubs among nurses and professional groups

Sponsor performances by local dramatic circles

Provide trees, greens, holly, lights at Christmas

Decorate auditorium at special holiday seasons

Take part in National Hospital

Day receptions and other social affairs

Arrange for Sunday religious services and for special days

Provide favors for trays on Christmas, Easter, Valentine's Day and other occasions

Serve as hostesses when large groups visit the hospital

Act as waitresses when groups come to hospital for meals

Children's parties

Story telling hours for children

Dinners and receptions for graduating classes

Group parties for student nurses

Motor rides for student nurses

Make arrangements for graduation day and provide entertainment

Birthday tea and shower of gifts for hospital

PUBLICITY AND PUBLIC EDUCATION

Supply speakers, lantern slides and movies to various local organizations, church groups, women's clubs, junior league groups on hospital matters

Arrange with local picture houses for showing hospital movies

Help publicize National Hospital Day

Encourage patronage of hospital drug store, beauty parlor and tea room

Supply feature articles to local publications

Obtain pictures of individuals for newspaper society columns in connection with benefit performances, etc.

Sponsor essay contests in schools

Aid in printing and distribution of hospital bulletins containing feature stories and illustrations

Arrange for tours of hospital by special groups

Furnish guide service for individual tours of hospital

Arrange open house once a year for the public

Arrange exhibits at local fairs, bazaars or in department stores

Sponsor monthly health forums

Describe hospital's activities and needs to individuals whenever occasion offers

MISCELLANEOUS SERVICES

Make scrap books

Make jellies and preserves

Landscaping services by garden clubs in helping lay out grounds, securing trees and shrubs, planting bulbs, etc.

Junior aids serve as ushers or candy and cigarette girls at balls, horse shows and functions

Occupational therapy

Appendix III

CLEVELAND POLICY ON SOLICITATIONS BY INSTITUTIONS THAT ARE MEMBERS OF THE WELFARE FEDERATION*

(Approved April 2, 1937)

THE BOARD OF trustees of the Welfare Federation feels the matter of solicitations constitutes a serious problem. It believes that the regulation of these solicitations cannot be completely reduced to a set of fixed rules, and it recommends, therefore, that any project of money raising character should be referred to the federation for consideration by its solicitations committee and approval or disapproval.

The Welfare Federation believes the solicitations committee should review these projects in the light of the following principles. It is contemplated that as the committee has experience in reviewing such projects it will be able to make suggestions from time to time regarding the modification of the principles governing solicitations to the end that after a few years' experience a set of permanent principles will have been crystallized.

1. All proposed solicitations for money or other articles of value by or on behalf of member agencies shall be submitted to the Welfare Federation not less than 45 days in advance to allow time for the solicitations committee to recommend approval or disapproval and the board of trustees to act. Each member agency will be regarded as responsible for any solicitation on its behalf by whomsoever made.

2. A solicitation shall be defined as including not only a direct appeal of any character but also anything like an indirect invitation or publicity of such a nature as would indicate very strongly a need for assistance and any such action

*Reprinted by permission.

by a women's auxiliary or by any fully or partially affiliated organization or any such action by any party in which the name of the agency is used. Sales of merchandise, tickets, solicitations for memberships which are in support of the work but are not actual memberships in exchange for services and all other similar activities will be regarded as solicitations.

(The foregoing recommendation does not forbid all such activities but merely states that they will be regarded as solicitations and as such should come before the Welfare Federation for approval or disapproval.)

3. Agencies shall ask for approval of solicitations which have been recurring annually. If approval is given, it may be not only for the current year but for following years, but with the condition that notice be given of their annual recurrence at the time of any submission of budget estimates for the following year and that, upon request of the Welfare Federation, the agency resubmit its appeal for approval.

4. If during the year, because of an emergency, any agency finds itself short of meeting its budget, it is understood that such agency shall promptly bring that fact to the attention of the central budget and policy committee of the federation for counsel and action. Such procedure is the agency's first duty before considering an independent solicitation.

5. All proposed contracts, financial arrangements and fees shall be reported to the Welfare Federation at the time approval of the solicitation is requested and before any contract is made binding.

6. Any proposal from any commercial organization to any agency to allow the agency's name to be used in return for a gift shall be presented, with an explanation of all the proposed business arrangements, for review and decision in the light of all the facts. (Such arrangement will ordinarily be disapproved.)

7. A condition of approval of any solicitation shall be that value shall principally accrue to the agency or to the public or to both rather than to the promoters.

8. The breadth of the appeal shall always be taken into consideration by the federation along with other factors.

9. Where an appeal has a social character, every effort should be made to confine the appeal to those persons who are interested in the institution. This will prevent a wide public solicitation. Selling tickets to people for functions which they do not expect to attend is strongly discouraged.

10. The purpose for which the solicitation is made shall also be taken into consideration by the federation.

11. The federation shall ordinarily recommend against a solicitation for any item of expense which will increase the annual budget until the service has been reviewed and endorsed in one of the annual budgets.

12. On approving any solicitation, the Welfare Federation shall also study and advise as to the method of approach so as to protect the interest of the agency, the federation, the Community Fund and the public.

The above twelve rules shall become effective forthwith.

STATEMENT OF PRACTICES OF THE
SOLICITATIONS COMMITTEE OF THE
CLEVELAND WELFARE FEDERATION*

(November 30, 1938)

MOST TYPES OF solicitations have been discouraged, as they seemed to be a violation of the long standing agreement that financially participating agencies could not conduct other solicitations for funds than the joint money raising effort in the Community Fund.

However, in certain cases benefit performances have been allowed where tickets are sold only to board members and

*Reprinted by permission.

committee members of the organization and sold only on the basis of attendance, especially where there is no newspaper publicity. Other benefits which are reaching the general public have been approved when the name of the agency was not used in the sale of tickets, the tickets being sold exclusively on the merit of the entertainment rather than as a donation. Favorable consideration has sometimes been given performances in which clients took part when the emphasis was on the educational value to the client. No affairs have been approved which involve the solicitation of merchants for prizes or merchandise. The committee has also opposed Keno parties, raffles, lotteries and other activities outside the law. The committee is unfavorable to the plan of mailed out tickets in advance with a request that the receiver "either remit or return."

Occasionally benefit performances which have been discouraged by the federation were revised considerably, re-presented and approved. Where small articles were being sold, approval has sometimes been given if we have been assured that the article was to be sold on its merit, if telephone solicitations were being avoided and (in the case of sale of printed material) if no advertising was being sold in connection with it. The committee has favored sales of occupational products when the emphasis was placed on the value of the occupation rather than on the profit from the sale. The solicitation of magazine subscriptions in the name of an agency has been disapproved. The committee has been critical of solicitations if conducted during the period of the Community Fund campaign or two months prior to it.

Membership campaigns have been approved which were confined to those families some member of which would use the facilities of the institutions, or which were for small amounts and were based on long established custom and confined to a small group. Some campaigns for second-hand clothing, radios, furniture and so on have been approved, also the acceptance of unsolicited gifts which have been offered certain organizations for specific purposes and certain solicitations for Christmas gifts. It is the general policy of the committee to discourage, as far as reasonable, projects whose primary purpose is raising money for current operations of the organization. The committee is not in favor of use of benefit performances in capital account campaigns.

The acceptance of unsolicited gifts from service clubs, fraternal and other similar groups interested in the work of the agency has been approved, provided in each instance the group was advised by the agency that membership in the Welfare Federation precludes the use of the name of a member organization in any money raising projects.

Appendix IV

GIVING INFORMATION
TO THE PRESS*

THE FOLLOWING CODE for uniform procedure was prepared by the Cleveland Hospital Council, the Cleveland Academy of Medicine and the press of that city. It has been approved by the public education committee of the American Hospital Association.

This code has been adopted by
COMMUNITY GENERAL HOSPITAL

Responsibility for providing information is to be placed on one individual in the hospital to whom all inquiries are to be directed, namely, JOHN A. DOE.

For police cases the following items of public information may be given without the patient's consent:

1. Name: (a) Married or single, (b) color, (c) sex, (d) age, (e) occupation, (f) firm or company employing patient and (g) address.

2. Nature of the Accident: (a) Injured by automobile, explosion, shooting; (b) if there is a fracture, it is not to be described in any way except to state the member involved, and (c) more than a statement that it is simple or compound may not be made.

3. Injuries of the Head: (a) Simply a statement that the injuries are of the head may be made; (b) it may not be stated that the skull is fractured; (c) no opinion as to the severity of the injury may be given until the condition is definitely determined, and (d) prognosis is not to be made.

4. Internal Injuries: (a) It may be stated that there are internal injuries but nothing more specific as to the location

*Reprinted by permission.

of the injuries and (b) a statement that the condition is
very serious may be made.

5. Unconsciousness: (a) If the patient is unconscious
when he is brought to the hospital, a statement of this fact
may be made; (b) the cause of unconsciousness, however,
should not be given.

6. Cases of Poisoning: (a) No statement is to be made
that a patient is poisoned; (b) no information as to kind of
poisonous substance, such as mercuric, chloride, phenol or
carbon monoxide may be given; (c) no statement concerning
the motive, whether accidental or suicidal, may be given,
and (d) no prognosis may be made.

7. Shooting: (a) A statement may be made that there
is a penetrating wound; (b) no statement may be made as
to how the accident occurred, *i.e.* accidental, suicidal, homi-
cidal or in a brawl, nor may the environment under which
the accident occurred be given.

8. Stabbing: The same general statements may be made
for stabbing as for shooting accidents.

9. Intoxication: No statement may be made as to whether
the patient is intoxicated or otherwise.

10. Burns: (a) A statement may be made that patient
is burned, also the member of the body involved; (b) a
statement as to how the accident occurred may be made only
when the absolute facts are known, and (c) no prognosis
may be given.

11. Attending Physician: Hospitals may state to the
representatives of newspapers the name of the attending
physician of private patients and refer such representatives
to the physician for information about the case, but the
newspapers shall not use the name of the physician without
his consent.

12. Pictures: When newspapers request the privilege of
photographing a patient in the hospital, such permission
will only be given (a) if in the opinion of the doctor in
charge of the case, the patient's condition will not be jeop-
ardized and (b) if the patient (or in the case of a minor,

the parents or guardian) are willing to have a photograph taken.

For other than police cases the following rule has been adopted: "If the patient is conscious and can communicate with the doctor or nurse in charge, or relatives, he should be asked whether he will permit any information to be given and his decision is final."

If the patient agrees to permit information to be given the conditions are identical with those quoted above except that item 3 (c) does not permit an opinion to be given as to the severity of head injuries even when the condition is definitely determined.

Appendix V

MOTION PICTURES FOR THE
LAITY APPROVED BY THE
AMERICAN COLLEGE OF SURGEONS*

Title	Procurable from:
EMERGENCY TREATMENT FOR FRACTURES 1 reel; 16mm.; silent	Aetna Casualty & Surety Co., Hartford, Conn.
GOOD HOSPITAL CARE . . . . 2 reels; 35mm.; sound	American Coll. of Surgeons, Chicago, Ill.
THAT MAN MAY LIVE . . . . 2 reels; 35mm.; sound	American Coll. of Surgeons, Chicago, Ill.
YOUR MOUTH . . . . (By Edwin N. Kent, D.D.S., Boston) 1 reel; 35mm.; silent	American Dental Assn., Chicago, Ill.
CLARA CLEANS HER TEETH . . . . . . (By Thomas B. McCrum, D.D.S., Kansas City, Mo.) 1 reel; 35mm.; silent	American Dental Assn., Chicago, Ill.
FIGHT CANCER WITH KNOWLEDGE . . . film strip; 60 frames; 35mm.; silent; colored	American Society for the Control of Cancer, New York, N. Y.
THIS GREAT PERIL . . . . 2 reels; 35mm.; silent	American Society for the Control of Cancer, New York, N. Y.
CINEMATOGRAPH OF LIVING CELLS . . . 2 reels; 16mm. and 35mm.; silent	American Society for the Control of Cancer, New York, N. Y.
VARIOUS ASPECTS OF CELLS IN LIVING TISSUES . . . . (By Robert W. Chambers, M.D., New York) 3 reels; 16mm. and 35mm.; silent	American Society for the Control of Cancer, New York, N. Y.

*Reprinted by permission

336

SEEING HOW YOU SEE . . . . Belgard & Spero, Inc.,
1 reel; 16mm.; silent   Chicago, Ill.

BEHIND THE SHADOWS . . . . National Tuberculosis Assn.,
1 reel; 16mm.; sound and silent   New York, N. Y.

THE TRAIL OF THE CIRCUIT RIDER . . . The Duke Endowment,
(Portrayal of the work of the Duke   Charlotte, N. C.
Endowment in caring for the sick,
especially in rural districts.)
7 reels; 35mm.; sound

BODY DEFENSES AGAINST DISEASE . . . ERPI Classrooms Films, Inc.,
(By Paul R. Cannon, M.D., Chicago)   Long Island City, N. Y.
1 reel; 16mm. and 35mm.; sound

DIGESTION OF FOODS . . . . ERPI Classrooms Films, Inc.,
(By Anton J. Carlson, M.D. and   Long Island City, N. Y.
H. C. Swann, M.D., Chicago)
1 reel; 16mm. and 35mm.; sound

HEART AND CIRCULATION . . . . ERPI Classrooms Films, Inc.,
(By Anton J. Carlson, M.D., Chicago)   Long Island City, N. Y.
1 reel; 16mm. and 35mm.; sound

MECHANISMS OF BREATHING . . . . . ERPI Classrooms Films, Inc.,
(By Victor Johnson, Ph.D., Chicago)   Long Island City, N. Y.
1 reel; 16mm. and 35mm.; sound

REPRODUCTION AMONG MAMMALS . . . ERPI Classrooms Films, Inc.,
(By H. H. Strandskov, Ph.D., Chicago) Long Island City, N. Y.
1 reel; 16mm. and 35mm.; sound

THE NERVOUS SYSTEM . . . . ERPI Classrooms Films, Inc.,
(By Ralph W. Gerard, M.D., Chicago)   Long Island City, N. Y.
1 reel; 16mm. and 35mm.; sound

HOW THE FIRES OF THE BODY ARE FED . Films of Commerce Co.,
1 reel; 16mm. and 35mm.; silent   New York, N. Y.

ACUTE APPENDICITIS . . . . Eastman Kodak Company,
(By Edward Martin, M.D.,   Teaching Films Division,
Philadelphia, Deceased)   Rochester, N. Y.
1 reel; 16mm. and 35mm.; silent

BREATHING . . . . Eastman Kodak Company,
(By C. E. Turner, M.D., Boston)   Teaching Films Division,
1 reel; 16mm.; silent   Rochester, N. Y.

CIRCULATION . . . . Eastman Kodak Company,
  (By C. E. Turner, M.D., Boston)   Teaching Films Division,
  1 reel; 16mm.; silent   Rochester, N. Y.

DIGESTION . . . . Eastman Kodak Company,
  (By C. E. Turner, M.D., Boston)   Teaching Films Division,
  1 reel; 16mm.; silent   Rochester, N. Y.

THE SKIN . . . . Eastman Kodak Company,
  (By C. E. Turner, M.D., Boston)   Teaching Films Division,
  1 reel; 16mm.; silent   Rochester, N. Y.

TUBERCULOSIS AND HOW IT MAY   Eastman Kodak Company,
  BE AVOIDED . . . .   Teaching Films Division,
  (By C. E. Turner, M.D., Boston)   Rochester, N. Y.
  1 reel; 16 mm.; silent

AFTERCARE OF POLIOMYELITIS . . . . . Harvard Infantile Paralysis
  (By Arthur T. Legg, M.D., Boston)   Commission,
  2 reels; 16mm.; silent   Boston, Mass.

THE ADVENT OF ANESTHETIC ETHER . . Mallinckrodt Chemical Wks.,
  1 reel; 16mm.; silent   St. Louis, Mo.

THE MANUFACTURE OF   Mallinckrodt Chemical Wks.,
  ANESTHETIC ETHER . . . .   St. Louis, Mo.
  1 reel; 16mm.; silent

EMERGENCY CARE FOR SAFE TRANS-   Massachusetts General Hos-
  PORTATION IN FRACTURES OF THE   pital, Fracture Clinic,
  LONG BONES . . . .   Boston, Mass.
  1 reel; 16mm.; silent

PREPARATION OF INFANTS' FOOD . . . . Mead Johnson & Co.,
  (By Robert A. Strong, M.D.,   Evansville, Ind.
  New Orleans)
  2 reels; 16mm.; silent

MAN AGAINST MICROBE . . . . Metropolitan Life Ins. Co.,
  1 reel; 16mm. and 35mm.;   New York, N. Y.
  sound and silent

CONQUEST OF DIPHTHERIA . . . . . . Metropolitan Life Ins. Co.,
  1 reel; 16mm. and 35mm.; silent   New York, N. Y.

HOW TO LIVE LONG . . . . Metropolitan Life Ins. Co.,
  film strip; 28 frames; 35mm.; silent   New York, N. Y.

WORKING FOR DEAR LIFE . . . . Metropolitan Life Ins. Co.,
  1 reel; 16mm. and 35mm.; silent   New York, N. Y.

TRANSPORTATION OF FRACTURES OF
THE EXTREMITIES; TRANSPORTA-
TION OF FRACTURES OF THE SPINE . .
1 reel; 16mm.; silent

Hubley R. Owen, M.D.,
319 S. 16th St.,
Philadelphia, Pa.

FIRST AID TREATMENT IN FRAC-
TURES OF THE LOWER EXTREMITIES . .
1 reel; 16mm.; silent

Kellogg Speed, M.D.,
122 S. Michigan Ave.,
Chicago, Ill.

FIRST AID AND TRANSPORTATION OF
BACK INJURIES . . . .
1 reel; 16mm.; silent

J. E. M. Thomson, M.D.,
1307 N Street,
Lincoln, Neb.

AROUND THE CLOCK WITH YOU AND
YOUR BABY . . . .
(By Lyle G. McNeile, M.D., and
Donald G. Tollefson, M.D., Los
Angeles)
3 reels; 16 mm.; silent

Donald G. Tollefson, M.D.,
511 S. Bonnie Brae St.,
Los Angeles, Calif.

BEHIND THE SCENES IN A MODERN
HOSPITAL . . . .
2 reels; 16mm.; silent; colored

George U. Wood,
Peralta Hospital,
Oakland, Calif.

INDEX

A

Accidents in hospitals,
informing newspapers, 200
prevention, 74
Addleman, Perry, 39, 42
Administration, 86
accurate records, 87
complex task, 86
humane aspects, 87
need for competence, 251
standards, 317
training, 87, 297
trends, 166
trustee responsibility, 86
Administrator,
aiding public relations counsel, 117
as public relations counsel, 46, 121
community service, 146
education, 87, 297
need for well qualified, 87, 251
personal contacts of, 127, 146, 220
responsibility for public relations program, 116, 304
responsibility for publicity, 173, 194
responsibility in ameliorating hospital costs, 97
supply of able, 88
Admitting department, 64, 133
Advertising Age, 303
Albany Hospital, 145
Alcoholics, 59
Alumnae list, 157
Amalgamation of hospitals, 77, 278
Ambulance service, 65
Amelioration of hospital costs (see Costs of hospital care, amelioration)
American Association of Fund Raising Counsel, 262, 267
American College of Hospital Administrators, 297

American College of Surgeons,
aids graduate education, 295
conventions, 284, 296
fights fee splitting, 295
might grade approved hospitals, 108
motion pictures, 209, 210, 336
public education activities, 296
standardization program, 294
American Hospital Association,
ethics for hospital publicity, 48
obstetric standards, 73
on hospital and medical care insurance, 108
on hospital care insurance, 106
principles governing subsidies to voluntary hospitals, 100
public relations work, 292
American Institute of Public Opinion, 255
American Medical Association,
code of ethics, 46
on hospital and medical care insurance, 108
public education activities, 296
American Public Welfare Association, 100
Analysis, value in publicity, 44
Ancillary services, 104
Anesthesia department, 67
Annual reports, 155
advance planning, 157
brevity, 156
contents, 156, 164
distinctive examples, 158
distribution, 155
Grady Hospital, 161
illustrations, 157
low pressure promotion, 171
makeup, 170
need, 155
quotations on hospitals, 170
Strong Memorial Hospital — Rochester General Hospital, 158
value of prompt publication, 157

Index   351

Hospitals (cont.)
(see also Administration
Care, well rounded
Hospital cooperation
Publications
Responsibility
Service, good hospital)
Hospitals, governmental,
free and part-free patients, 98
increasing load, 9, 98
need for public relations program, 1, 5, 9, 243
new tax funds for, 243
Hospitals, small, 56, 70
Hospitals, voluntary,
campaigns for new funds, 243
distinctive nature, 165
financing, 165
free and part-free patients, 98
need for public relations program, 1, 5, 9, 14, 243
new sources of income, 11, 99, 106, 109
problems of, 9
set pace for hospital service, 9
subsidies, 11, 99, 109
tax exemptions, 98
working with governmental agencies, 99, 109, 165
Hostess, 65, 136
House magazine, 171
aids employes and auxiliary in public relations, 129, 143
costs, 172, 174
description of The Pilot, 172
discussed by McCleery, 172
distribution, 171, 173
for low pressure promotion, 171
place in public relations program, 176
"ready made," 175
relation to fund raising, 175
responsibility for, 173
technics of producing, 172
value, 129, 143, 174
House organ (see House magazine)

Humane aspects of hospital care,
importance, 87, 129, 131, 147
to indigent, 134
training nurses in, 132

I

Imitation, constructive uses, 26
Impressions of patients, 137
Improvement, hospital, 152
Inclusive rate plan, 102
benefit to public relations, 104
effect on nursing, 105
is sound, medically, socially, financially, 103, 104
lowers unit cost of ancillary services, 104
pleases patients and staff, 103
Income,
earned, 29
new sources for voluntary hospitals, 11, 99, 106, 109
Indigent, 98
importance of courtesy to, 134
service through insurance plans, 109
subsidies for care, 11, 99
Information, Please, 224
Institutes for administrators, 88, 297
Insurance, hospital care, 106
a public service, 106
contracts with government for care of indigent, 109
control, 108
developing national public relations program, 294
expanding to include medical care, 108
increasing hospital income, 29
might sponsor radio series, 230
Pennsylvania Hospital Association supports, 284
publicity in Duluth, 289
rate structure, 106
value in public relations, 82, 106, 288, 294

Personal contacts (cont.)
  telephone operators, 135
  trustees, 127, 146, 220
Personal interests (see Interests, personal)
Personnel, 127
  education regarding hospital, 128
  factor in rising hospital costs, 97
  personal contacts in public relations program, 127
  relations improved by public relations program, 307
  (see also Personal contacts)
Personnel administration, 129
  health program, 76
  labor unions, 130
  need in public relations program, 129
  recognition of unusual service, 169
Pharmacy, 66
Philanthropists, 25, 245
Physical therapy, 68
Physicians,
  attracted by good hospital, 22, 139
  ethics of, 46, 225
  must not be overshadowed by equipment, 147
  on hospital radio broadcasts, 225
  (see also Staff, medical)
Physicians' offices, 137 (fn.)
Pilot, The, 172, 235
Pledges, collection of, 264, 268
  (see also Campaigns, fund raising)
Policies, hospital,
  standards for evaluating, 315
Poll, public opinion (see Public opinion poll)
Preparation,
  for campaign, 265
  value in campaigns, 31
Press-agentry, 2, 5

Prestige, hospital, 168
Prevention, disease, 75, 76
Pride, civic, 22, 23
Principles,
  governing subsidies to voluntary hospitals, 100
  of fund raising, 37, 241, 270
  of good hospital service, 56
  of public relations program, 34, 39, 51
Printing for hospital publications, 183
Private duty nursing (see Nursing)
Professional audit, 74
Professional education (see Education, professional)
Promotion (see Low pressure and High pressure)
Propaganda, 18
  Bernays' theory of, 26
  dangerous, if false, 19, 35
  group leaders, 26, 36
  honest, 19
  uses stereotypes, 18
Prospect lists, preparation, 178
Protection,
  hospitals as community protection, 22
Public attention, competition for, 6
Public health department,
  cooperation of hospitals, 75
  responsible for disease prevention, 75
  studies hospital records, 77
  uses hospital laboratories, 76
Public health information, 51
Public meetings, 218
  addressed by hospital representatives, 146, 220
  audience participation, 220
  health lectures, 219
  highspotting public relations program, 152, 218
  in publicity for Minnesota Hospital Service Association, 290

R

Tax exemptions for voluntary
hospitals, 98
Tax funds,
for governmental hospitals, 243
(see also Governmental subsidies)
Telephone service, 135
Testing public opinion, 254
public opinion poll, 254
questionnaires, 260
Therapy (see Gas, Fever, Intravenous, Occupational and Physical therapies)
Thought, allowing time for,
value in public relations program, 30
Toronto Star, 280
Toronto Western Hospital, 280
Touro Infirmary, 136
Tours, hospital,
by men's groups, 146
on National Hospital Day, 233
recordings for radio, 227
value to auxiliary, 144
Town Crier, 224
Town Meeting of the Air, 224
Training courses (see Education)
Trends, in hospital administration and operation, 166
Tri-State Hospital Assembly, 285
Trustees, 85
acting on recommendations, 116
duties, 85
leadership, 85
must understand needs, methods and purposes of public
relations program, 114
need for united opinion, 249
personal contacts, 127, 146, 220
qualifications, 85
reorganization of board, 248
representative and confidence
inspiring, 248
responsibility for administration, 86

Trustees (cont.)
responsibility in ameliorating
costs, 81, 97
responsibility in public relations program, 113, 305
standards for, 313
Tuberculous patients, 58

U

Unions, 130
United Hospital Fund,
fund raising, 80
motion pictures, 209
survey, 276
University of Chicago, 297
*University of Chicago Round
Table*, 223
Unmarried mothers, 61

V

Vanity, 24
Vassar Brothers Hospital, 181
Vocational guidance, 227
Voluntary hospitals (see Hospi-
tals, voluntary)

W

Weaver, Henry G., 255
Welfare agencies, 79
Welfare councils, 79, 276
White, William Allen, 189
Windham Community Hospital,
145
Wireless (see Radio)
Women's auxiliary (see Auxil-
iary)
Wood, George U., 209
Woollcott, Alexander, 224

Y

Young, Kimball, 35